HRT
Licensed to Kill and Maim

The unheard voices of women damaged by
hormone replacement therapy

Martin J Walker

photographs by
Robert Schweizer

SLINGSHOT PUBLICATIONS
London
2006

HRT: Licensed to Kill and Maim
The unheard voices of women damaged by
hormone replacement therapy

Slingshot Publications,
BM Box 8314,
London WC1N 3XX.
www.slingshotpublications.com
www.zero-risk.org

First Published June 2006

ISBN: 0-9519646-7-4

Type set by Viviana D. Guinarte
in Palatino LT
Printed in Italy
Cover design and photo lay-out: Andy Dark
Editing: Rose Shepherd
Photographs: Robert Schweizer

British Library Cataloguing in Publication Data:
A catalogue record for this book is available from the British Library.

Dedicated

To all the women
who have suffered adverse reactions
to HRT, and to the relatives
of those who have died as a consequence
of using HRT. To the children, husbands
and families of those whose lives have
been damaged by HRT.

Acknowledgements

In writing this book, I have tried to give a voice to women adversely affected by HRT. Their correspondence with the Menopausal Helpline was sometimes funny, often erudite and always moving. Maggie Tuttle was the power behind the book; she has unflagging energy and a strong commitment to the women who turned to her. Those who consistently supported the Menopausal Helpline also supported the publication and distribution of the book, most particularly the Muswell Hill branch of estate agents Kinleigh Folkard & Hayward, who provided Maggie with office facilities during her campaign, Joyce and Leslie Lesser of Southend, who gave administrative help, and John, Maggie's postman, who delivered the thousands of letters from affected women that flooded in to Maggie's flat on top of Muswell Hill in North London. Finally, we must mention Lindsey, without whose typing and administrative skills Maggie would not have coped.

For my part, I thank voluntary readers Anne, Marianne, Mark and Viviana, who each made distinct and valuable contributions to the manuscript, and, of course, in particular Rose, who has an editing skill and craft which that is profound.

I continue to be surprised at the number of £awyers – friends of long standing – who are willing to give free time and advice on my books. Thank you for your commitment and generosity.

This is the place where I can also acknowledge all those people who have kept me afloat and writing over the past few years. Thanks to all of the following who have helped me with funding and support, without which I would not have survived: Stephen, Elaine, Eric, Liz, Frederica, John, Gordon, Jorge, Mar, Jane, Joanna, Rebecca, James, Judith, Judith, Sagrario, Lucrecia, Emilia, Tony, Elena, María Jesús & sisters, Teddy, Andy, Rose, Loïc, Jim, Bob, Sharon and Sepp. I have to thank my partner, Viviana, for being infinitely tolerant, giving me consistently good advice and emotional support. Last but not least, comes our son, Juan, who may never have kept quiet while I was working, but unflaggingly presented humorous and relaxing interludes when I stopped.

CONTENTS

APPENDICES

We have too often perturbed natural systems for
short-term gains, but with disastrous long-term consequences.
Quite apart from science, I feel instinctively that it is
a terrible mistake to interfere with anything as
delicately poised as the endocrine system.[1]

Scarecrow: My straw has come out!
Dorothy: Doesn't it hurt you?
Scarecrow: No, I just keep picking it up
and putting it back in again.[2]

No man putteth a piece of new cloth
unto an old garment, for that which is put in
to fill it up taketh from the garment,
and the rent is made worse.[3]

Got myself a crying, talking,
sleeping, walking, living doll.
Take a look at her hair, it's real,
and if you don't believe what I say
just feel.[4]

---

1 Professor Samuel Epstein MD. Cited in Schell O., *Modern Meat: Antibiotics, hormones and the pharmaceutical farm*. Random House. USA, 1984.

2 *The Wizard of Oz* (Metro-Goldwyn-Meyer, 1939), starring Judy Garland.

3 Matthew 9: 16.

4 'Living Doll', written by Lionel Bart, sung originally by Cliff Richard.

Preface

I WAS ASKED to write this book by Maggie Tuttle, who, as you will learn, set up an organisation called the Menopausal Helpline (MHL) in London in 1996. Maggie, who herself had a bad experience with HRT, wanted more than anything to give a voice to the thousands of women with whom she had come into contact who had also been damaged.

Because, when I began writing, I wanted to work from the stories of the women I interviewed and the data collected by the MHL, and, to some extent, because I wanted to find my own way of writing about HRT, I did not read the literature. Perhaps 'literature' is too grand a word to describe the handful of books that present a critical analysis of oestrogen therapies and the damage that they have done to women.

Towering amidst this writing is the work of Barbara Seaman. Her radical and critical analysis of hormones was first expressed in *The Doctors' Case Against the Pill* in 1969, then in *Free and Female*[5] in 1972. After limbering up with these two books, Seaman went on to write the definitive critical *Women and the Crisis in Sex Hormones.*[6] This was the source for almost all the critical information on sex hormones that followed over the next 25 years. Then, in 2003, as if to show that she would

---

5 Seaman B. *The Doctors' Case Against the Pill.* New York: P H Wyden; 1969.

Seaman B. *Free and Female: The sex life of the contemporary woman.* New York: Coward, McCann & Geoghegan; 1972.

6 Barbara Seaman and Gideon Seaman MD. *Women and the Crisis in Sex Hormones.* New York: Rawson Associates Publishers; 1977.

not leave a stone unturned nor any pickings for anyone who came after her, Seaman wrote *The Greatest Experiment Ever Performed on Women*, a beautiful piece of historical journalism.[7]

Following Barbara Seaman closely is Sandra Coney with her book *The Menopause Industry: How the medical establishment exploits women*.[8] In Britain, Dr Ellen Grant has made a considerable contribution to the field, especially in respect of the Pill, with her book *Sexual Chemistry*.[9] In 1991, Hamish Hamilton published Germaine Greer's book, *The Change: Women, aging and the menopause*.[10] This inter-disciplinary text, written with wit, irony and intellectual rigour, takes the reader on a kaleidoscopic journey through the menopause. Despite its erudition, at its core the book has three practically instructive chapters on 'treatments': allopathic, traditional and alternative.

The National Women's Health Network (NWHN), a campaigning group co-founded in 1975 by Seaman in Washington DC with Alice Wolfson, Belita Cowan, Dr Mary Howell and Dr Phyllis Chesler, published *The Truth About Hormone Replacement Therapy* in 2002.[11] There are a couple of excellent distillations in chapters in longer books, notably Lynne McTaggart's *What Doctors Don't Tell You*,[12] and John Robbins's *Reclaiming Our Health*,[13] together with some long feature articles in books and magazines, Internet releases and a few alternative health

---

7 Seaman B. *The Greatest Experiment Ever Performed on Women: Exploding the estrogen myth*. New York: Hyperion; 2003.

8 Coney S. *The Menopause Industry: How the medical establishment exploits women*. Alameda, CA: Hunter House; 1994.
Coney S. *The Menopause Industry: A guide to medicine's 'discovery' of the mid-life woman*. London: Women's Press; 1996.

9 Grant ECG. *Sexual Chemistry: Understanding your hormones, the Pill and HRT*. London: Cedar; 1994.

10 Greer G. *The Change: Women, aging and the menopause*. London: Hamish Hamilton; 1991.

11 National Women's Health Network. *The Truth About Hormone Replacement Therapy: How to break free from the medical myths of the menopause*. Prima Publishing, 2002.

12 McTaggart L. *What Doctors Don't Tell You: The truth about the dangers of modern medicine*. London: Thorsons; 1996.

13 Robbins J. *Reclaiming Our Health: Exploding the medical myth and embracing the source of true healing*. Tiburon, CA: H J Kramer; 1996.

books, exceptionally Maryon Stewart's *Beat the Menopause Naturally* [14] and Marilyn Glenville's *The New Natural Alternatives to HRT.*[15] These texts represent almost the sum total of critical analyses written about this important subject.

Inevitably, there are a number of books which deal critically with hormone additives and supplementation because their main subject is women and cancer. Sharon Batt's book, *Patient No More: The politics of breast cancer,*[16] is a brilliant and thorough investigation of the politics which exist deep in the heart of the business of cancer. Written while she had breast cancer, the subjective narrative makes it readable and involving.

Other books which look at HRT, and especially DES, while talking about cancer are: *Preventing Breast Cancer: The politics of an epidemic* by Dr Cathy Read, and *Breast Cancer: Poisons, profits and prevention* by Liane Clorfene-Casten.[17]

The many other hundreds of books and 'scientific' papers available on HRT overwhelmingly fail to put up opposition to hormone supplementation and the threat it poses to women, and most of them fail radically to address questions of drugs marketing and the history of scientific endeavour in this area. Many of them are written as if by the pharmaceutical companies that produce HRT. The area of HRT is an area where populist writers for women have generally failed to critically examine the issues.

When, at the end of writing the book, I came to read these core texts, I inevitably got depressed. Barbara Seaman and Sandra Coney's books are both exceptional works of counter culture and investigative writing, well researched and uncompromisingly campaigning. It did briefly occur to me that I might have wasted my time, but then I began to consider what my book contributes that Seaman and Coney don't specifically cover.

---

14 Stewart M. *Beat the Menopause Naturally.* Natural Health Publishing; 2003.

15 Glenville M. *The New Natural Alternatives to HRT.* Kyle Cathie Ltd; 1997.

16 Batt S. *Patient No More: The politics of breast cancer.* London: Scarlet Press; 1994.

17 Read C. *Preventing Breast Cancer: The politics of an epidemic.* New York: HarperCollins; 1995. Clorfene-Casten L. *Breast Cancer: Poisons, profits and prevention.* Monroe, ME: Common Courage Press; 1996.

I concluded that there were positive differences in this book. First, I would like to think that I have not written a book solely about HRT, but also about the hidden conflicts between pharmaceutical companies, physicians and patients, especially in Britain. In a subtext I have also tried to look at the way in which groups of people fight back against iatrogenic illness and the toxic corporations that cause it. Finally, I have gone deeper than other writers into the structure of companies that produce HRT, and have tried to draw some conclusions from the analysis of these organisations.

If I have one slight criticism of *The Menopause Industry* and *The Truth About Hormone Replacement Therapy*, the books by Coney and the National Women's Health Network, it is that they seem to me to place too much emphasis on scientific studies of treatments, often quoting their conflicting results. To my mind, industrial pharmaceutical science has been in such parlous shape for so long now that there seems little point in referring to it, except inasmuch as it influences cultural or commercial attitudes. A great deal of the information put out by pharmaceutical companies today is lies, much of it is distortion, and all of it is concerned more with marketing than with health care.

I suppose that I have approached the whole question of HRT from a perspective of two principles – first, that it is probably almost always wrong to introduce synthetic chemicals into your body, and, second, that of, 'If it isn't broke, don't fix it.' Unless there is clear proof that synthetic chemicals will effect some kind of cure, in the case of serious illness, or safely eradicate unbearable pain, the light is rarely worth the candle.

There is no clearer case, as I say throughout the book, of scientists and pharmaceutical companies inventing illness to treat with drugs that they have already developed – in this case HRT – as part of some *other*, often secret, agenda. And it stands to reason that, when drug companies try to foist their discoveries on the public, they will create research and clinical studies to support sales. In the case of HRT, companies invented completely spurious advantages for hormone replacement, which later proved to be complete fabrication. The fact that the companies used 'scientific' studies to back up their assertions tells us much about present-day industrial science. It hardly seems worth quoting studies unless one is prepared to delve deeply into this quagmire and investigate conflict of interest and issues of research funding.

There are, in this book, four long case histories. In relation to these, especially Maggie Tuttle's, I think that I should explain why they seem to introduce extraneous material, which might, at first sight, not appear to shed light on HRT. It has long been my belief that writers of documentary books should try to make their descriptions of people as rounded as possible. I felt a particular duty to do this in this book, for several reasons. First, I know myself from my own illnesses and conditions that their severity is measured in part by comparing them with the condition of my prior life. To some degree a person's character and experience of life structure their reaction to illness and, especially, adverse reactions to drugs. This is one of the reasons why I have spent time describing the lives of the women in the case histories before they suffered such reactions.

Second, it seems to me that a 'case history' should be much more than that. If one is to pursue the view that medicine and healing is about the whole person, the story of a person's illness has itself to be holistic and entail much more than a pseudonym and a quick list of symptoms. People affected by illness are clearly much more than a cipher for the illness or for the writer's point. Finally, and perhaps most importantly, this book, as well as being about HRT, is about how various women have responded to iatrogenic illness, how they have taken a first step towards legal action or joining a campaigning group. It is in this nexus between illness and social action that we can realise hope for the future, especially in the battle against pharmaceutical companies. In this sense, it is important to describe the characters of the women in these case histories as they responded to their illness.

When I first started the book, I had some trepidation about writing about women's health. These concerns were increased when I found that the best critical and analytical material written on HRT had all been written by women. My fears were even further heightened when the NWHN, whose work I admired, neglected even to answer my accumulating e-mails asking for information. I have tried my best over the past year to think my way through this and to badger myself into believing that they did not refuse to respond because I was a man. As I got into the book, however, a couple of things became evident. Clearly, the traditional and more conservative women's health groups, especially those in Britain, which have become dominated by pharmaceutical company money, have been infiltrated by men. And the whole iatrogenic assault carried out on women through HRT has been organised and enacted mainly by men. As well as being a man, I have experience in writing about these areas.

Second, this book is not just about HRT, but also about reactions to iatrogenic illness. I would have been hard pressed to find a group of men who have responded in a similar manner to iatrogenic assault as the women who contacted the Menopausal Helpline. Because of the historical understanding of oppression and manipulation in many areas of their lives, women appear to respond with more alacrity and sense of personal strategic organisation, not to say grievance, to medically-precipitated illness than men do.

When I think of male protests against iatrogenesis, my mind throws up individuals, often individual professional medical men; it seems to be rarely the case that men, in England at least, group together to deal with iatrogenic illness in a collective or campaigning way.[18]

It could be that men are so deeply implicated in the damage that medicine does, that even when they see the damage they find it difficult to extricate themselves from their more powerful and instrumental brethren. This problem and this process are illustrated well in Henry Jenner's book about the dangers of breast implant surgery.[19] In the book he describes how he was viewed as a traitor by other male surgeons when he began to discuss his feelings and knowledge of the risks to women.

It is also the case that men often objectify their illnesses and see them as something separate from themselves, their past and their feelings. In this sense, men are less likely than women to form groups and to discuss how they might deal with their illnesses. Men, rather than women, will perhaps be happy with a conversation with a (probably male) doctor, readily believing the apparently rational picture that is presented to them by him.

---

18 There are notable exceptions to this, especially in the campaigns by gay men against AZT and other pharmaceutical AIDS regimes. There are also odd areas of male interaction against orthodox medicine, such as the campaign in England against hydrocortisone creams, often given to young men for skin conditions.

19 Jenner H. *Silicone – Gate: Or the scandal behind breast implants;* 1995.

A great deal of the book is about adverse reactions. Throughout the past 15 years of listening to people with a variety of chemically-induced illnesses, the one rule of thumb that I have adopted is to always believe what they are saying about their symptoms. Any other approach appears pointless to me, and I know from some experience that disbelief is always the first necessary step for those on 'the other side' who try to discredit sufferers. It is also the case that to even entertain disbelief when listening to accounts of people's illnesses means the erection of a whole schema of complex psychological reasoning. At the end of this journey, unless you conclude that people are actually lying – that is, falsely reporting symptoms which they do not have – it is still necessary to believe that the pains and feelings that people are describing are real. Consequently, I have never veered from this initial commitment of absolute belief in people's narrative accounts of their illnesses.

It might, however, be necessary for the writer to keep an open mind about the *causes* of illness, and on some occasions it might be hard to have the same belief in the subject's account of this. However, in this book, as in my previous two, many of the people who describe illnesses also describe social processes in which they have challenged pharmaceutical companies, as well as their doctors and other health professionals. Whether or not they have won their cases, the journey through such processes as the law or statutory complaints procedures is often a good guide to whether or not people are attributing a reasonable cause to their condition.

As well as explaining what might be the consequences of using HRT, I hope that this book lays down some hopeful guidelines for people wanting to fight back, either individually or collectively, legally or with extra-judicial campaigns. That the book will bring an end to the prescription of HRT would be a vain and arrogant hope, given the superb quality of critical work and the recent scientific studies that precede it. At least, however, the information compiled through the Menopausal Helpline will now be 'out there', adding weight to eventual change.

It is always a humbling experience for a writer to talk to people who, after being personally affected, begin to educate themselves and campaign on a particular issue. In writing this book, I was struck by the inner strength of many women, not only to deal with and overcome seriously debilitating conditions of ill health, but to learn and to focus their energies towards arguing their cases against experts and, perhaps most profoundly, still to argue their case calmly and rationally when they have been abused by their detractors. Such people's commitment to both theory and practice usually outstrips the often cynical and detached approach of professional workers.

Unfortunately, there exists no level playing field or democratic forum where the debates generated by campaigns such as that against HRT might be aired. What is more, in medicine at least, the most powerful agencies show no stomach for honest discourse, relying instead on misinformation and spin. I hope to right the balance, to some extent, with this book by giving a public voice to those women who have suffered and have then been obstructed in reaching the public with their stories.

I have tried to give as much notice as possible to the work of other preceding or contemporary writers. We should never lose sight of the fact that a culture of resistance is a historical continuum, and we should always look first at the history of our ideas and respect those who have trodden a similar path before us.

Martin J. Walker, 2006

PART ONE

Prologue

Hormones and Their Replacement

Ordinarily the body's pituitary glands and ovaries work in exquisite tandem, constantly adjusting oestrogen levels to fit the body's need of the moment, like a car set on automatic. Taking HRT, which delivers a constant level of oestrogen, is like having a car stuck in a single gear.

Dr Ellen Grant[1]

THE VIEW THAT contemporary medical science has of the human person is still primarily based upon a 19th century idea of mechanical engineering. Within this idea, almost all body parts can ultimately be transplanted, and everything can be replaced by a synthetic equivalent.

Although the idea of hormones has permeated the fabric of popular culture almost entirely in the form of 'sex hormones', agents relating to emotional states and sexuality, they play a considerable part in the whole biological working of the human mind and body. Produced by different organs and glands, and transported to different cells, in a complex network of demand and provision, over 30 hormones govern a wide range of physical and psychological incidents and conditions.

---

1 Grant ECG. *Sexual Chemistry: Understanding your hormones, the Pill and HRT.* London: Cedar; 1994. Cited in McTaggart L. *What Doctors Don't Tell You: The truth about the dangers of modern medicine.* London: Thorsons; 1996.

3

Hormones determine the course of growth and eventual height, the stimulation of secreted milk in mothers. They maintain sodium and phosphate balance in the kidneys and sugar levels in the blood – insulin is a hormone. They are responsible for development and maintenance of the male and female sex characteristics, while also regulating reproduction. They are almost entirely responsible for the management of digestion in the human body.

Apart from having huge tasks such as these, hormones, their distribution and strength, also determine a multitude of tiny details that make up an individual's quality of life. They determine processes, such as secretion of saliva in the mouth and of liquids around the eye, the secretion of lubricants in the vagina and the density of bone. Hormone imbalance can cause oily or dry skin, pre-menstrual tension, low energy and fatigue.

Hormones are perhaps the most pervasive and connected elements in the human chemistry, and their natural good balance is essential to quality of life. While most original constituent parts of the body, from blood to a variety of organs, can be replaced from other sources within broad general parameters with apparently relatively minor knock-on effects, the introduction of non-individual specific hormones to the human body can have myriad different, continuing effects.

Together, hormones and their producing and receiving sites are known as the endocrine system, and physicians who work with these systems are called endocrinologists.[2] Endocrine glands release hormones into the blood, which transports them to target receptor cells, which they are genetically programmed to join. The interaction between all the hormone-producing glands and their target cells is infinitely complex. Messages are constantly being passed within the endocrine system, informing both control sites and producers when to adjust their levels of production of hormones or hormone-stimulating chemicals.

---

2 In their battle to sell HRT to the public, the pharmaceutical companies have sought, in many circumstances, to cut out the endocrinologist. Much better to have the general practitioner, who knows next to nothing about endocrinology, push the drugs to vulnerable women. In their ideal world, indeed, the drug companies would want to sell HRT directly to the public, who know even less about endocrinology.

The glands and organs of the endocrine system are: the hypothalamus, pituitary and pineal glands, which are situated in the brain; the thyroid, which is situated in the front of the neck, just below the voice box; the adrenal gland, which is in two parts and situated at the upper ends of the kidneys and the pancreas; in women, the ovaries, which are situated on both sides of the uterus, and, in men, the testes. In addition, most of the major organs of the body, including the heart, the stomach, the intestines and skin, produce hormones, as well as performing to their main functions.

The pituitary gland produces, among other things, growth hormone, prolactin, which initiates and sustains lactation; thyrotropin, which stimulates the thyroid to produce thyroid hormones, and corticotrophin, which stimulates the adrenal glands to produce its hormones. It also affects the nervous system, secreting endorphins, signals to the ovaries and testes to make sex hormones, and controls ovulation and menstruation in women.

The thyroid gland produces thyroxine and triiodothyronine. These hormones control the metabolic rate and determine energy levels.

In the kidneys and pancreas, the adrenal glands regulate the salt and water balance in the body, as well as stress responses, metabolism, the immune system and sexual development and function.

The male sex hormones produced by the gonads, the testes, are called androgens, the most important of which is testosterone. This hormone controls the male sex characteristics, both primary and secondary, including muscle growth and growth of facial and body hair. The female gonads, the ovaries, produce oestrogen and progesterone, which regulate the development of all the female sexual features and reproductive functions, including menstruation and pregnancy.

A complex relationship between the pituitary gland – sometimes called the 'master gland' because it controls so many varied functions – and the hypothalamus, within the brain, ensures that the pituitary gland produces hormones in relation to the emotional mood of the individual and to external factors such as temperature and climate change and light exposure.

Female reproductive hormones begin their development and their regulation in the hypothalamus and pituitary gland. The hypothalamus first releases the gonadotropin-releasing hormone, which in turn stimulates the pituitary gland to produce follicle-stimulating hormone (FSH) and luteinising hormone (LH). These two instructing hormones then command the ovaries to secrete oestrogen, progesterone and testosterone.

Hormone balances change throughout the course of a person's life, depending on when and how the identity develops with age. Hormones move with differing regularity and energy at different times in the male and female bodies. After sexual maturity, which comes earlier in women than in men, hormone levels in women fluctuate cyclically over a much wider range than those of men. At female menopause, ovarian secretion shuts down. In men the testes continue to produce testosterone, but at an increasingly slower rate. In very old age, the brain hormonal environment is similar in the two sexes.

The function of hormones and what they do to the human body has changed historically. Now that women in developed societies, for example, have fewer children and are less often pregnant, they have three times as many periods, and higher levels of circulating oestrogen than their great-grandmothers did a century ago.

A good example of the complexity of the endocrine system and the human historical condition is the hormone melatonin, which is produced by the pineal gland. Melatonin is an antioxidant which goes through the body scavenging 'free radicals', damaging toxic elements that build up in the body.

Melatonin is produced when the eyes are in complete darkness. In previous societies without electricity, levels of melatonin were kept up during the long periods between sunset and sunrise. With the development of electricity in the early 20th century, light and darkness patterns that had previously dictated human behaviour, changed radically. It is possible that some contemporary bodies never experience complete darkness, and for this reason they produce little melatonin. Some scientists believe that changing light pattern and lack of melatonin could be one of the factors contributing to the increase in cancer.

The production of hormones can be affected by stress, infection and, in the contemporary world, the taking into the body of hormone-mimicking chemicals. Imbalance of hormones can lead to a variety of illness-

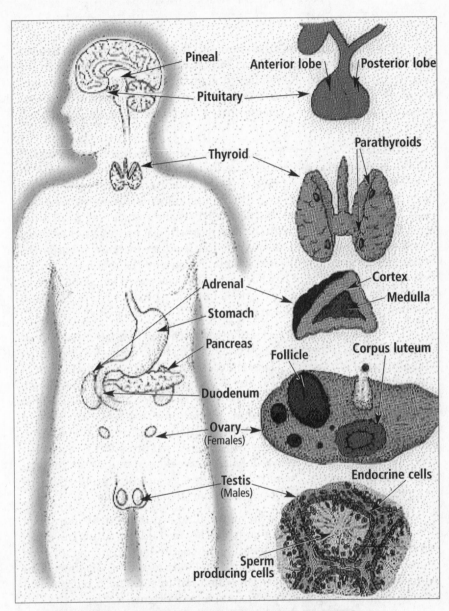

HORMONE-PRODUCING ORGANS AND GLANDS

Taken from: http://users.rcn.com/jkimball.ma.ultranet/BiologyPages

es, which originate in both the mind and the body. Levels of oestrogen and progesterone can both inhibit and encourage tumour growth in the breast, the uterus and the ovaries. It is thought that levels of hormones are also linked to diseases of the mind such as Alzheimer's, schizophrenia and more common ailments such as depression, anxiety and alcoholism.

Although, in theory, it is possible to give synthetic or 'other animal' hormonal supplements to 'top up' a low level of a specific hormone, in practice it is dangerous to give any kind of hormonal supplementation. Even if it were possible to take exact measurements, not only of the levels of a particular hormone, but also of levels and functioning of all other aspects of the body that might be affected, artificial processes of delivery cannot imitate nature and always provide a sudden increase in hormones into a delicate and complicated system. Because of the massive distribution and consumption of sex hormones that has arisen since the Second World War, many of the less serious but widespread adverse effects of hormone imbalance have been poorly recorded or researched.

There is a recognised series of illnesses caused by malfunctioning of the hormone producers in the body, which include: goitre (over-production of thyroid hormones), Hashimoto's thyroiditis (under-production of thyroid hormones), gigantism (over-production of growth hormone), Type 1 and Type 2 diabetes (created by the lack of production of, and the inability to utilise, insulin), Cushing's syndrome (excessive amounts of glucocorticoid hormones, resulting in symptoms that can include obesity, growth failure, muscle weakness, acne, high blood pressure), Grave's disease and adrenal insufficiency leading to weakness, fatigue, abdominal pain, nausea, dehydration and skin changes. A lack of thyroid-stimulating hormones is suspected of playing a part in osteoporosis.

While the most serious forms of illness produced by hormonal imbalance might be diagnosed quite quickly in children, adults can experience imbalances and less quantifiable conditions over long periods without physicians diagnosing them. In relation to a series of ailments, in women especially, male physicians often fail to consider a biochemical imbalance, preferring to suspect psychological origins.

Unfortunately, the mechanistic way in which we describe the complex work of hormones gives the lay person no ready vocabulary to describe the experience of feeling unwell or 'different' from normal. However, while it is true that hormone imbalances can directly affect the psychology of both men and women, most imbalances are accompanied by clusters of clear physical symptoms, such as dry skin, dry eyes or itching, which a skilled physician ought to try to elicit from the patient.

Why have the 'sex hormones' achieved the status they have, both in popular mythology and in scientific research? The complete answer to this question is complex, but a summary answer might be that the ultimate goals of life science are threefold. First, to produce an individual who has lifelong freedom from the challenge of disease; second, to gain control of human reproduction so that it can be taken out of the insecure hands of the common people; and, third, to produce a human race that can live for eternity.

While these three goals have to address many serious side issues, some issues are central. The lowering supply of oestrogen to the female body and the end of the reproductive cycle appears to be the key to the process of ageing. There can be no doubt that science sees the possibility of extending the reproductive cycle of women, while prolonging their sex lives, as part of its project to create an ageless human being. The increasingly popular use of hysterectomy and oophorectomy (removal of the womb and ovaries) in women before the menopause, encouraged by the medical profession in developed societies, and the following up of these operations with oestrogen implants, would suggest that covert research is going on in this area.

The 'Wham Bam Thank You Mam' approach of British and North American* physicians to giving and taking away hormones from women over the last half century, in no sense matches the infinitely complex natural modulation of the human female person. The automatic assumption that synthetic hormones would inevitably play a useful role in making the human body function better is one of modern science's most perverse and ill-founded conclusions.

---

* The terms North America and North American, rather than America and American, are used to refer to the USA throughout this book in recognition of the fact that the US is only one country in the American continent, or the continent of the Americas.

Introduction

The proponents of HRT have never proved that there is an oestrogen deficiency, nor have they explained the mechanism by which the therapy of choice effected its miracles. They have taken the improper course of defining a disease from its therapy.

Germaine Greer[3]

Everybody knows that the boat is leaking.

Leonard Cohen[4]

EUGENICS AND THE IDEA of designer people are still very much at the heart of life science. Equally, the struggle to overcome imperfections in the human body and personality has always been widely perceived as a reputable part of medicine. Whether for good or ill, it remains one of the principal objectives of modern science to re-create, with amendments, the human form. Although progress in these areas is always portrayed as being of consequence to medicine and primarily devoted to the prevention or curing of illness, almost all this science is actually motivated by a search for the holy grail, a process of replicating a human person, all the functions of which can be controlled.

---

3 Greer G. *The Change: Women, ageing and the menopause.* London: Hamish Hamilton; 1991.

4 'Everybody knows', written by Leonard Cohen and Sharon Robinson, sung by Leonard Cohen.

For over half a century, drug companies have accumulated great profits by pumping life-changing and life-threatening quantities of hormones into women, who have rarely had any knowledge of just how deeply and insidiously these mainly synthetic substances can affect their physiology, their biology or their consciousness.

While mechanistic medical scientists have proved sceptical about the use of vitamin supplementation, pointing to the fact that all aspects of the process, from consumption to absorption to excretion, have to be considered, allopathic physicians and drug company scientists have rarely voiced similar concerns in relation to hormone supplementation. Thousands of women have died, while others have spent years in illness and misery, after becoming, in the words of the author Barbara Seaman, subjects in 'the greatest experiment ever performed on women'.[5]

Since the British licensing system came into effect, there have been around 160 hormone replacement products, in a variety of presentations, floated on the British market. Of these, 85 are currently authorised, and the remainder have been withdrawn by their makers for commercial reasons. None of the products has been withdrawn by the licensing authorities for any reason.

Some of these preparations have been manufactured from the urine of pregnant mares, while others have used entirely synthetic hormones. Most of the preparations prescribed to women for effects of the menopause are based upon oestrogen, the main hormone of the female reproductive system, the production of which declines as a woman reaches the change of life.

In questionnaires returned by women who contacted the Menopausal Helpline[6] in the late 1990s, 25 different preparations are reported. These are marketed in the form of pills, implants, creams or patches. Oestrogens and progestogens (steroid hormones with progesterone-like activity) are also present in the contraceptive 'Pill', and oestrogen is present in the breast-cancer drug Tamoxifen and some other anti-cancer medications.

---

5 Seaman B. *The Greatest Experiment Ever Performed On Women: Exploding the estrogen myth*. New York: Hyperion; 2003.

6 See Chapter 3, Adverse Circumstances.

Despite the fact that producing companies have, over the years, added to the marketable value of hormone replacement therapies by suggesting – in defiance of findings to the absolute contrary – that they act against heart attack, breast cancer, Alzheimer's disease, stroke and deep-vein thrombosis, in both Britain and North American brands of HRT are licensed for a relatively narrow band of conditions.

First, they are approved for what the US Food and Drug Administration (FDA) entitles 'moderate to severe vasomotor symptoms of the menopause', and for conditions related to either hysterectomy or oophorectomy (removal of the womb or ovaries), including, in both cases, vaginal or urethral atrophy and primary ovarian failure. Secondly, until recently, HRT was prescribed for osteoporosis, either in actuality or as a prophylactic.

In reality, however, the prescription net for the treatment is far wider. Many women accept the prescription of HRT simply because their doctors think that they may be reaching menopause and might want to stay 'young at heart', or because those doctors guess at the possibility of their patient developing osteoporosis. Other women seek out HRT and doctors who will prescribe it, because they are determined to stay attractive and sexually active for longer than they imagine they might do 'naturally'. To a lesser extent, in North America, oestrogen products are prescribed for breast and prostate cancers, even though, as detailed below, as early as the 1950s, oestrogen was identified with increased risk of breast cancer.

Throughout the 1990s, in North America, there were six preparations available that were licensed for both 'symptoms of the menopause' and osteoporosis. These products were – and are – manufactured by a range of pharmaceutical companies, including Wyeth (formerly Wyeth-Ayerst), Lilly, Solvay, Schering and SmithKline Beecham. In Britain, the implant, Riselle, which is currently prescribed to around 15,000 women, is produced by Organon. Wyeth Pharmaceuticals has led the market in HRT products since the 1940s and, up until the critical findings of a number of studies in the late 1990s, they controlled around 70 per cent of the market.

Both oestrogen and progestogen, when taken as supplements, can cause recognised adverse reactions, which are noted on the packaging or the patient information leaflets given out with treatments, on the data sheets and in compendiums of drugs data. It is now apparently accepted by all the pharmaceutical companies that oestrogens taken over long periods can trigger endometrial cancer, breast cancer and gall bladder disease, heart attacks, strokes, deep-vein thrombosis and pancreatitis. Lower-level imbalances can cause, among many things, breast tenderness, hair loss, fluid retention, weight gain, the sensation of burning skin and irregular bleeding. Progestogen can cause breast tenderness, distension, oedema, abdominal cramps and pre-menstrual-like syndrome, as well as anxiety, irritability, depression and drowsiness.[7]

Although it had occurred to physicians as early as the 18th century that they could tinker with body chemistry in both males and females, with a view to putting off ageing or aiding sexual potency, it was not until after the Second World War that doctors argued that it was actually in the interest of women to maintain artificially high levels of hormones during or after the menopause.[8]

Oestrogen was first isolated in the 1930s, and was chemically synthesised at the end of that decade. In the 1940s, Wyeth Pharmaceuticals produced what it described as a 'natural' oestrogen replacement called Premarin, extracted from (*pre*)gnant (*ma*)res' u(*rine*).[9]

---

7 Most of these adverse reactions are noted with supporting studies in effectiveness and costs of osteoporosis screening and hormone replacement therapy. Vol. II: Evidence On Benefits, Risks, and Costs. Washington, DC: OTA; 1995. Other, later studies support those which are not found in this publication. And the data sheet which accompanies HRT has a long list of recognised adverse reactions, although nothing is said about their frequency.

8 Ernest Henry Starling introduced the term 'hormone' in his Croonian lectures to the Royal College of Physicians in June 1905. Previously, Claude Bernard (1813-78) and Charles Edouard Brown-Sequard (1817-94) had introduced the idea of internal secretions, but neither had thought of them as specific chemical messengers.

9 Many women using Premarin do not know that it is produced directly from pregnant mares' urine. This is a particularly disgusting form of animal exploitation, depending as it does on getting mares pregnant before chaining them in stables to harvest their urine during that pregnancy. In 1995, the *Today* newspaper exposed the woeful state in which mares whose urine was used to make HRT were kept. The newspaper described conditions on Canadian farms as 'factory farming at its worst'.　　　　　　　　　　　(*cont.*)

After the Second World War, especially in North America, other companies began to produce synthetic oestrogen replacement therapy (ERT). Doctors were quick to prescribe ERT to address a perceived connection between cancer and low oestrogen levels. By the late Fifties, synthetic ERT was being prescribed to women as an aid to easy and successful pregnancy, and to help with 'women's problems', on the flimsiest and most flawed of medical evidence.

During the 1960s, sensing a billion-dollar market, pharmaceutical companies developed the argument that the menopause – the time when women cease to be child bearers – was a medical condition. They promoted the attitude that the end of the women's reproductive cycle actually heralded an end to their experience of sexuality, accompanied by a continuing state of ill health. Oestrogen replacement could, they suggested, change both these circumstances, relieving the adverse effects of menopause and returning women to their younger sexual selves, by topping up hormone levels that declined naturally at menopause or as a result of the surgical removal of the ovaries.

The role of oestrogen in the creation of cancer and other serious conditions has been known for many years. In the 1952 Merck Index, which lists trade-name drugs and all their chemical formulations, the medical use of oestradiol (one of the oestrogens) is shown as a replacement therapy in oestrogen deficiency. However, the book specifically cautions against the use of this therapy by any patient who has a history of breast or genital cancer. Despite this caveat, hormone replacement therapy became one of the first drugs sold in great quantity in a public market created by the pharmaceutical industry.

As with many drug-marketing operations, hormone replacement therapy did appear, on occasion, to have beneficial uses. In those cases of women who had had their ovaries removed at an early age, and who had, therefore, suffered an early menopause, there appeared to be a genuine, if cosmetic, case for artificially introducing hormones. Cosmetic, because the introduction of hormones could never return their bodies to their nat-

9 (*cont.*) Wyeth-Ayerst, manufacturers of Premarin and Prempak-C, commented that there existed codes of conduct for farms. At that time, Wyeth-Ayerst, a subsidiary of American Home Products, farmed pregnant mares' urine from 485 farms, in Canada and North Dakota in the USA (*Today*, 16 January 1995).

ural state and because, as soon as they stopped taking the 'medication', the menopausal state was destined to return.

In all other cases apart from hysterectomy and oophorectomy, however, the marketing of hormone replacement therapy was widely based upon the apparent desires of male physicians to experiment on women, and, ultimately, to control their reproductive and ageing processes.

From the 1940s to the 1960s, millions of women, particularly in North America, were prescribed diethylstilbestrol (DES), one of the first synthesised oestrogens, formulated in 1938. Although it was originally prescribed to prevent miscarriage and premature birth, before long it was being touted as a 'miracle cure' for any female reproductive problem. In North America, it was handed out to women with no known risk of miscarriage in the misguided belief that it would produce bigger, healthier and stronger babies. DES was thought to be effective against acne and prostate cancer, it was given as a morning-after contraceptive, and was even used to inhibit the growth of adolescent girls who feared being too tall.

In the 1960s, however, it became apparent that the use of oestrogen replacement therapy by menopausal women increased their chance of endometrial cancer (the endometrium is the lining membrane of the womb). One study found that in women who had used the treatment for seven years or more, there was a fourteenfold increase in the incidence of this disease.[10] Research in the 1990s would further show that women who had taken DES had a 35 per cent increased risk of breast cancer. It has been suggested that approximately 60,000 North American women will die of this cancer as a consequence of having taken the drug.

DES mothers, duped and well meaning, also bequeathed to their children a dangerous inheritance. In 1971, the *New England Journal of Medicine* documented a rare form of vaginal cancer in adolescent daughters of women who had taken DES when pregnant. Thousands of 'DES sons' and 'DES daughters' were born with malformations of the genitals. Studies from the 1930s and 1940s, which had revealed that DES caused cancer in laboratory rats, were ignored by industry and regulators alike.

10 Ziel HK, Finkle WD. Increased risk of endometrial carcinoma among users of conjugated estrogens. *N Engl J Med,* 1975; 293:1167-70.

The most ardent proponents of vivisection can apparently take or leave the findings that it throws up if it suits them.[11]

As a bitter irony, it was found that, far from promoting bonny, bouncing, full-term babies, DES actually *increased* the risk of miscarriage. After a series of costly court cases, it was taken off the market, but the concerns continue. Researchers are now watching DES grandchildren to see if disease and abnormalities pass on to the third generation.

Medical researchers should have learned something from the DES tragedy, yet the desire to manipulate women's hormones continues unabated, even as the evidence stacks up of very serious health risks connected with HRT in successive formulations.

Following the finding of links between excessive oestrogen and both endometrial cancer and hyperplasia (a pre-cancerous abnormal overgrowth of the endometrium, causing irregular and excessive bleeding), the drug companies introduced a conjugated treatment in which progestogens were taken together with the oestrogen. There was also a drive by some doctors and some pharmaceutical companies to get women to have their uteruses removed so that they could continue taking 'safe' oestrogen.[12]

In 1977, Beresford, Weiss and Voigt et al reported in *The Lancet* on the risk of endometrial cancer in relation to use of oestrogen combined with cyclic progestogen therapy in postmenopausal women.[13]

Throughout the 1980s and 1990s, a series of studies showed that synthetic human hormones, introduced into women's bodies as contraceptives or as hormone replacement therapies, even as anti-cancer drugs, had the capability to produce not just cancer, but thrombosis and cardiovascular problems.[14]

---

11 See *Hormone Experimentation and the Second World War* for more of the DES story.

12 Robbins J. *Reclaiming Our Health: Exploding the medical myth and embracing the source of true healing.* Tiburon, CA: H J Kramer; 1996.

13 Beresford SA, Weiss NS, Voigt LF, McKnight B. Risk of endometrial cancer in relation to use of oestrogen combined with cyclic progestagen therapy in postmenopausal women. *The Lancet* 1997;349:458-61.

14 Anyone wanting to review these studies can begin by drawing on the six studies from the 1990s cited in Appendix VI, as well as those cited in the chapter.

A British study published in the *British Journal of Obstetrics and Gynaecology* in 1987, which followed 4,544 women for an average of five-and-a-half years, showed that breast cancer risk was one-and-a-half times greater in HRT users, while the risk of endometrial cancer nearly trebled.[15]

A Swedish study published two years later, in 1989, which followed 23,000 women over time, found that HRT doubled a woman's chances of getting breast cancer.

In 1995, the *New England Journal of Medicine* reported a study involving 121,700 women, which found that those taking HRT for more than five years during menopause increased their chances of developing breast cancer by 30 to 40 per cent. In women between the ages of 60 and 64, there was a 70 per cent increase in risk after five years.

In 1996 came the first reports that HRT obscured breast cancer findings in mammography tests for women by making breast tissue denser. A study looking at 9,000 postmenopausal US women with breast cancer found that those on HRT were 71 per cent more likely to have a false negative result. Not only was hormone therapy predisposing them to cancer, but it was increasing their risk of death by militating against early detection.

In October of that year, newspapers reported on three studies from Britain and North America, published in *The Lancet*, which revealed an increase of between two and four times in the risk of deep-vein thrombosis in women taking HRT.[16]

In 1997, another paper published in *The Lancet* showed, yet again, increased cases of breast cancer. In 1998, the *Journal of the American Medical Association*[17] reported the results of the Heart and Estrogen/Progesterone Replacement Study (HERS), involving 2,763 postmenopausal women with a mean age of 66.7 years, with a history of coronary disease. The study showed conclusively that HRT conferred no

---

15 Hunt K, Vessey M, McPherson K, Coleman M. Long-term surveillance of mortality and cancer incidence in women receiving hormone replacement therapy. *Br J Obstet Gynaecol* 1987;94:620-35.

16 *The Lancet.*, October 1996.

17 *Journal of the American Medical Association* (1998; 280-605).

overall benefit to people with heart conditions: those on HRT and a control group on a placebo had the same incidence outcome. In the first year of HRT use, however, there was a higher, but non-significant, incidence of heart attack.

Despite this accumulating scientific evidence of increasing health problems for women, and considerable areas of ignorance about introducing synthetic and 'other animal' hormones into the human body, between 1960 and the year 2000, the drug companies developed and expanded a fabulous, mythical identity for HRT. With next to no supporting evidence, the manufacturers, particularly Wyeth, argued that HRT not only smoothed the passage through the menopause, but was also a defence against osteoporosis, stroke, Alzheimer's disease,[18] coronary heart disease and deep-vein thrombosis. The companies never went as far as suggesting that the treatment was a cure for dying, but they came as near as damn to it.

Despite the fact that hormone replacement was not licensed for anything other than menopausal difficulties, and despite the fact that it was contraindicated in a wide range of cases, HRT was prescribed 'at the drop of a hat', particularly to 'cure' osteoporosis.

In December 2000, a US Government scientific advisory panel recommended that synthetic oestrogen used in HRT be added to the list of cancer-causing agents.

In July 2002, new findings from a major North American study, which compared a placebo group with women taking Prempro, a combination of oestrogen and synthetic progestogen, confirmed the findings that those using the therapy stood a greater chance of developing breast cancer, with a greater probability that the tumours would not be picked up in the early stages by mammograms. The increased breast cancer risk for the HRT group treatment was assessed to be 26 per cent, and there was also a higher incidence of strokes and blood clots among users.

---

18 In November 1995, Californian research workers reported that the incidence of Alzheimer's fell in relation to the amount of HRT taken. The announcement of the results, from a study conducted between 1981 and 1982 of deaths in a retirement village, immediately prompted British clinical researchers, who had paid no attention at all to previous studies which had claimed damaging effects of HRT, to do similar studies.

The study, which followed 16,608 women aged 50 to 79, who had not undergone a hysterectomy, began in 1997 and, by 1999, the alarm bells should already have been ringing, when an independent data and safety monitoring board (DSMB) employed on it observed small but consistent cardiovascular adverse effects. However, none of these results crossed the clinical boundaries set by the study, so it was not discontinued. In the years 2000 and 2001, participants were belatedly given information about increases in heart attacks, stroke, pulmonary embolisms and deep-vein thrombosis. Still, the study continued, because even then no clinical boundaries had been crossed. Not until May 2002, did the study find that adverse events of breast cancer crossed the designated boundary, and on the basis of these data, the oestrogen-plus-progestogen component of the trial was stopped.

By the time it was wound up, this strand of the study had recorded in the HRT group a 41 per cent increase in strokes, 29 per cent increase in heart attacks, 100 per cent increase in blood clots, 22 per cent increase in total cardiovascular disease, and a 26 per cent increase in breast cancer. Claude Lenfant, Director of the NHLBI, said: 'The cardiovascular and cancer risks of oestrogen plus progestogen outweigh any benefits – and a 26 per cent increase in breast cancer risk is too high a price to pay, even if there were a heart benefit.'

In December 2002, the US National Institute of Environmental Health Sciences labelled steroidal oestrogen a 'known carcinogen'. In August 2003, one strand of the British 'Million Women' study was called off because results published in *The Lancet* showed that HRT caused breast cancer. Professor Valerie Beral, Director of the Cancer UK Epidemiology Unit, said, 'We estimate that over the past decade, use of HRT by UK women aged between 50 and 64 has resulted in an extra 20,000 breast cancers, oestrogen-progestogen combination therapy accounting for 15,000 of these.'[19] A North American research paper estimated that cases of breast cancer in the US caused by HRT, could be as high as 120,000.[20]

---

19 Beral V; Million Women Study Collaborators. Breast cancer and hormone-replacement therapy in the Million Women Study. *The Lancet* 2003;362:419-27.

20 Null G, Dean C, Feldman M, Rasio D, Smith D. Death by medicine. *Life Extension Magazine*, March 2004.

In February 2004, two Swedish HRT trials were stopped. One published in *The Lancet* found an increased risk of the recurrence of breast cancer in women who had previously recovered from the disease and who were taking HRT for 'acute menopausal symptoms'.

In March 2004, a second strand of the Women's Health Initiative (WHI) study, which had been looking at the effect of oestrogen replacement in relation to heart disease, was also called off. The study had found that the use of oestrogen supplementation increased the risk of strokes, while showing no signs of averting heart attacks, as its manufacturers and prescribing physicians were still obdurately claiming that it could. (The incidence of coronary heart disease in women increases after the menopause, so, runs the simplistic argument, HRT must have a cardio-protective effect.)

One thing that could be seen with certainty following the publications of these critical studies was that, in the main, doctors loyal to pharmaceutical companies used science to defend themselves only when it suited them. When science threatened the financial base of the pharmaceutical industry, they suddenly ceased to believe, and put everything down to personal choice.

Over the period that the critical studies were published, all the research scientists, Department of Health officials, FDA staff, drug companies' representatives and general practitioners played the 'risk game'. They washed their hands of responsibility and suggested that it was patients who determined what happened, who 'made up their own minds', once they had been told all the facts by their physician.

Some medical experts did make plain statements about the catastrophe that science had begun to structure. In Germany, Professor Bruno Muller-Oerlinghausen, chairman of the German Commission on the Safety of Medicines, compared HRT to thalidomide, saying that it had been a 'national and international tragedy'.[21]

---

21 Thalidomide, a drug for depression developed in West Germany and licensed in the mid-Sixties, led to the birth of between eight and ten thousand cases of phocomelia: children born with deformed limbs or no limbs at all. This pharmaceutical disaster precipitated Europe and US changes in drug monitoring and regulating systems. In Britain, the 1968 Medicines Act resulted in the setting up of the Medicines Control Agency and the four committees instigated to oversee the licensing of new drugs. A few years after the Act,   *(cont.)*

By March 2004, the month that the adverse findings of the WHI were made known, even World Health Organisation (WHO) officials were making clear statements, distancing themselves from the treatment. On March 5 at a conference in Sydney, Australia, the co-ordinator of the WHO said that hormone replacement therapy was 'not good for women'. Alexandre Kalache said that science sometimes makes big mistakes and it had done so with HRT. Professor Jay Olshansky, a Public Health Professor at the University of Illinois, said, 'Scientists now suggest that in most cases HRT should not be used. It's harmful for some and of no use to others.'

Despite it having been dispensed in Britain since the 1970s, little information about the minor or the major dangers of HRT was picked up over the past 30 years by the regulatory agencies. Had doctors, governments and regulators been paying attention over three decades, they would have seen that hormone replacement therapy was producing serious adverse reactions in many women.

Perhaps Department of Health officials did know about the adverse reactions women had been suffering, and perhaps they too had been playing the risk game. After all, as buyers and monopoly suppliers of huge quantities of drugs for distribution throughout the health service, their contracts and other business dealings with drug companies, involving millions of pounds, might have been, on balance, more important than the quality of life of a 'small' number of women.

By the end of the first quarter of 2004, it was clear that the tide was beginning to turn, and that HRT would eventually be seen as a scientific and medical mistake. For the moment, the drug companies, the regulatory agencies, and, in Britain, the government, tried to slip away as quietly as possible from the scene of the crime.

But even at this late stage, the experts and the organisations supported by the drug companies, were trying to find a small patch of safe ground on which to fight their last rearguard action. This patch turned out to be osteoporosis.

---

21 (*cont.*) following a focused academic campaign, rules were put in place, which compelled members of these four committees to declare their interests in pharmaceutical companies and products.

In October 2004, the Women's Health Initiative published its final results. On HRT, the study concluded that women who had taken the combination hormone therapy had *doubled the risk* of developing blood clots (venous thrombosis).[22] The study found that conjugated equine oestrogen (from pregnant mares' urine) increased rates of venous thrombosis.

Even when the full truth is out about the number of premature deaths caused by different forms of HRT, questions will remain to be answered. These questions go to the very heart of the relationship between pharmaceutical companies and physicians, the prescription of pharmaceutical medicines in a socialised health care system, and the nature of science and its links with medicine.

When the results of the aborted British 'Million Women' study were published in 2003, the chief of breast cancer medicine at Memorial Sloan-Kettering Cancer Center in New York, Dr Clifford Hudis, made a simple statement, which raised what must be considered *the* important question about HRT, science, medicine and health: 'The whole health benefit story for hormones has really unravelled.'

Hudis also put the adverse reaction of breast cancer into context, posing the question: 'This will give women something to think about. Do you want to take an intervention like oestrogen plus progestin that will reduce hot flashes (flushes) 90 per cent, probably, at the cost of having a 1 in 25 chance of having this abnormal mammogram, which might be more significant? I think a lot of women with modest symptoms will now say, "wait a minute."'

Despite the fact that hormone replacement therapy in various forms has killed, maimed and made thousands of women ill over the past half century, the latest revelations about the treatment have seemingly raised no issues regarding the criminality of the companies concerned. It seems that quite different standards are used in judging the criminality of drug companies from those used in judging, say, toy companies which produce a product which is a danger to children.

---

22 Cushman M, Kuller LH, Prentice R, Rodabough RJ, Psaty BM, Stafford RS, Sidney S, Rosendaal FR; Women's Health Initiative Investigators. Estrogen plus progestin and risk of venous thrombosis. *JAMA*, 2004;292:1573-80.

What is more, once the scientific dust had settled and many women had voted against HRT with their feet, the official view appeared to be that Wyeth, the drug company most significantly involved, had lost half its market and that this, in itself, was sufficient punishment.[23] Even more disturbing, the future 'rump' market for HRT now appears to be secure because, as Victoria Kusiak, Wyeth vice-president, said in February 2004, the average user of HRT is now a 51-year-old woman who takes the hormones for less than two years. On hearing this, well informed women might have wondered why it had taken half a century and mounting deaths to return to the protocols laid down for the original prescription of oestrogen replacement therapy.

Even better-informed people, including physicians, should also be asking: 'What is the point of prescribing HRT to ameliorate the symptoms of the menopause, if when women stop taking it their menopause begins all over again, even more severely?' And, 'How can we continue to use HRT as a prophylactic against osteoporosis when its use over long periods has consistently been shown to introduce high risks to women?'

Despite apparent acceptance of the serious adverse effects of HRT, the drug companies, depending on the short memory span of the media, began almost immediately to rebuild their markets. By 2006 there were a growing number of studies which began to advocate extensive use of HRT.

Now in her early sixties, Maggie Tuttle was born in the English Midlands. She had an interesting younger life as a popular singer and social campaigner. In 1979, when she was 37, after losing a baby and suffering irregular periods, she was prescribed hormone replacement therapy by her general practitioner. From the first time she took HRT, although her periods stabilised, Maggie felt unwell, with a confusion of different feelings and physical symptoms.

---

23 This is a standard free market answer to this kind of problem: The simplistic equation is that if a company product proves to be too great a risk to consumers, then they will cease to buy it and the producing company will make a loss. Unfortunately, this equation is based on conditions of perfect information, something which the drug companies have manifestly failed to provide over half a century.

For 15 years, Maggie attended a large number of doctors, who all told her that her newly experienced symptoms were due not to HRT but to a variety of new illnesses. Sure in her own mind that her symptoms were actually adverse reactions to HRT, and that she was the victim of iatrogenic illness – illness created by professional physicians – Maggie changed her prescriptions many times and experimented with various alternative treatments. Nothing, however, stopped the terrible pains in her back and shoulders, hot and cold fevers, sweating or the extreme fatigue that had descended on her. Perhaps worst of all were the times when she literally lost her mind, suffering bouts of unconsciousness while going about her everyday life.

In 1995, after a period on a new prescription, which led to her hair falling out, Maggie did the only thing that she had so far failed to do: she stopped taking HRT. Stopping was not easy and, fearing the consequences, she put an advertisement in a local newspaper, asking if anyone had any advice, either about HRT or alternatives to it. Three months after she stopped taking hormones, most of Maggie's symptoms had gone and her hair had begun to grow back.

The response to her newspaper advertisement, however, did not allow her to put her experiences behind her. Within weeks of the ad appearing, she was besieged by mail, phone calls, even personal callers, all wanting to report to her either their adverse reactions to hormone replacement therapy or the death or serious illness of a relative, which they were sure had been caused by the therapy.

In late 1995, as a response to these communications, Maggie set up the Menopausal Helpline (MHL) from her flat atop Muswell Hill in North London. From that point onwards, for the next five years, she gave her life to the cause. She read and researched the subject and became increasingly angry about the effects of the therapy reported to her. She pitted herself fearlessly against the drug companies, the medical establishment and their various agents.

Initially, the media appeared to aid Maggie in her campaign and she gave a number of newspaper interviews and appeared on television. In one of those rare examples of an academic who is not afraid to back a popularist, anecdotally-based campaign, Klim McPherson, Professor of Public Health and Epidemiology at the London School of Hygiene, in an article in *The Sunday Telegraph*, was happy to give the following comment in support of the Menopausal Helpline: 'It's a common notion amongst enthusiastic gynaecologists that the menopause is God's mistake and that their job is to correct it. They like doing hysterectomies and they like HRT. They genuinely believe they are doing women a good turn. But the downside has not been talked about.'

Over the next five years, however, the going got rougher. The MHL was carefully pushed out of the limelight and 'more balanced' media reporting replaced Maggie's sometimes raucous and, it was said, 'anecdotal' voice.

When Maggie wound up the Menopausal Helpline in 2003, despite having helped thousands of women, despite television and radio interviews and continuing exposure in newspapers and magazines, and despite escalating scientific reports of the detrimental consequences of HRT, she felt bitter because the voice of 'the women' she had represented had still not been properly heard.

Maggie Tuttle was used to campaigning, and over the five years of the existence of the MHL, she managed to present a good public record of the damage that HRT was doing to women. However, even in an 'open' society with a liberal media, especially in the field of medicine, it is difficult to push a patients' campaign to the fore.

The public discourse around health has become highly specialised and dependent almost entirely upon a professed 'objective' knowledge of biology and science. The representation of vested interests, such as that of the drug companies, infiltrates every aspect of public information, despite almost always being anecdotal, well spun and often untruthful. The world of professional medicine and the machinery of its exploitation are perhaps the most secret and the most corrupted by power and profit outside the industries of oil, chemicals and politics.

Maggie Tuttle's battle to publicise the adverse effects of HRT turned very quickly into one that highlighted all the principal characteristics of the conflict between the medical state and the individual, between the pharmaceutical corporation and the 'consumer', disabled *as* a consumer by medical professionals, and between the laity and the unholy alliance of professional physicians and science.

This book, although primarily about hormone replacement therapy, is not only about this therapy. It pursues social and political arguments intended to add to the debate about the power of the State and corporations, and the powerlessness of the consumer in the field of medicine.

Besides asking how it could be possible for a therapy that adversely affects a large number of women to retain its place in contemporary medicine, the book also asks how patients can defend themselves against the growing iatrogenic assault mounted by the drug companies and allopathic medicine.

PART TWO

Chapter One

The Personal and the Political

The peasant, even the humblest peasant, particularly the humblest peasant, thinks he is safe in his obscurity and comparative anonymity. Let me be, he says, let me till the soil and I will mind no other business but my own, but he never was, never is and never will be safe.

John Bingham[1]

After first meeting her in London, I travelled by train from Madrid to La Manga in the south-east of Spain, to interview Maggie Tuttle again. At Atocha station, where only a few months before, bombs aboard trains had killed 200 people, I took the opportunity to buy English newspapers.

I would be travelling for five hours. En route, the geography of Spain changed gradually from the larger, cosmopolitan towns to the more arid landscape and villages of the south. The journey, which began with the rich architecture of the 19th century, ended with goat herders who, in an uneasy settlement with the brave new world of the EU, shepherd their straggling flocks along the sides of the motorways.

I read the newspapers continuously, from Madrid to Cartagena, until my head was full of the war in Iraq, the murder of thousands of civilians and the developing terror-reasoning of British and US politi-

---

1 Bingham J. *A Fragment of Fear*. London: Panther; 1967.

31

cians. I began to think how the 'war on terror' makes us all feel insignificant. I wondered for a moment what I was doing, travelling to interview a woman about her adverse reactions to HRT, when the world was in turmoil, with huge matters of the post-modern era being enacted.

I was reminded of an English doctor who had been facing criticism about his medical practice for a number of years, and who after 9/11 said, 'What has just happened, makes our dispute about health of little consequence.' Was this right? Did these matters of global criminality actually take precedence, in some moral hierarchy, over the problems of everyday life facing citizens?

I came down to earth quickly when I realised that the restriction of individual power has probably been a calculated aspect of mass politics throughout history. Today's emphasis on global security, on the war against terrorism, obscures so efficiently the everyday threats and dangers that exist for individuals and communities in developed societies. In a society obsessed with security, there is no longer any possibility of a real debate on a subject such as iatrogenic[2] death. When society is on a war footing, internal criticism diminishes to a smoking wick. Lights no longer burn for individual liberty, whether for those accused of terrorism or those damaged by powerful industrial interests.

Perhaps even more important than this, in some perverse way, pharmaceutical companies take their marketing battles forward with the soldiers. The ethics of pharmaceutical production get automatically and inextricably bound up with wars. This is not only through politicians who have interests in these companies, but also through their involvement in vaccines for troops and the whole issue of biological warfare and the 'protection' of the metropolitan populations sucked into war. American Home Products, previously the parent company of Wyeth, producers of HRT, also manufactured toxic dioxin, containing herbicides and pesticides similar to Agent Orange, the long-term effects of which are still suffered by the Vietnamese people.

At the end of the day, the gathering spectre of ideological oppression and global hegemony can only be challenged by people with a deter-

---

2 My Microsoft spell check does not recognise this word and thinks it is in a foreign language.

mination to build strong communities. Personal, everyday problems in the community should be the building blocks of democracy; they are, in effect, the reason for democracy.

In this sense, the destruction of an individual life through adverse reactions to a pharmaceutical is at least as important as, if not more so than, the external threat of terrorism.[3] The pharmaceutical industries, together with orthodox medicine, have killed and maimed thousands more people in developed and developing societies than Al Qaeda and all other terrorist organisations put together. Yet their directors, staff, organisers, theorists and representatives consistently escape political, ethical, moral or financial censure.

When Maggie Tuttle set up the Menopausal Helpline, even though she had herself gone through 15 years of painful bad health, she was unprepared for the agony that would consequently flow into her life. As if she had opened an invisible gate, the diaspora of the iatrogenically injured descended upon her.

Maggie is, on the surface, a disorganised and emotional woman, her face lined with habitual concern. She is a quivering nerve of life; she smokes heavily and has a throaty laugh. No one could be more different from the organised, rational and professional 'new' women who have made careers from reassuring other women about their health and lifestyles. Over the past ten years, Maggie has read almost everything that has ever appeared on the Internet about hormones.

A small woman with black hair, Maggie can 'do' colourful working class or much softer female entrepreneur, without a change of clothes. A smart woman, full of energy, she talks ten to the dozen, departing from her initial narrative like a bag of fireworks catching a spark.

---

3 It is now thought that the arthritis drug Vioxx has been instrumental in the death of between 30,000 and 60,000 people and, in the 1990s, the heart drug Tambocor, which was found to cause cardiac arrest, killed an estimated 50,000 individuals in North America; this is more than the number of combatants killed in Korea or Vietnam, and more than the total deaths in every commercial aeroplane crash in the history of US aviation.

Maggie says about her work with women prescribed HRT: 'I never cried as I did for the women who contacted me. I used to cry uncontrollably, sometimes because I knew that we could do very little except support each other.'

As a writer, trying first to tease out the underlying truth, and then to assemble it as a coherent narrative, I have only two options with Maggie: I either interrogate her, forcefully and with discipline, or let her talk and try, later, to plot an intellectual path through her ideas. The first approach makes me feel like an army inquisitor trampling on Maggie's rights and identity; the second makes me feel as if I have been asked to summarise James Joyce's *Ulysses*. I veer between these two approaches, all the while putting my representation of her in jeopardy.

Maggie is a born fighter; she has a straightforward determination to put things right. She is the kind of woman produced by the late Sixties and Seventies in great number, a raw, vibrant, tough, street-fighting woman who has habitually launched campaigns based on her own experience.

In the late Sixties, Maggie began campaigning against the prison industries' organisation, for trade union rates of pay for working prisoners. Then, in 1971, she set up the Prisoners' Wives and Families Association, an organisation that she ran from her bare-floorboarded kitchen in Muswell Hill.

Maggie is a strangely detached person, part of, but not integrated with, her time. Now she says that she didn't see herself as a campaigner, nor did she know anything of the women's movement. She was, she says, just a woman who wanted to campaign for other women. She campaigned because she saw women virtually faced with starvation when their partners went to prison.

In the late Seventies, Maggie helped to set up the Vanguard Community for ex-hospital psychiatric patients. In the 1990s, she championed the cause of child minders, and she was chairman of the Childminders Association in 1994/5. For periods, she has also been a health visitor and given talks in prisons.

In 1984, Maggie had a new man in her life. She had already had four miscarriages, losing one baby at six months. She was told that she had a hormone imbalance, which should be remedied. Her private practitioner told her that he would put her on HRT. When she asked if it would do her any harm, she was told simply that it wouldn't. 'How long can I stay on it?' Maggie asked, and was told that she could stay on it for ever. 'In fact,' the doctor said, 'I have women on it who are now in their sixties: it keeps you young.'

Maggie was given Premarin, and from the first day she took the drug, a hammering began inside her head. Maggie's account of her 15 years on HRT reads like a literary version of Hieronymus Bosch. She talks of a pain that became so severe that she found herself on the floor, on her knees, holding her head. Although Maggie had thoughts that it could be the HRT which caused her sudden ill health, the drug and her doctor, undermined her and her reasoning about her own body. When she went back to the doctor she initiated a process through which many women have travelled, which would lead her to question her own instincts and reason. On this journey, the original medical problem, the treatment and the adverse reactions to the treatment, all became separate and unrelated.

During her treatment, she felt, she says now, like a woman of 150. During this time of torture, after the second prescription, not one doctor suggested that the conditions from which she was suffering might possibly have their origins in the HRT that she was taking.

The pains in Maggie's head never went away, and with them came a dull ache at the top of her head, like a pressure on her shoulders, which led her to hold her head in her hands, as if only that would keep it on. It felt as if she were being dragged round the room by her hair. In her ears she felt a fluttering, which she describes as like a bird wafting its wings. On occasion, her ears were filled with ringing and other high-pitched sounds.

She suffered what should have been recognised by any doctor as allergic reactions, which led to unremitting itching down the side of her legs and around the area of her pubis; she would scratch her legs until they bled. From the beginning, her eyes began to dry up, but on some days they would feel as if they were watering, and her nose would fill with virtual mucous, with nothing to show for it when she blew her nose.

Her joints ached continuously. Sometimes her hip joint simply gave way and she would collapse. Her arms became too heavy for her to brush her long black hair, and her spine was tender to the touch. As in the case of other women, Maggie was sent by an HRT advocate doctor to a surgeon who wanted to operate on her spine. She refused.

She was always short of breath, and sometimes she would have to gasp for air. Her mouth was dry, and she was forced to drink liquids constantly. She later found, after research, that quite often women on HRT fail to produce saliva. On one occasion, when she found difficulty breathing, she was rushed to hospital and operated on, after being told the patent untruth that her airways were blocked.

HRT gave Maggie low blood pressure and high cholesterol. She wanted to go to the toilet all the time, but when she got there she was unable to produce anything. Even after she came off it, travelling to Egypt or Spain, tracking down doctors to talk to about HRT on behalf of the Menopausal Helpline, she always felt cold, and at other times her body would burn as if, she says, she were sitting on top of a fire. Her skin got thin and dry, and she became emotionally labile, crying for no reason. On some days she became very depressed. Her breasts grew much bigger, became more solid and were unbearably painful.

At her worst, Maggie had to employ a physiotherapist to come to her home three times a week to give her massages, because, by this time, she was doubled up with joint stiffness and pain. She used to get spells of dizziness and her finger and toenails would break. If she cut or bruised herself, the wound seemed to take for ever to heal; and she got frequent abscesses in her gums.

Perhaps one of the things that most affected her social life was the fact that her memory dribbled away to next to nothing. This became so serious that she had to carry a small book around with her, in which she made notes of everything she had seen, been told or arranged. Her hair began to thin and then to fall out heavily. Eventually, she had to wear a wig. Her weight drifted up to over ten stone, when it had always been eight. She felt constantly bloated and she had excessive menstrual bleeding. She had frequent heart palpitations and sometimes experienced an uncontrollable spasmodic jerking of the muscles in her arms and legs.

Throughout her years of purgatory, Maggie was misdiagnosed with cancer, hepatitis B and ME. She was prescribed sleeping pills, diagnosed as having an under-active thyroid. She was tested for blood clots and strokes. She was frequently X-rayed, scanned, had her urine and blood sampled. Her thyroid was tested and she received advice from countless dieticians, rheumatologists, gynaecologists, trichologists, dental surgeons, endocrinologists and neurosurgeons. The great majority of these professionals told her that there was nothing to find in any diagnosis or test, and that, most probably, the symptoms that she was experiencing were all in her mind.

Maggie blames years of conditioning about doctors and the marvels of medicine for her inability to come to her own conclusion that her life was being destroyed by HRT. 'Only a few years ago,' she says, 'no one dared speak out against the medical profession. So, as I was doing the rounds of the doctors, changing from one form of HRT to another, I would ask, "Is it the HRT that is doing this?" And every doctor would reassuringly say "No".'

Maggie is not scientifically minded, nor, although she is voluble, is she particularly articulate; she knows, as they say, what she knows. Right at the top of the list of things that Maggie knows is the straightforward fact that in 1997, when she stopped using HRT, apart from some permanent and continuing symptoms of damage, with which she has learned to live, her ill health disappeared. The most telling of these recoveries was an increase in her bone density over the seven years after she stopped taking HRT. Although not as voluminous as it was previously, her hair is now fairly thick. Her eyebrows have not grown back, however, and Maggie laments the fact that it costs her £300 a year to have them tattooed on.

❦   ❦   ❦

Any attempt to dent the confidence of the largest global corporations, in the absence of constitutional or democratic pathways, is difficult and almost bound to lead to failure. The Menopausal Helpline (MHL) was one of the many campaigning groups that emerged over the last few decades of the 20th century made up of victims of drug damage; they sought changes in the pharmaceutical industry and its relationship to doctors and consumers. Some campaigns have organised battles against specific drugs and their side effects, while others, like those to keep vitamins and food supplements free from arbitrary regulation, have attempted to wage a general campaign against the pharmaceutical industry.

Like many campaigners before her, Maggie found that, with HRT, there was no easy route to publicity or to change. When she wound down the organisation in 2003, she was exhausted and had relatively little to show for her efforts, apart from the comforting knowledge that she had been there for many hundreds of women who had gone through experiences similar to her own.

Having been joined at the MHL by a small number of other women, Maggie fought against the setting up of a better-organised professional or volunteer organisation. Maggie *was* the telephone answering service of the MHL. As a consequence she not only spent many nights talking to women from all over the world, but she began to accumulate massive debts in the form of telephone bills.

> When I set up the Helpline, I had little idea of any overall structure, but always envisaged it as a voluntary organisation. From the beginning I funded the organisation entirely. Throughout the life of the Helpline, I was always against professionalising the organisation or trying to raise funds by commercial ventures.

Maggie dedicated her life to an attempt to bring the side effects of HRT into the public arena. She not only spoke to the newspapers, went on television and talked on the radio, but also wrote to the Medicines Control Agency (MCA),[4] she wrote to the pharmaceutical companies and she entered into an ultimately frustrating dialogue with the Department of Health.

The MHL was easily dismissed by the pharmaceutical companies and doctors as presenting only anecdotal evidence. But this, of course, is at the very centre of the contemporary battle of communities of different kinds against corporations and science. As individual human beings, we have, naturally, only our own stories. The lie of science is that it can subsume the needs of a limitless number of individuals into one story.

---

4 The MCA has now become the Medicines and Healthcare Products Regulatory Agency (MHRA).

One of the reasons Maggie Tuttle turned out to be a magnificent ambassador for women suffering adverse reactions to HRT, was that she is a medical scientist's nightmare, who, although well versed in the literature on HRT, expresses herself in the manner of an embattled working-class woman.

Maggie's whole demeanour is 'anecdotal'; her life is made up of verbal narrative, as if it is vitally important for her to keep you in touch with her world. She tells stories continuously, narrating and threading her way through the cases about which women have written to her. Maggie relates the stories both to her own experience and to her theoretical paradigm – although she would not call it that – constructed over years of night-time thinking about the problems of HRT.

During its seven-year formal existence, between 1996 and 2003, the Helpline received over 10,000 letters from women either asking for information or relating their histories in detail.

Because the MHL was Maggie's personal initiative, it never really worked out its objectives. It did, at one point, include the idea of setting up clinics to help women cope with the adverse side effects of HRT. It aimed to strengthen the instructions for the reporting of side effects to the MCA and to mount a campaign to educate doctors to understand and treat adverse reactions. It sought to set up a central advisory service in the NHS to advise women on alternative therapeutic approaches to the menopause and other hormone-affecting conditions (see Appendix IV).

Maggie's first thought and primary aim, however, was to help other women who were suffering. She thought, no doubt, that if you demonstrated that something was wrong, the good people in the world would ensure that it was put right. Her relatively disorganised campaign was rather like trench warfare, and it is greatly to her credit that, for over six years, she held her position and was not ground into the dirt or deflected by a more powerful and experienced opposition.

Within a short time of Maggie setting up the MHL, two other helplines had predictably opened, HRT Aware and The Amarant Trust, both partially paid for by pharmaceutical companies producing HRT.

One of Maggie's strengths as a campaigner was her determination to follow up every argument that emanated from officially sanctioned agencies. Trained in the old school during her days with prisoners' wives, she knew always to follow through, never to let the other side get away with anything, most particularly, to have the contradictions down on paper.

From the beginning, however, there were behind-the-scenes moves to damage both Maggie and the MHL. In the beginning, Maggie applied to make the MHL a charity. In May 1996, the Charity Commissioners wrote to Maggie via a legal services group, which had made inquiries about the registration of MHL. The Charity Commission, which spends limitless energy in supporting charities that act as front organisations for drug companies, had, they told Maggie, received letters expressing objections to the registration of the organisation. The Charity Commission's fair policy of transparency stopped it from sending copies of the letters to the applicants, or even informing them from where the complaints originated. However, it is quite clear from the nature of the complaints that drug companies and professional medical organisations were involved.

Summarising the six objections to registration, the Charity Commission claimed that Maggie had 'made anecdotal and unscientific statements about the side effects of HRT'; the 'Menopausal Helpline is dedicated to the opposition of the use of HRT'; 'Information given [by the MHL] is not backed by a medical committee of any sort ... the information provided is not unbiased'; 'MHL received financial support from "fringe medicine" products'; and 'The proposed name of this organisation, "Menopause Helpline", would cause confusion in the eyes of the public as there are a number of helplines available, manned by medically trained personnel.'

Evidently, the Charity Commission was of the same mind as Wyeth-Ayerst and other drug companies that, in order to have an understanding of the menopause and adverse drug reactions, you have to have a medical training. That the pharmaceutical companies could influence the Charity Commissioners with this kind of rubbish would have had Britain's greatest charitable philanthropists such as Thomas Barnardo turning in their graves. After all, it has been the case for over a century that what is primarily needed in any charity is an energetic amateur – in this case, an energetic woman who had personal experience of the adverse reactions to HRT.[5]

---

5 See Chapters 6, 7 and 8 for the interaction between the drug companies and the voluntary sectors.

As part of Maggie's concern always to follow through the arguments, in 1999 someone approached the Charity Commission on behalf of the Menopausal Helpline, to complain about the HRT-promoting charity, The Amarant Trust. The Charity Commissioners wrote back that they could not comment on the Trust's charitable status. In a throwaway paragraph they said, 'I understand that the Trust does receive donations from HRT drug manufacturers, but these are neither its sole or primary source of income.'

Maggie carried on a correspondence with the Medicines Control Agency (MCA), trying to glean as much information as possible about the monitoring, regulation and prescription of HRT. Many of the letters she received have a bland and patronising air. A letter to the NHS executive and other branches of government produced the same distant and uncomprehending replies about the adverse effects of HRT, while at the same time stressing – without reference – the treatment's therapeutic virtues.

In a 1998 letter dated November 17, 1998, replying to Maggie's request for funding, following a meeting with Frank Dobson, the Secretary of State for Health, Elizabeth J. Connell of the Women's Health and Maternity Services of the NHS, utilised a strategy often used by the drug companies, in claiming beneficial results for a drug in areas for which it was not licensed. 'It has been shown recently,'[6] Ms Connell wrote, 'that [HRT] can prevent Alzheimer's disease.' Of course, nothing of the sort had been shown or proven. What had happened – *all* that had happened – was that Wyeth had publicised speculation that lack of oestrogen might be one of the factors that influenced the onset of Alzheimer's disease.[7]

6 Letter, 17 November 1998, from Elizabeth J. Connell, Women's Health and Maternity Services, NHS Executive, to Maggie Tuttle at the Menopausal Helpline.

7 In another 1998 letter to a supporter of the MHL, Connell reiterates this absurd statement about HRT 'preventing Alzheimer's disease'. In this letter Connell plants her feet solidly in favour of the drug company argument that HRT is a drug-based therapy that was a clear response to clinical conditions suffered by women: 'HRT does suffer from an image that it is a sort of "cosmetic" therapy, acting to bring back some lost youth and restore the sex drive. This is an unfortunate [for whom?] misrepresentation which detracts from the clinical benefits of easing painful symptoms of menopause and helping to prevent osteoporosis.' (Connell to T [name withheld] 26 November 1998.)

Connell's letter also suggested that HRT had been shown to 'protect against cardiovascular disease and stroke'. After Maggie received this letter, she wrote to the MCA, asking if HRT had been used to help heart disease patients. Mrs A. E. Belchem of the MCA stated clearly: 'I have also spoken to one of my colleagues in the field of HRT who has confirmed that, at present, there are no such [HRT] products licensed [for cardiovascular disease] in the UK.'[8] Staff in the NHS should not, of course, promote any drug for a purpose for which it has not been licensed; to do so is blatant quackery.

In September 1998, with the help of an accountant whose wife had been affected by HRT, Maggie worked hard to stage a conference at the Brighton Conference Centre, entitled 'HRT, Remedy or Time Bomb?' In organising this conference, there were many times when Maggie thought that she had overreached herself. She chose the occasion to release copies of a booklet on which she had been working with a journalist, Jackie Williams. The cheaply-printed, slide-bound text, entitled *Cause of Death HRT*, showed on its cover the death certificate of Irene Brankin, who died, aged 42, six weeks after starting to take HRT.[9]

Prior to the conference, Maggie managed to feed information about the 'other side' of HRT into the media, and for the first time a number of intelligent articles appeared, giving personal examples of what could go wrong. One of the best of these appeared in the *Jewish Chronicle* of September 25, 1998. Headed 'Weighty Risks of HRT', the article told the story of TV producer Pamela Kaufman, who 'suffered unstoppable weight gain after she was given an implant'. Pamela's weight had gone from her petite 'less than ten stone' to 15, after she was given an implant without her consent during a hysterectomy. Pamela's case was also taken up by the *Sunday Mirror*, which ran 'before' and 'after' photographs of her.

The *Sunday Telegraph* of September 13, ran an article entitled 'Thousands of women to sue after HRT is linked to death'.[10] This piece,

---

8 Letter from Mrs A. E. Belchem, Information Scientist, the MCA, 11 January 1999 to T (name withheld).

9 This death certificate (Appendix II) is, it seems, one of the only death certificates ever issued that clearly blames HRT for the death of the subject.

10 *Sunday Telegraph*, 13 September 1998, 'Thousands of women to sue after HRT is linked to death.'

which appeared just prior to the conference, highlighted the death of Irene Brankin. The following Sunday, the paper ran another article, headed 'Should women take HRT? [11] asks Wendy Cooper, 78'. The sub-heading explained that 'last week's *Sunday Telegraph* story had started an angry debate between advocates of HRT and those who fear its health risks. A large picture showed Wendy Cooper's aged body and small surfboard reclining in the sun on the sands of the Gower Peninsula in South Wales. This article again found space to advertise the conference.

The line-up for the Brighton conference was prestigious. Maggie and Sandra Simkin of the Campaign Against Hysterectomy and Unnecessary Operations on Women were the only lay speakers. All the other presentations were given by doctors: Dr Marilyn Glenville, who is author of *Natural Alternatives to HRT* and a doctor who ran five holistic clinics for women; Dr Helen Pensanti, a North American researcher and lecturer in PMS and menopausal symptoms; Dr James Zhou, Head of the Pharmacology and Herbal Medicine Faculty at Yale School of Medicine; Dr Yehudi Gordon, a gynaecologist at a leading London hospital; Dr Larry Milam, a North American homeopath and expert on nutrition; Dr Eric Endby, a Swedish biologist researching the treatment of osteoporosis; and Christopher Pick, a naturopathic physician and nutritionist.

Maggie put all her organising skills into the Brighton conference, managing the press like a professional and doing a large number of interviews. With the many authoritative speakers who attended, and the things that Maggie said to journalists prior to the event, Wyeth must have thought that the 'timebomb' was being placed directly beneath it:

> Maggie Tuttle, who has organised the conference and herself suffered devastating side effects from HRT, including hair loss, asks this question: 'Were you prescribed hormones to protect your health and instead landed up with symptoms such as hair loss, thrombosis, breast cancer, burning sensations, male characteristics, increased osteoporosis, unstoppable weight gain, endometriosis and more? Then this conference is for you and your voice must be heard.'

> Women will be attending from all over the world to testify to the adverse effects of HRT, which the Menopausal Helpline claims have not been

---

11 *Sunday Telegraph*, 20 September 1998, 'Should women take HRT? asks Wendy Cooper, 78'.

widely reported because of the massive promotional publicity by the drug companies, encouraging women to believe that HRT is the source of eternal youth.[12]

On the day of the conference, Maggie and the conference helpers were receiving a phone call a minute – she is sure about this because all the calls were monitored with the help of BT. On the Sunday following the conference, however, despite there having been doctors, television crews and newspaper reporters present, there was not a word in the press about the vital issues raised.

The conference was a considerable expense. Maggie borrowed £10,000 to finance it. And although it was a success, with some 400 people attending, it did not make a profit. Maggie thinks now that it finally cost her around £30,000. All the speakers and organisers stayed in the Grand Hotel in Brighton, with Maggie paying the bill.

The conference must have worried Wyeth executives, for they went to the trouble of writing to all general practitioners in the Sussex area. The medical director of the company warned both doctors and patients off the 'meeting', claiming not, of course, that their profits might be damaged, but that such a 'meeting' might cause concern to patients (see Appendix V).

Wyeth was not alone in being worried about Maggie's Brighton conference turning women patients off HRT. Dr Richard Burwood of Brighton Health Care NHS Trust was approached by the local newspaper, and told them that he was concerned about negative publicity arising from the conference. He told the local evening paper, the *Argus*, 'HRT can prolong the life of women ... women who take it live about 18 months longer than those who don't.' (This is a completely new turn in the hyping of HRT and I have not seen it quoted anywhere else.) 'Women on HRT are also 25 per cent less likely to get heart disease and 20 per cent less likely to have a stroke. The problem with this conference is that it will frighten women away who would have benefited from HRT'.[13]

An old-school campaigner, Maggie believed in getting out on the street. In May 1999 she organised a Saturday March on Downing Street.

---

12 *Liverpool Daily Post* (Welsh Edition), August 24 1998.

13 *Argus* (Brighton), September 23 1998.

Maggie Tuttle

It was Maggie who met with the police to organise the march's route, which eventually went down Whitehall from Whitehall Place, visited 10 Downing Street and ended up at the Department of Health. Experience of this march introduced Maggie to post-industrial politics and the negative effects of a modern democracy. The march and picket brought home to her how much things had changed since the Seventies.

About a hundred protestors attended, and a 5,000-signature petition was handed in at 10 Downing Street. The police attendant on the door told Maggie that Prime Minister Tony Blair was getting ready to go to watch a football match, so was unable to come down and take the petition. Maggie answered in her usual straightforward manner, saying, 'Tell him, he should be down here seeing us women.' We don't know what Cherie was doing at the time (perhaps being scrubbed clean of toxins in the shower by her lifestyle guru, Carole Caplin), but the failure of further attempts by Maggie to contact her, suggested that she had no sympathy for the cause.

The rebuff by the Prime Minister still rankles with Maggie, perhaps more than any other she received during the campaign. In the interviews I conducted with her, she returned to it time and again, as if Tony Blair's inability to come to the front door not only showed his personal lack of understanding, but was also an act of rudeness to her personally.

Just as there had been no response to the conference, there was next to no reporting of the march. Reflecting now on the strategy of marches, Maggie says that they are a waste of time unless you can guarantee media attention.

> If you have thousands upon thousands of women, then you can probably be effective. You have to have the mass behind you, but you also need the press on your side, and I think, personally, that live shows or live documentary programmes are the best way of contacting thousands of people. The good ones that I participated in were favourable to our cause.

Pharmaceutical, chemical and other companies that face product liability cases, go to the most extraordinary lengths to ensure that clear, unarguable legal decisions are not made against them.[14] Obviously, the doc-

---

14 For one of the best fictional accounts of this in North America see *The Runaway Jury*, John Grisham, Arrow Books, 1996 (not the film, which does not deal with tobacco companies and is much weaker for this reason).

tors, who might also find themselves facing actions, are the first line of defence against such actions.

In the case of HRT, doctors defend the pharmaceutical companies by stubbornly reiterating that there are no side effects. This argument is the bulwark defence of HRT. Anyone taking a civil action based on adverse reactions to the treatment, first has to face the fact that there are no expert witnesses considered to have sufficient stature to support their case: quite the opposite, there are legions of doctors, of indeterminable status, willing to swear blind on behalf of the producing company that they have never found a single case of adverse reaction to HRT. One admission would open the floodgates.

The second defence is the out-of-court settlement. Accompanying all such settlements is a signed agreement that, while the company does not accept fault, the case will never be resurrected, and that the plaintiff will not disclose the amount of any compensation.

The final line of defence, before a legal case comes to court, is for the company to have some kind of 'hold' over the lawyers who have taken on the case. This obstruction to justice might well be some 'cultural feeling' or some legal 'rule of thumb' that companies have fostered. Legal aid might be withdrawn for what appears to be a fair and independent reason. The lawyer might suddenly make the client aware that there is insufficient evidence on a certain matter for the case to go ahead. Or the hold might be a legal rule, which a company has worked to foster over years, such as the one acted on in English pesticide cases, that a group action stands or falls on the weakest case.[15] Although it might appear that the solicitor and barrister are simply at the command of these Byzantine twists to the legal system, it is very rare that solicitors in Britain make a stand against them in liability cases.

In March 1997, 18 months before the conference, Maggie began to think that she and other women who had contacted the Menopausal Helpline should sue the manufacturing drug companies.

In 1998, the women were granted legal aid to claim damages against Schering Health Care and Wyeth. The cases involved included Maggie's and that of Bernard Brankin on behalf of Irene. The women were sup-

---

15 This rule was introduced into English law after pressure from Wyeth.

ported by the Campaign for Informed Consent.[16] The main scientific expert supporting their case was Dr Ellen Grant, who had become a fierce opponent of 'exogenous' hormones. Dr Grant's research into the Pill had convinced her that the introduction of hormones into the human body would definitely 'increase cancers, heart attacks, strokes, migraines and the rate of suicide'.[17]

After contacting a law firm in the north of England, 24 women, Bernard Brankin and another man, got legal aid for a group action.

> One of the people considering independent legal action was Charles Knowles of Eccleshall, Staffordshire, whose wife had died after she had switched from HRT patches to an HRT pill. Mr Knowles said that his wife, who was 56, had decided to take HRT after suffering from the standard menopause symptoms. He claimed that she had been in good health and that she had not been called back for a check-up after taking the treatment for six months.[18]

In the *Daily Mail* of September 14, in a typical newspaper article that leant heavily towards the drug companies, two experts gave their view on the action. Kevin Gangar, a consultant gynaecologist at Ashford Hospital, Middlesex, said, 'I have never heard of a case in which a death caused by blood clot has been ascribed to HRT.' And author Dr Mike Smith said, 'If anything, the effect would be to produce a mild tendency to thin the blood.'

Joan Jenkins, founder and president of Women's Health Concern, said that she was sceptical about any of the HRT cases reaching court. 'HRT is the best thing that's happened to women, in terms of health, this century.'[19]

The group of claimants made their application for legal aid in October 1997, and by December 1997 there were 24 women involved in

---

16 Despite several Internet searches and some enquiries, I have been unable to find out anything about this organisation.

17 March 24 1997. Quoted in 'Women on HRT to sue over "blood clots"', an article by Gaby Hinsliff. See also Ellen Grant's books in the Bibliography.

18 Allison Daniele, 'Woman set to sue over HRT effects'. The *Guardian*, March 25 1997.

19 The late Joan Jenkins was in fact a staunch supporter of HRT from the beginning and involved other supporters and Wyeth in her organisation.

the action. All of them were claiming to have suffered serious side effects following the use of HRT. Inevitably, the cases were based upon a number of different illnesses, from deep-vein thrombosis or pulmonary embolism, through the whole series of life-ruining but not life-threatening adverse reactions suffered by Maggie and others.

As many claims for damages go, the initial stages of the case were dealt with quickly. Patients' records were traced – no easy matter in such cases, when the claimant is referring to treatments from different physicians over periods of up to ten years. Expert witnesses were gathered, research summaries produced, and outline documents examining the proof of causation prepared. Unfortunately for the claimants, in the cold legal light of day, except in a couple of cases, the link between HRT and a serious illness – in this case deep-vein thrombosis and cardiovascular disease – appeared tenuous. Claims had to be backed by scientific evidence that showed causation, and it was then necessary to show that the drug company had been negligent in failing to research the cause of these diseases or to warn the consumer about the risks.

From the beginning of the action, both 'independent' expert witnesses and counsel felt that the cases were not strong. While all the advisers showed considerable scepticism about almost all the claims made by the producing companies, except in the matter of the use of HRT for hot flushes, there was very little creditable evidence at that time that showed clearly that HRT caused heart disease, pulmonary embolism or deep-vein thrombosis.

The failure of the case, notification of which was sent to claimants in March 1999, came as a considerable disappointment. Claimants in cases of this kind build up expectations on the basis of their own feelings and experience. When the law and logic scupper their chances, they often feel aggrieved. The instructed solicitors had sent Maggie in the region of 17 letters between October 1997 and March 1999, keeping her in constant touch with the case. However, when it was called off, she felt so let down that she pursued a complaint against her lawyers through the Office for the Supervision of Solicitors.

The research carried out for the claimants' lawyers points out that, although there have been some out-of-court settlements, there have been no successful cases fought against pharmaceutical companies in Britain. The problem of gathering evidence for prosecuting claims against drug companies reaches back into the structure and nature of science and aca- demic writing. All too often the defendants have years of recorded and 'authoritative' science to back up their products, as well as protective reg- ulations, while the claimants have only 'fringe' scientists, and speculative radical criticism, which sometimes *appear* to be rooted in little more than prejudice.

One of the central problems for the claimants' lawyers in the case was that the producing companies had 'spread the muck' of apparent sci- entific benefits so deeply across the landscape of oestrogen replacement that it almost seemed like heresy for anyone to suggest that the drug did anyone harm. The other difficulty was that the data sheet information quoted so many adverse reactions to treatment that they could hardly be accused of not having warned patients.

Following the failure of Maggie's group to get to court, a Scottish claimant who had tried to take an action against her GP for very serious adverse reactions to HRT, also saw her case fail in the same way. In this case, the solicitors were forced to concede that, as the woman's consult- ant had suggested to her GP that she should take HRT for at least ten years, the GP would have been unlikely to dispute this.

Maggie's court case on behalf of her women went the same way as many other product liability cases in England: it disappeared down a black hole of which the defendants never even touched the sides. Looking back on the case now, Maggie has only a vague idea of what happened. In the main, the case was handled by her journalist friend, Jackie Williams, and it was she who kept contact with the solicitor. Maggie found the process very frustrating because, while she answered the Helpline phone for most of her waking hours, she was unable to be involved in the court case.

Behind the scenes, however, Bernard Brankin's case was settled out of court for £30,000 at around the same time as a North American woman who suffered cancer on HRT was bought off for just $40,000. With the death certificate, Brankin's case on behalf of his wife was the strongest in the group. The settlement was of no value at all to the campaign or to anyone taking any similar legal action. Out-of-court settlements do not constitute legal precedents. After the settlement, Bernard drifted out of contact with Maggie and the MHL.

In Britain, class actions, or actions by groups of people, are much harder to get off the ground than they are in North America. Every victim has to fight his or her case individually. This is ironic when one considers that the situation has arisen entirely because the drug manufacturers and physicians have refused to see the patient as unique individuals.

In 1998, Maggie met housewives' favourite smarmy, Dr Hilary Jones, on the *Richard and Judy* television show, and there was an enormous debacle. Maggie not only shouted Jones down, but used the 'p' word on morning television. While telling him in no uncertain terms that he was wrong to say that HRT simply returned hormone levels to normal, she asked him, not *sotto voce*, if he 'hadn't come across cases of women growing penises'. Of the hundreds of letters that poured into the Helpline after that particular confrontation, only one doubted Maggie's tactics in acting like a fishwife.

What the audience did not know was that this was a confrontation that Richard and Judy wanted to engineer. After Maggie had won the 'first round' on the early morning programme, the producers wanted to bring both protagonists back on after nine o'clock, made up as if they had been in a boxing match. Maggie would have nothing to do with this trivialisation of her cause, but she did return to the programme after nine o'clock to engage in another argument.

As Maggie slowly came out of her own personal illness caused by HRT, as her life began to stabilise and, as she began coming to terms with the personal financial cost of running the Helpline since 1996,[20] she realised that she had to finish her Helpline work and to draw a line under this part of her life.

In 1999 she began a move to Spain. Although she wanted to keep the Helpline, she also wanted to provide a therapeutic retreat for women from different countries affected by HRT. In 2002, she organised a conference in Spain to discuss the adverse reactions caused by HRT and to get women from other countries together.

---

20 Since 1996, the Helpline had cost Maggie in the region of £100,000. To raise this money she had sold property that she owned in London.

Maggie speaks almost guiltily now about the Helpline. Despite still owing over £10,000 as a consequence of running it, and despite doing more than any other person in Britain to fight the case of women who suffered after taking HRT, she is afraid she might not have done enough.

> I have done everything I can over the years to highlight the problem: interviews, demonstrations, conferences, publicity. I do think that through the Menopausal Helpline women have been able to speak about menopause. More and more women are able to come out about this and speak to the press about their experience. As well, the Helpline was responsible for putting women in different areas in touch with each other, so that they could get support. That continued after I stopped. Also, a number of women associated with the Helpline have done a lot of research into their own condition. I personally would like to think that we have forced the truth out as well as adding to the information. Women have said to me, 'We have won, if only because we campaigned.'

I met Maggie for the first time in 2002 when she contacted me over a court case in which she had become involved. She was, she told me, being sued under copyright law by Jackie Williams, the woman who had offered her help to the Menopausal Helpline.

The Menopausal Helpline was set up in the last months of 1995, and by the time she was approached by Jackie Williams early in 1996, Maggie had already received letters and phone calls from thousands of women. Jackie said that she had seen Maggie being interviewed on television and thought that, although she herself had not taken HRT, she might be able to help.

Maggie was glad to have the help of a 'journalist'. She asked Jackie if she would write a book about the women who had been affected, and, together, they began to plan it. Over the next four years, they both worked on this project, with Maggie financing Jackie in her research. Jackie travelled to Florence, Egypt, Sweden, Spain and around the UK, gathering research material and interviews. Maggie drove Jackie to many places to interview both lay sufferers and experts, she bought source books and introduced Jackie to a number of doctors and other professionals with whom she had come into contact. And, of course, Maggie passed on information that came into the Helpline. In 1998, Jackie took charge of the court case.

Although it had been decided that the booklet on which Jackie and Maggie had been working would be presented at the Brighton conference, and although Maggie had made a point of mentioning it in interviews in the lead-up, as the date approached Maggie and some associates had to put pressure on Jackie to produce it. Still, the two women appeared to be on the best of terms during the conference.

Maggie paid the £1,500 for the printing of the first and only 300 copies of the A4 'booklet'. The publication had the names of both Maggie Tuttle and Jackie Williams on its front cover.

Following the conference, however, Maggie and Jackie had a number of disagreements. Jackie, together with a friend whom she had brought into the Helpline group, argued for professionalism in the organisation. In fact, they reiterated a number of the arguments that had been put by the Charity Commission, and that were undoubtedly being put by the pharmaceutical companies, about the Helpline.

One of Jackie's complaints was that Maggie was giving advice without medical training, to people who consulted the organisation. She also wanted to set up an office and to have this staffed, and she proposed that callers should make financial contributions in exchange for advice. In Maggie's opinion, this kind of professionalisation was the quickest way to put an organisation beyond the reach of the women for whom it should speak. She was adamant that those who contacted the Helpline should not be used in any way, and despite the fact that she had been approached by numerous commercial organisations, she was determined never to give a stake in it to any vested interests.

After the conference, the only contact that Maggie had with the book – most copies of which had sold at the conference – was the continuing distribution of its synopsis. Both she and Jackie Williams had worked on this, and Maggie began sending it out with both of their names on it. It was a useful document for focusing on the issues involved. Around March 1999, Jackie and her friend resigned from the Menopausal Helpline.

As Jackie and Maggie drifted even further apart, Jackie appeared to become concerned that Maggie would republish the booklet on HRT, which she now considered to be owned and authored by herself rather than being owned by the MHL, and jointly authored, as had previously been accepted. After a series of letters to Maggie went unanswered, Jackie Williams took her case to court in an attempt to obtain personal copyright of the manuscript and to constrain Maggie from having any ownership or control over it.

In the middle of the turbulent period of moving to Spain, Maggie found that she was called to court in England to face a trial. Worried at having to appear on an issue about which she knew nothing, she employed a firm of solicitors to defend her. Within a year, before the substantive issue in the case had even come to court, Maggie already owed the lawyer £13,000.[21]

It was with the court hearing pending that Maggie first contacted me and asked for my help.[22] I was loath to get involved in the court case because I knew nothing about copyright law. However, when I saw the papers I had no doubt that I could do better than the very ordinary, but very costly, defence that her lawyer had prepared. When the case was finally heard, Maggie conceded the copyright of the report without argument. She then asked the court for costs to be awarded against Williams on the grounds that her actions in taking the matter to court were precipitous and had cost Maggie, a charity worker, £13,000. The judge awarded almost half Maggie's costs against Jackie Williams.[23]

Through this involvement in Maggie's court case, I got involved in writing this book. Maggie was desperate to make public the plight of

---

21 Jackie Williams had embarked upon the court case in person, which meant that her costs were minimal. However, if she had won a case outright and been able to show some maligned intent to breach copyright on Maggie's behalf, she might have been entitled to damages and, certainly, Maggie would have had to pay her costs.

22 From the mid Seventies, I had acted for people who had been wrongly arrested or wrongly imprisoned and wanted to defend themselves rather than use a solicitor. When I met Maggie, we found that we had both been working for prisoner organisations, just up the road from each other, in the Seventies.

23 The peculiar nature of civil litigation in England made this court order highly ineffective. So far these costs have not been paid.

what she consistently refers to as 'The Women'.[24] Despite the fact that Maggie was unable to continue the work of the MHL, and as anarchic as she is, I personally agreed with her about not forming a more 'professional' representative organisation. My experience of many campaigning organisations since the late Sixties is that their radicalism rarely survives the transitions and, anyway, this is the door through which, in time, the drug companies enter.

It seemed to me that the women who consulted the Helpline wanted to talk to and to seek empathy from someone with a burning passion, who had gone through what they were going through, not to engage with a politically correct 'women's' counsellor with, perhaps, a couple of toes in the HRT camp.

I learnt a lot about Maggie from her case. Like many people driven to set up campaigning organisations, apart from being slightly eccentric, she is also quite egocentric – she probably would have got little done had she not been. Her approach to the court hearing, the financial losses that she had accumulated as a consequence of it, and her complete preoccupation with the pain of the women whom the Helpline had set out to help, were all indicative of the kind of person she is.

Maggie has a transparent integrity. She suffered at the hands of the medical profession and she then contacted other women who had similar experiences. From that point on, Maggie had only one objective, and that was to make public what had happened to them. Even at the cost of her savings, even at the cost of any job or personal life, Maggie wanted to expose the problems of HRT. She was not even faintly interested in who had the rights over a relatively insignificant manuscript or who might make money from it. Nor was she interested in being the founder of a women's organisation that had to depend on grants and professional advisers. She did not have the slightest wish to advance in any kind of career for herself. She wanted only to talk to other women about the adverse effects of HRT and to propagate their stories.

---

24 I have only read a couple of sentences from *Cause of Death HRT*, because seeing Williams's penchant for legal actions, I did not want, even subconsciously, to draw on any of it for this book. Nevertheless, even reading a couple of sentences and glancing at its overall plan, I could see that the work was not that substantial.

Women of the Menopausal Helpline

In my opinion, there is no sound basis for assuring any woman that any dose of any oestrogen, given for any reason, is safe.

John Bailar[25]

THE FOLLOWING THREE chapters are about the problems suffered by women on HRT who contacted the Menopausal Helpline. The Helpline was never a well-organised affair, stemming as it did from Maggie's very individualistic sense of justice. Although it might have been better for posterity and social science if Maggie and her friends had made detailed records of everyone with whom they dealt, what was left behind by the MHL was quite astonishing.

As soon as it started, the Menopausal Helpline began to receive stories recounted by women who, like Maggie, had suffered adverse reactions to HRT. Maggie always did her best to answer the letters that were sent to her, but, from the beginning, hundreds and then thousands of letters arrived, and it was difficult.

The manufacturers of HRT had not been behind in including as many adverse reactions as possible to HRT in the patient literature that accompanied their products. The listed adverse side effects, indeed, reached bizarre proportions. There was hardly a health problem that HRT did not create in the consumer. For the manufacturers, this listing was, of course, their best defence against any future complaint; doctors

---

25 John Bailar, statistician at the National Cancer Institute cited by Sharon Batt. In *Patient No More*, op. cit.

could be blamed for not checking patients' histories and for not carrying out sufficient tests prior to prescription. At the same time, it was clear that if the treatments were prescribed only for the few women that they suited, the drugs would not be money spinners. In fact, the massive number of women using HRT over the years consists of many women who use it for a couple of months and then, because of the adverse side effects, stop taking it.

In Maggie's opinion and that of many other Helpline contacts, some of the adverse reactions described in relatively inconsequential terms by the producers of HRT, doctors and government agencies, could completely destroy a woman's quality of life. But the core problem with reviewing adverse reactions to HRT, and regulating on the basis of them, is that the producing companies have, through the NHS and other agencies, run a constant campaign marketing the apparently 'beneficial' effects of the treatment.

HRT might, if properly administered, stop hot flushes, but even at the least damaging end of the risk curve it might also cause the growth of facial hair or cause hair loss on the head or a constant burning sensation; some women might think this a poor and unnecessary exchange. At a slightly more advanced point on the risk curve, a woman taking it for a relatively short period at low dosage might develop pancreatitis and gall bladder disease.

But deep at the root of the propaganda about HRT, the most important and unarguable fact remains: if you are taking a hormone replacement to counter adverse effects of the menopause, as soon as you stop taking it your menopause will probably start again. This time you might be in for an even rougher ride. Of course, you could stay on it for the rest of your life, in which case, day by day, your chances of breast cancer, heart attack or thrombosis would rise.

In the case of HRT specifically, and medicine in general, a number of factors have aided corporations and physicians in dodging criticism. Health has always been a very private matter, and, especially in Britain, doctors have enforced that privacy, even, until relatively recently, by refusing to let the patient see his or her own records, which are also the only record of doctors' professional behaviour.

Issues relating to sexuality, to menstruation, to the menopause, and inevitably to ageing, hold fears for many female patients, just as issues such as impotence, prostate cancer and also ageing, do for men. Even in enlightened times, most people probably want to keep the most intimate aspects of their health identity to themselves. At the same time, these glitches in life's progress presented the pharmaceutical companies with a massive and developing market for drugs sales.

While it might appear possible that women doctors would deal more sympathetically with women patients going through the menopause, a medical training often ensures that they put the rules of science and professional medicine before the politics of their gender. Consequently, in general, women doctors seem to have followed the same pattern in prescribing HRT as their male colleagues. As medicine is, however, dominated by men, women's medical issues are still dominated by male doctors, who are more often than not linked to either the medical establishment or pharmaceutical companies. This is particularly true in the area of menopause.

During the years between 1996 and 2003, the Menopausal Helpline received around 10,000 letters from women either asking for information or relating what had happened to them. In 1999, the Helpline began sending out a questionnaire on the adverse side effects of HRT (see Appendix I – MHL Questionnaire.) Between 1999 and 2003, almost 700 of the survey forms were returned.

Apart from having a long checklist of adverse reactions, the forms asked what kind of preparation the women had used and for how long. Both the letters from women and the survey forms were assiduously kept, and cases were always responded to, giving suffering women information about alternatives and putting them in touch with others with similar problems.

The three chapters that follow have taken information from the 697 survey forms (from women using different forms of HRT), together with quotes from 53 of the most detailed letters sent in to the MHL, and draw some general conclusions from the contents of other letters.

I arrived at these 53, having selected around 200 of the most detailed from the thousands received by the MHL. These, I whittled down to 145, and wrote to their authors seeking their consent to quote from them. I received 58 replies, of which 53 gave that consent.

None of the information, in either the letters or the questionnaires, gives us any indication of the numbers or percentage of women who have suffered adverse reactions after taking HRT, either generally or of specific brands. On the whole, letters and questionnaires were received and requested on two or three occasions when Maggie appeared prominently, either on television or in a major newspaper, and they were inevitably highly self-selecting.

There are many different forms of HRT, mainly manufactured by a small number of companies. The returned questionnaires on adverse reactions cited 22 different brands of HRT. They vary in constituent hormones and method of delivery; some oestrogens are synthetic, while others are produced from the urine of pregnant mares (which does not of course make them 'natural', nor stop them being mixed with other damaging chemical substances). Some HRT oestrogens are administered with progesterone, others on their own.

HRT is delivered in pill form, via patches, and by way of implants that disperse hormones unevenly over a six-month period, and that continue to produce hormones long after they are *supposed* to have biodegraded. Preparations can also be administered as creams, which again deliver hormones unevenly over a period of hours.

All forms of HRT have adverse reactions, some of them more severe than others. Some of them – notably implants – crudely cause serious adverse reactions, simply because they are uncontrollable. Many adverse reactions are caused by either too much oestrogen or progesterone, or too little. These hormone deficiencies, or in some cases overdoses, have startling effects on the subtle interaction of many glands and secreting organs of the body.

Some forms of HRT, in some women, produce almost immediate adverse reactions; others create problems only after they have been taken for longer periods and deleterious chemicals have built up in the body, or hormone levels have passed their saturation points. Some women get adverse reactions months after coming off HRT, when their oestrogen supply plummets to an all-time low. Synthetic hormones are not the same as natural ones, and their chemical make-up can cause adverse reactions in the form of allergies and intolerances. The chemicals listed on the patient information leaflets as only traces can build up over time, while some women even find themselves allergic or sensitive to the plastic or adhesive used on patches.

Despite the many different brands of HRT, I have not mentioned these when quoting from women's stories below. It is not the task of this book to recommend one form of HRT over another, or to suggest that one form provokes little adverse reaction, while another provokes massive reactions. The view expressed throughout the book is that neither doctors nor manufacturers of HRT can realistically give assurances about the safety of hormone replacement therapy to anyone.

Chapter Two

Changing Ros

I can only say that we are not all the same and I wish that doctors would see this.

Woman affected by HRT [1]

Professional callousness, negligence and sheer incompetence are age-old forms of malpractice. With the transformation of the doctor from an artisan exercising a skill on personally known individuals into a technician applying scientific rules to classes of patients, malpractice acquired a new, anonymous, almost respectable status.

Ivan Illich [2]

Since she has been on HRT, Ros has been changing, literally, she tells me, the minute I get into the car at the railway station where she has driven to meet me. Ros, who has red hair, laughs almost all the time, and at our first meeting it is difficult to tell how serious she is. As I settle into the car, she thrusts her head towards me. 'See,' she says, with her strong Norfolk accent, 'you wouldn't see it, of course, you don't know what to look for, but I have acromegaly, my jaw is growing.'

---

1 Letter to the MHL.

2 Illich, Ivan. *Medical Nemesis: The expropriation of health*. London: Calder & Boyers; 1975.

I later learn that acromegaly is a rare condition caused by autonomous secretion of growth hormone. Overproduction of growth hormone can be caused by the suppression of adrenalin, normally produced when the body is under stress. In turn, all these conditions and others are precipitated by an excess of oestrogen.

Later in the interview, Ros tells me twice, taking pride in it, that she is very 'in yer face', but in the car on first meeting her, I don't know how to respond. She continues to talk, however, without expecting a response until we reach her home on the Essex-Suffolk border. I quickly realise that I'm not going to be able to grasp the unregulated outflow of her pent-up story, so I sit back and look at the countryside of the Harwich Peninsula. Ros is still talking when we sit down at the pine table in her newly-appointed kitchen. Now, however, I can put on the tape recorder, and, anyway, she has slowed down. Perhaps she is wondering what comes next, thinking that she has already told me everything as she drove.

One of the interesting things about interviewing people is that you find they often take a great deal for granted. They begin to talk to you as if their very life suppositions are the same as yours and any other sensible person's. People who have been forced to consider their own illness for long periods, talk to you in a kind of shorthand, leaping over what they believe is common knowledge between you.

The interviewer and interviewee share an intimacy based upon their desire, on the one hand, to impart information, and, on the other hand, to glean it. Interviewees, a little like allopathic doctors, focus in a very detailed manner, almost mechanically, on their illness, rarely thinking to give contextual information. The interviewer, a writer in this case, is, however, not so much interested in the exact biological nature of the illness as in how the subject perceives it, how it has changed them, and, perhaps, how they conceive of their rights. What the subject considers an irrelevant part of their story often has to be prised from them.

In 1988, Ros was 39 and married to Harry, a bodybuilder ten years her senior. Harry worked in the local port container depot, he had brought a son to the marriage, and later he and Ros had a daughter. Ros's marriage to Harry lasted 20 years. Both children are now adults, and Ros and Harry, who split up a couple of years ago, have a firm and supportive friendship. Ros readily understands how her illness, created by HRT, was partially responsible for the break-up of their marriage.

In the late Eighties, Ros worked for a home-visiting agency for elderly people, franchised out by the district council. Working with a team, she was responsible for placing elderly people already living in council accommodation into new accommodation that better suited their needs. After she left that job, she became a mobile deputy warden, covering two care homes in her area. During her two years as deputy warden, Harry's uncle became ill and she began to care for him.

Looking back on this period, it seems to Ros that she was always busy. Every morning, she got the children up, made the family breakfast then drove the 15 miles to Clacton, where she did a day's work, returning in the late afternoon to make the dinner. She began to notice, at this time, that she was experiencing hot flushes and feeling dizzy.

Her local GP was quite certain that she had begun the menopause. So certain was he, indeed, that, without any further discussion, and without taking a case history of her family's medical background or ordering any blood tests, he prescribed HRT, in pill form. Six months later, when Ros attended the surgery again, she told the doctor that, far from feeling better, she actually felt worse than she had done on first coming to him. According to Ros, her doctor said, 'Well, that's the menopause for you, we'll up the dose.'

Over the next six months of taking HRT, Ros noticed her periods had become heavier and that she had become very bad-tempered. She had, she says, repeating again in her East Anglian accent, 'always been a bit in yer face', but this was different. Now she was, she says, positively irascible. Then the tiredness started, and within a short time she had become a frequent visitor to her GP, who, when she demanded to see another doctor, sent her to a gynaecologist.

After an examination, the gynaecologist told Ros that she had five fibroids in her uterus.[3] According to the consultant, Ros's ovaries needed removing because they had become atrophied. Ros told the gynaecologist that she noticed that during the time she had been taking HRT, her

---

3 Fibroids are benign growths composed of smooth muscle and connective tissue. Fibroids weighing more than 20 pounds have been reported.

breasts had become bigger and felt very solid. What the gynaecologist did not tell Ros was that the conditions she was experiencing could be caused by the circulation of high levels of oestrogen. In 1991, when she was 42, Ros had her womb and ovaries removed.

Six weeks after her operation, Ros went back to see the gynaecologist, who told her that she should discuss with her doctor how she would like to take an inevitably-increased dose of oestrogens. Her GP gave her three choices: pills, a patch or an implant. Because it seemed to fit in best with her lifestyle – she wasn't a pill person, she said – Ros chose the implant.

This, her doctor assured her, could just be popped in, and would disperse its oestrogen over time, then biodegrade. Ros was given the maximum permitted 100 milligrams, a dose banned in some countries.[4] She was not given any kind of analytical tests to discover exactly what her hormone parameters were.

Ros accepted the idea of an implant, and the implant itself, without worries or doubts about the judgement of her doctor. The gynaecologist had told her that she would have to be on HRT for the next 20 years, and her doctor had given her a choice. Both these things seemed to mitigate the possibility of any bad consequences or adverse side effects.

Ros was given her first implant in the February after her hysterectomy; her second in November. Soon after this, she went on holiday to Malaysia. Looking at the videos of that holiday she saw that she had gained weight and realised that her dress size had gone from a 12 to a 14.

While the family watched the holiday videos with friends, Ros was struck by a comment of her daughter's. 'This is my mother asleep on the beach,' her daughter said. 'She's ill – in fact, she's always ill.' Ros thought, 'Is that right? Am I always ill?' It was then, for the first time, that she saw the person she had become since beginning to take HRT. She now had frequent headaches, which she had never had before. And, it wasn't just her head; all the bones in her face ached as if they had been frozen. She was always grumpy, as she put it, always tired, and felt sick much of the time.

---

4 Hormone implants for women are not approved in North America by the FDA.

Over the next nine years, her visits to the doctor became ever more frequent, as different parts of her body began to 'play up'. From a healthy, energetic woman who had seldom had the need to see her GP, she appeared to her family and others to have become a hypochondriac. She visited her doctor for problems with her sinuses, her stomach, her bowels, and she saw a consultant for each of these conditions. At one point, one of her legs felt as if it had been cut off at the knee. Like her jawbone, her legs ached painfully and then were consumed with numbness. Eating became painful because, unbeknown to her, she was developing ulcers around the diaphragm at the neck of her stomach.

The continuous pains in her jaw sent Ros back time and again to her dentist, who, although sympathetic, kept reassuring her that he could find nothing wrong with her teeth. She made a number of phone calls to the HRT manufacturers, thinking that they might be able to shed some light on her multiple painful condition. On one occasion, when she was persistent, she was told by Organon: 'This call will be logged as a nuisance call.' Ros laughs menacingly at the recollection.

Despite her constant questions about whether or not HRT could possibly be the cause of her declining health, Ros was still not given an oestrogen-level test. In the year 2000, however, she had a prolonged bout of thrush and was sent to the genito-urinary department of her local hospital. There they took a blood sample, and the doctor commented on the fact that her oestradiol was high. Oestradiol is the most potent oestrogen hormone, secreted by the ovary and delivered in 'natural' or synthetic form in HRT. The level quoted by the doctor that December was 2,110.

By April of 2001, Ros was as ill as she had ever been in her life. Describing this condition now, her breath leaves her body like a death rattle as she says, 'So ill. You can't imagine how ill.' When her iatrogenic illness was at its worst, Ros couldn't walk and had to crawl across the floor.

By August of 2001, Ros was at her doctor's surgery every week. She looked haggard, she says, and her face looked as if she had had a stroke. Now she found difficulty in breathing, and sleep had become impossible. She was constantly dizzy, never more so than when she lay down. Her blood pressure dropped. When Ros was really ill she couldn't close her eyes for fear of becoming dizzy and falling over. She was weak and exhausted. In the middle of August when she was at her most ill, she went again to her dentist, the pains in her jaw were worse than they had every been and she thought the pain must have something to do with her teeth; she also sensed that her front teeth had moved forward slightly.

When her dentist looked at her teeth on this visit, he said, for the first time, that it looked as if she had a protrusive jaw, something that he had not noticed before. He looked at her records and told her that she had been complaining about an aching jaw since 1989 when she went on HRT. Still, however, he couldn't find anything wrong with her jaw. On her next visit back to the doctors, she told him that she knew she was ill and that she was actually growing. She asked her doctor what her oestrogen levels were meant to be. He told her that he didn't know. Ros put on her most cutting tone and said, 'You've been putting implants in me for ten years, and yet you don't know what my oestrogen levels are supposed to be?' When Ros left the surgery, she told her doctor, trying to convince him, that she was really ill. Yes, 'You're always ill,' he said.

Ros went to the hospital and demanded that her oestradiol be measured; it came back with a test result of 2,100. Still trying to work, she fell off a ladder and her injuries forced her to take sick leave.

Finally, unable to think what she could do, she rang the HRT manufacturers and asked them what the average level of oestradiol should be. She was told 600. When she told the company that hers was over 2,000, they suggested she was mistaken. Full of fury, Ros went straight from the phone call, back to the hospital genito-urinary clinic and asked for a copy of the blood-test results, together with the accompanying paperwork.

Yes, her levels were 2,110, and the graph on the lab report stated 800 was the absolute maximum – *although this is twice as high as the normally quoted maximum of 400*. She then went to her GP and demanded that her last implant be removed. She listened in shock and stupor as he told her that this was not possible. She also asked for a growth hormone test. When the results came back, the level, which should ideally have been nine, was 21.

By the time Ros found that the implants had come near to killing her, the last implant had turned to a biodegraded jelly and had begun to disperse in her body. It was impossible to remove it, to counter its effects or to lower her oestrogen levels.

ROS

Looking back on what was happening to her from the perspective of her knowledge now, Ros sees that the extra oestrogen had 'knocked out' her adrenal glands, and, consequently, growth hormones were being pumped into her system.

A range of effects caused by overdosing on oestrogen is well documented, from clinical cases in humans. Apart from constant and general ill health as a consequence of a series of body functions being affected, the most significant effects include the growth of fibroids and the atrophying of the ovaries, falling blood pressure, a rising level of growth hormone release and impaired adrenal function.

When I spoke to Ros in 2004, her level of oestradiol was 512, which was still high enough to continue the overproduction of growth hormones and interfere with her adrenal function.

$$\mathbb{V} \qquad \mathbb{V} \qquad \mathbb{V}$$

Everyone responds differently to personal injustice, whether it is a trespass by a neighbour over a property boundary, or an iatrogenic injury by a doctor or a hospital. Individuals have different ideas about which disputes are 'worth the bother', about how much energy can be expended. People are differently polite or embarrassed by public conflict. Some are naturally argumentative, while others can't wait to get out there and test their strength. Sometimes, individuals want to forget about conflict and simply get on with their lives.

While writing my book *Dirty Medicine*, I often observed the quandary that alternative practitioners and doctors who embraced holistic medicine were faced with when they were attacked professionally. By and large, most practitioners decided that their work as healers was more important than fighting to clear the damage that had been done to their reputation. In North America, one practitioner, however, cleared the decks and devoted two years to defending himself against the attack upon him by self-appointed, so-called 'quackbusters'.

Decisions about strategies are equally complex and based on many factors, from the individual's personality to the degree of the insult and the accessibility of means of redress. While some respond with measured fatalism, employing the recognised social instruments, considering that they have no power and few options, others rashly take up cudgels. Some burn themselves out after a short show of temper, while others sit down calmly, developing a mission, planning strategies and resolving battle plans. Some people brush aside the damage done to them, while others strive for decades to right wrongs that others consider of little consequence. Many strategies are necessarily dictated by available funds.

As social structures become more complex, the route to the resolution of conflicts between people also becomes more difficult. In the early village, any conflicts between parties, all of whom probably knew each other (if they were not, indeed, related), might have been easily resolved. Although it has to be said that in all societies the poor and the powerless always have difficulty in resolving conflicts with the rich and the powerful.

Contemporary Britain has not gone down the same road as North America with respect to legal claims for damages.[5] As a consequence, there exists no clear-cut route that the medically injured may take in their search for justice. The judicial system should give a voice to the damaged, and apportion blame, as well as initiating some form of compensation to claimants. In Britain, the most powerful corporations have, in the area of drug product liability, gained complete control of the judicial system.

In many cases of iatrogenic illness, victims find that their primary goal is to return to health, but others consider that their return to health can be helped only by fighting to right the wrong that has been done to them. Some victims are too ill to fight battles, and their hopes and their cases become invisible. Those individuals who do fight back have a doubly hazardous course in front of them, for, as well as learning about their legal or legitimate rights, they also have to familiarise themselves with the details of their medical condition and its treatment, while coping with their illness.

Women seem to be particularly good at learning about their illnesses and taking an analytical and campaigning stance. While men seem to objectify their illnesses, seeing them, as it were, as separate from them-

---

5 The social and moral conflicts that surround product liability litigation for compensation in North America are seriously and entertainingly discussed in two of John Grisham's novels: *The King of Torts* (NY: Doubleday; 2003) and *The Runaway Jury* (London: Arrow; 1996). We might also mention the brilliant *A Civil Action* by Jonathan Harr (NY: Vintage Books; 1996).

selves, women acknowledge them as a part of themselves, and tend to understand that the road to recovery is locked into their whole perception of themselves. Many of the women adversely affected by HRT took to a medical education like ducks to water. When I suggested to Ros that I would probably find difficulty in understanding the medical aspects of the condition brought on by her adverse reactions to HRT, she laughed and said, 'If *I* can pick it up, it can't be rocket science.'

Such a remark obscures a self-evident truth about some women campaigners around medical issues: even if they did have to learn rocket science, a very personal and overpowering sense of injustice would drive them to do it, and to do it well.

In autumn 2001, Ros went to see a Department of Health and Social Security (DHSS) doctor to be assessed for her right to claim state benefit. Physicians involved in this programme are usually like police doctors: they go through the motions, but, at the end of the day, the patient knows that the doctor's assessment will be tempered in part by strategic needs. The doctor Ros saw, however, turned out to be surprisingly well up on the campaign critical of HRT; he mentioned *What Doctors Don't Tell You* [6] and then put her in touch with Maggie and the Menopausal Helpline. Maggie, in turn, put Ros in contact with a number of other women who had been through similar experiences.

From the beginning, Ros focused her campaign for justice on the fact that her excessive oestrogen intake had produced massive overproduction of growth hormone.

Ros knew that she would be on thin ice were she to argue the case for all her various states of ill health induced by HRT. After all, with her doctor taking next to no notice of her, there was scant record of what had become very real physical complaints.

Whenever Ros approached the doctor about her increased rate of growth, which she claims she could sometimes actually feel, she was told not to be silly, so she determined to educate herself about her condition. Now, like other women, she speaks about it with a fluency that leaves a

---

6 *What Doctors Don't Tell You* is a journal started by Lynne McTaggart, a North American writer and journalist. For some years it has been the only consistent voice raised against the mistakes and corruption of allopathic medicine in Britain.

lay person like me struggling to catch up. Even before Ros contacted Maggie, she had learned how to use the Internet on a computer that her sister was about to throw out. Having learnt how to gather information, she set about investigating the science behind her complaint.

When Ros was told by her doctor that her symptoms could not be relieved because her implant could not be taken out, she went straight to a solicitor whose advertisement she had seen on television. The first solicitor to deal with her case appeared uninterested, so it was transferred. The firm used £12,500's worth of legal aid, mainly on finding Ros's medical notes, and despite their claims of 'no win, no fee', Ros has herself had to pay £5,000 towards her case.

At the solicitors' suggestion, Ros began a case against both her doctor, who had given her continuing prescriptions for HRT without taking either a blood test to establish her oestrogen levels or a careful case history about family illness, and the gynaecologist consultant, who advised an increase in her dose of HRT without giving her a blood test.

From the beginning of her action, her orthodontist was her best support. Clearly surprised to have a patient whose jawbones were creating terrible pain without any obvious signs of problems related to her teeth, he has monitored Ros's bone growth over a three-year period. He has produced computerised evidence of unstable bone growth that should not be occurring in a woman of Ros's age.

Throughout the case, Ros did not actually see her solicitor, and all her discussions with him were conducted over the phone. It is Ros, in the main, who searched for papers and gathered the evidence. This pattern is all too common in medical negligence cases, which tend, in England, to be treated like low-level consumer complaints. Many solicitors working in large practices that advertise 'no win, no fee' work are more concerned about harvesting legal aid than with fighting, with any commitment, for justice.

As soon as Ros began her search for evidence, the system shut down on her. She found it increasingly difficult to get tests done on the NHS or to get hold of her records. Her blood-test results for the second half of the 1990s disappeared from her files. For the medics involved in Ros's case, there was now a race against time: if they could obstruct her for as long as possible, her oestradiol test levels would eventually return to their normal parameters, and, anyway, the case would run out of time.

But, as in nearly all the other HRT cases brought through uncommitted solicitors, what really killed the case off was the solicitor's ignorance in approaching an expert witness who was actually an expert in prescribing HRT, but not in its dangers and adverse reactions.

The 'expert witness' approached by the lawyer concluded, 'I do not believe there is any hard evidence that any of Mrs Gale's symptoms would have been related to the hormone implant she received … although I would concur with the view that she was almost certainly over-prescribed this medication.' According to this expert, the over-prescription was not a problem, because, as he had said earlier in his report, plenty of women had high oestrogen levels. What this really means is that, although Ros was over-prescribed, and although insufficient tests were carried out to record her oestrogen levels, either no one had made a research correlation between HRT overdosing and growth hormones, or the expert had not searched the literature and taken a more embracing approach to the reporting on bone growth and hormones.

Of course, the 'expert testimony' that there was no hard evidence that any of Ros's symptoms can have been related to the hormone implants, was probably completely honest and straightforward, but inevitably it was based upon the 'expert's' own particular experience, which, as we will see in the rest of this book, is often insubstantial when it comes to adverse reactions or to following the most up-to-date research. Worse, when women do present devastating adverse reactions to HRT, those experts tend to discount any connection, and will often refer patients on to a psychiatrist: their experience counts for nothing when they learn nothing from it.

While the expert agreed that Ros's doctors' care had been 'suboptimal', he suggested that none of the symptoms described by Ros would have alerted her GP to the adverse effects of HRT. Here again, the problem is multiple: the GP was entirely ignorant of Ros suffering any adverse reactions to HRT, and probably, like many other GPs, didn't even bother to record all the details of those reactions. And even if he had, given this prescriber's blind spot, it is unlikely that he would have recognised them for what they were.

Without making any specific suggestions about this particular expert witness, it is clear from his introduction to the report that it is not part of the convention of expert witnesses to state any conflicts of interest. Although the expert says clearly that he 'deals with patients on HRT', the question of whether or not he prescribes this treatment is left hanging in the air. There is no clue as to who might fund his research or his department.

In my opinion, Ros had a near-faultless attitude to her predicament. She approached her legal case with scepticism. She was forceful and dynamic about her commitment to seeing her doctor and the drugs company punished for the illness she has suffered, but she never banked on winning. She accepted that her solicitor would do little without her constantly pushing, and she realised she had to do most of the initial research in her own case. Her Plan B was always to hope that a journalist or a writer would give full exposure to her situation. In all this, the MHL acted to galvanise her, putting her in touch with others who have been similarly affected, while encouraging her to fight back.

It's April 2006, and I'm talking to Ros on the phone, just sorting out a few odds and ends about her story before the book goes to the printers. She tells me that she has sent me some extra papers. My heart sinks. Constant reworking of the manuscript has left me worried when someone says that they have sent more documents. Then, before I can reply, she fires off a question in her own inimitable way, with a rising inflection, hinting at some deep significance.

'So why is it that they don't print a range on your oestradiol test?' I try to focus on the conversation.

'You know, why don't they give the range references?'

I had the picture of the test results form in my mind now. First there is a main heading for the category of tests, then listed below a heading for the specific tests. Reading from left to right you find the results of the specific test, expressed as a number, then on from that there is the reference range so that you know whether your reading is inside or outside the range:

Cortisol (9am) –   –   –   –   301 nmol/L   (150 –680)

I thought back to one of Ros's test results forms I *had* seen, which had showed her oestradiol levels to be alarmingly high. It hadn't had a reference range on it, but someone had scrawled on the bottom of the test paper, 'Tell her it's low.'

'Don't they? I asked.

'Well they haven't on mine, I've sent it to you.' [7]

'What about other people you have been in contact with?'

'No, they don't have it either.'

My mind goes back to some of the other women who have shared their stories, who have expressed dismay at being blatantly lied to by consultants who have told them that dangerously high oestrogen levels are not actually high at all.

'Are you saying that there is some kind of conspiracy, Ros?'

The arch, almost scratching tone in her voice, makes me feel inadequate as a writer and an investigator.

'Conspiracy? Of course there's a conspiracy!'

And I thought that *I* was supposed to be the conspiracy theorist, but I know that other women have said this to me in exactly the same exasperated voice. The only matter to be resolved is semantic. Is there a conspiracy in the sense of a wide network of doctors giving women HRT in different forms and then pooling information of the resultant effects, or do doctors simply resort to common templates when they 'cover up' for their mistakes in prescribing HRT?

---

7 See Appendix VII: Ros's serum test results.

Chapter Three

Adverse Circumstances

The problems of three little people don't add up to a hill of beans in this crazy world.

Humphrey Bogart: Casablanca.

A sense of health is not the mere absence of disease, but that which concerns the individual's actions and their growth; not something which can be 'given' but something they, themselves, must take.

The Peckham Experiment[1]

Am I unlucky or is someone at fault?

Letter to the Menopausal Helpline

In 1926 the first steps were taken to set up a pioneer health centre in South London. By 1939, when the project had become known as the 'Peckham Experiment', the large modern building of the health centre, designed to accommodate around 7,500 people, included a school, a swimming pool, a ballroom, a library, self-service cafes, mother-and-baby groups, pre-school and toddlers groups, together with classes and lectures in everything from sewing to economics. On Saturday nights the centre regularly held dances with orchestras and bands.

---

1 Pearse IH, Crocker LH. The Peckham Experiment: A study in the living structure of society. London: G Allen and Unwin; 1943.

As well as all this, there were doctors and surgeries for the whole family. All families who signed up had a full range of tests carried out, and a health profile was formulated before any preventive or remedial treatments were begun.

The Peckham Experiment was built on money raised by a small committee of lay people to deal with the health needs of their community. The medical practice of the centre was based upon a number of ideas: the service of science to humankind, the fostering and development of self-help, and the idea that wellness was a positive state quite different from the mere absence of disease.

The approach of the biologists and physicians who worked at the centre was that good health was a continuous fact, and that healthy babies, for example, were not simply produced by good early feeding, but by assuring the pre-conceptual good health of both the mother and father. There were classes in Peckham in pre-conceptual care, and the organisation of the activities in the centre tried to ensure the everyday happiness and health of the whole family.

The ideas of the Peckham Experiment survive today only in the most rudimentary manner in the idea of the community health centre. The failings of the original project in post-modern eyes are easily imagined; it was, although privately funded, a 'public' project by design, and despite its insistence on self-help and education, it might today be seen as 'communistic'. Certainly, the project was dominated by the idea, very prevalent in the 1920s and 1930s under both capitalism and communism, that it was possible to organise both individual and social health scientifically. The emphasis at Peckham was not on the study of long-established traditions of health care, but on the brave new world of biology, the microscope and collective callisthenics.

When, however, we look at what is going wrong with modern medicine and its practice, we can see that there is much more than the 'seeds' of a good idea in the Peckham experiment. Most things in society work best in small communities. In today's primary health care system, there are so many possibilities of rifts between doctors and their patients, that there is a constant danger of communication breaking down, with plenty of opportunity for patients to remain ignorant and for doctors to take advantage of that ignorance.

Even within a system of socialised medicine, today health is considered to be primarily a private matter. There is nothing wrong with this *per se*, but in the shadow of collective privacy, we all suffer a lack of knowledge about both health and the system that our society has organised for its care.

In previous, smaller, communities with less mobile populations, where doctors stayed in practices for longer and everyone in the community knew everyone else, a practitioner might have knowledge of three generations of one family.

Reading through women's letters and then interviewing a number of women, it became clear to me that one of the most upsetting fractures in the continuity between doctor and patient is that which occurred after women had reported extreme adverse reactions to HRT. They were told that these reactions were not real, or had to be seen as new illnesses. At this point, often bereft of friends and sometimes of partners, the patients literally had no one to turn to.

However many books I may write, I shall remain haunted by the description given by a number of women of going through traumatic pain and sickness in an empty house. When someone says to you, 'At this point I was crawling around on the floor, too ill to stand', you begin to wonder if you have slipped into another, more gothic, universe.

In our complex society, loss of contact or understanding between the patient and doctor can mean the complete separation between the individual and their care, especially if people happen to live alone. Again, in a smaller, more intimate society, the doctor or friends would probably learn of the patient's distress and be able to press for a second opinion.

Perhaps there is another problem involved in the conundrum of dislocation between patient and physician in the case of adverse reactions. Could it be that doctors today are less likely to reassess a treatment, because they have been consistently told that it has been tested scientifically and has been proven to work without serious fault? This is one step on the road to blaming the patient for their illness. Perhaps, even in a society where there are extremely few successful legal cases against doctors, professionals are still worried about being sued if they admit that they have made a mistake.

On top of all these things, in the case of HRT there is the fact that many male doctors are simply arrogant and self-serving. Pragmatic and 'scientific' to the point of lacking all social skills, some really do believe that women are neurotic, irrational hypochondriacs.

So that we can more readily understand the failure of doctors to deal with adverse reactions in the case of HRT, it is worth sketching an idealised picture of the relationship between the doctor and patient. Bearing these possibilities in mind, it might be easier to see how serious adverse reactions can be created and then ignored by the modern medical professional.

$$ \text{❦} \qquad \text{❦} \qquad \text{❦} $$

In essence, an idealised picture does not differ that much from the lives of most contemporary physicians living outside the inner city. There is, however, a different emphasis on the doctor's role in the community and their use of a much broader range of non-pharmaceutical therapies.

Through preventive health programmes, many members of the community should know their doctors, who would be frequently seen at large. The doctor would be more of a personal acquaintance than a distant professional. Doctors would usually be well aware of the socio-economic, geographic and environmental circumstances of their patients. The general practitioner would spend as much time out of the surgery as inside it. All general practitioners would be trained in at least one other therapeutic approach besides allopathic medicine.

The community health centre would not simply contain the general practitioners, but a large number of other health-related groups and classes. The health centre or surgery would provide a forum for people to form their own groups. Whether they were of mothers, fathers or patients with particular illnesses, these groups would arrange their own activities and discussions, some of which might inform the direction of practitioners.

There would be an emphasis on environmental health, nutrition and children in all the practices of the health centre, which would include surgeries of non-allopathic practitioners. Patients could move at will between different modalities, using the ones that they alone, or they and their regular practitioner, thought appropriate. All practice committees would have lay representation, and something like a newsletter would keep all patients in touch with the practice and its staff.

Any new patient coming to a health centre or surgery would be given a choice to register with available doctors; this would entail the patient being provided with the history of the doctor and a statement of his or her approach. New patients would have a non-consultative meeting with the doctor whom they favoured. This meeting would provide an opportunity for the new patient to ask the practitioner any questions and to make a decision about whether or not to register with him or her.

All new patients at a health centre or surgery would be given a complete physical check-up, together with laboratory tests for a series of functions. The first proper consultation would be to discuss this check-up and these tests, regardless of what the patient felt was wrong. All practitioners would have to make at least one visit to the home of the patient, whether the patient was in good or bad health, every couple of months. All practitioners would be more proactive and concerned with prevention than they are at present.

The first signs of ill health would be reported to the general practitioner, who, during consultations, would resolve a diagnosis and a prognosis. Everything would be explained in lay terms to the patient, and all the possible ameliorating or curative treatments from any number of therapeutic approaches would be discussed. Doctors would always have enough time to talk to patients, and, in circumstances where the problem was of an intimate nature, the patient would be able to choose to whom he or she wanted to talk.

The patient would be apprised not only of available pharmaceuticals, but also of all herbal and homeopathic remedies that might effectively treat the illness or condition. The first choice of therapeutic practice should lie with the patient. In the case of those patients who wanted to learn more about their own health, there would be education courses in all aspects of well being, from anatomy to nutrition, through the history of medicine to the rudiments of different therapeutic practices. The aim of these courses, which would also be offered in schools and colleges, would be to create a population educated in its own health and some culture of health care.

The cost of different treatments, together with tables of efficiency, would be shown to patients to help them to make a decision on medicines or therapies. Any side effects of pharmaceuticals would be pointed out and a checklist drawn up of the patient's risk factors. In some cases involving drugs or procedures with known serious risks, the physician might put the patient in touch with others who have received this same treatment. In any event, the net of discussion would be spread as far as reasonably possible. In cases where treatments or illnesses might seriously affect the mood or physical capability of the patient, discussions might include, if the patient agreed, spouse or partner, parents, sons and daughters.

In all local communities, there would be an independent office staffed by a complaints practitioner. This person would hear any complaints or problems in relation to a doctor or the treatment that the patient had been given, and would have the authority to refer a patient to another practitioner for a second opinion.

Doctors would not be in receipt of any kind of products, favours or inducements, even calendars, mugs or pencils, from pharmaceutical companies, and no one working in the community health centre would be subsidised by any pharmaceutical interests. No representatives of any company producing any kind of treatment would be allowed on to the property of the health centre or be able to contact practitioners individually.

The doctor would have access to a National Formulary that would give the constituents of all treatments, allopathic and non-allopathic, and best-practice advice in all therapies for all conditions. By law, local dispensaries close to a surgery would have to carry or be able to obtain quickly a wide range of herbal, homeopathic and natural medicines, as well as allopathic preparations, quoted in the formulary. Dispensaries should not be allowed to advertise any product inside the shop or in the shop window.

In the case of the prescription of serious drugs or surgical processes – except of course in emergencies – there would be a cooling-off period, so that the patient, with the help of directions from the doctor, could seek out more information or conflicting opinions about the treatment. All general practitioners would have access to different kinds of independent information about the drugs that they prescribed, and would be able to guide the patient towards this information.

Health centres might have an open meeting every three months or so, which all practitioners and patients could attend, to discuss the work of the centre. Ideas discussed at these meetings, as well as disclosure of funding and salaries, would be raised at the monthly practice meetings of all practitioners, and would help to inform decisions. On any important matters concerning the health centre, as many patients as possible would be involved in discussions and decision-making, by ballot if necessary.

In the life of the patient and doctor beyond the doctor's surgery, we might expect certain things. If the patient were in pain and lived alone but were not being sent to hospital, there might be a system where either the patient reported in or someone visited the next day to check on them. We might, for instance, expect that when a doctor was going to prescribe a potent pharmaceutical product, he or she would sign off with his patient by saying, 'If you have the slightest side effects or uncomfortable feelings when you begin taking this drug, or if you notice any changes at all in your mood or your appearance, you can reach me on this number and we will appraise the situation.'

We should expect all physicians, great and small, to carry with them a deep and unrelenting sense of responsibility for the prescription of any remedy. We should also expect the physician to report any new information about treatments to the appropriate government or local authority agency.

As we follow the prescription for and adverse reactions suffered by patients throughout the rest of this chapter, one thing becomes horribly clear: some doctors have been giving out HRT as if it were nothing more dangerous than spring water. Then, when their patients have complained, they have simply refused to acknowledge, let alone take any responsibility, for the adverse reactions suffered. They have been doing this for years and they have been supported by an NHS that has, for decades, been in the pocket of Big Pharma.

The Prescription and Use of HRT

The development, theory and clinical use of hormone replacement therapy resembles nothing so much as a weird tale from science fiction. At every stage of their distribution and consumption, the drugs have caused havoc, because the idealisation, motive and purpose of their manufacture conflict in a thousand circumstances with their use in reality.

Almost all the problems with HRT are created in the space between scientific theory and human practice. The claims of manufacturers, distributors, marketing men and physicians for HRT, in thousands of instances, take no account of the reality of doctor-patient relationships, medical practice and the non-conforming diversity of women's physical and psychological make-up. It is this last aspect that turns HRT from what seemed like 'a good idea at the time' into the most dangerous of therapies.

The supplementation of the female body with hormones to avoid or ameliorate a natural life change is fraught with moral, ethical and technical dilemmas. The moral and ethical questions loom over the production and consumption of HRT, casting doubt on the very motive and direction of medical science in respect of women. Unfortunately, science and medicine have slipped the hawsers of ethical debate in this area, turning the issue into a medical question in which the only criterion is a slight and putative improvement in health.

Ideally, any doctor faced with a woman patient who describes acute or problematic manifestations of the menopause would first reassure that patient and him- or herself about the non-medical nature of these manifestations, and then help the patient to assess just how problematic they were.

The first and most important criterion for the prescription of HRT is that the patient is *suffering adversely* after beginning the menopause. Not all clinicians are definite about the fact that the menopause is solely the result of falling levels of oestrogen. Even if it is, not all women suffer adversely during 'the change'. However, like all serious life changes, the menopause can be frightening, with untoward things happening to the body. It is in these circumstances – or even in anticipation of these circumstances – that many women consult their doctors.

In relation to osteoporosis, this, like many other conditions, is not an indisputable fact of life for all women after the menopause. While general advice about osteoporosis should be given to all women over the age of 50, and bone density tests should be made available to them if they want them, hormone replacement therapy has always been too dangerous to give as a prophylactic therapy, especially when there are many more effective and less problematic alternatives.

It has taken medicine and the pharmaceutical companies over 50 years to realise that proper biometric testing has to be carried out before any hormone supplement can be introduced into the body. In fact, in reality, it will be a long time into the future, and require a large number of yet unenvisaged, more specific tests, before individual quantities of suitable hormones can be safely introduced into any human body. When we read about adverse reactions and the way in which doctors have prescribed HRT in the recent past, we find that the word cavalier is not strong enough.

As most women do not have tests for hormone levels in the years before they reach the menopause, most doctors can have nothing but a rough idea of whether or not their patients' levels have fallen dramatically. But an increase in biomedical testing is not, anyway, a simple answer to effective medical diagnosis. A diagnostic ability is only *aided* by testing; it begins with real discussion between the doctor and the patient, and the patient's description of symptoms that, from the doctor's empirical knowledge, signal the first stages of the menopause.

There is a problem common to all aspects of health care in the British system of socialised medicine: that is, the tendency for all allopathic doctors to prescribe a pharmaceutical, rather than discuss all the alternatives with patients. This is, after all, what pharmaceutical companies bank upon.

In most circumstances, women receive a prescription for HRT after attending their doctor's surgery for some kind of health problem. It is perhaps because of this existing malaise that many women cannot clearly recognise the adverse reactions that they begin to experience on taking the drug. New, low-grade health problems tend to get lost among other problems that existed prior to the prescription. Another clear reason why women, and perhaps even doctors, do not recognise adverse reactions for what they are, is that they can appear some time after the woman begins taking the treatment, when constituent chemicals have built up in the body. Add to this the fact that HRT produces such a wide range of varied and seemingly unrelated reactions, and it is not surprising that many women go on living with adverse effects of HRT for a very long time.

What follows are quotations from women about the prescription of HRT. Where possible I have sometimes quoted the women verbatim. In some cases, however, for reasons of economy and clarity, I have had to summarise what women wrote or told me in interviews. In these instances I have written up these accounts in the first person, staying as faithful as possible to the letter and the spirit of their account, because told in the third person they read oddly and disturb the narrative flow. In order to show the changes in subject, the quotes alternate in Roman and italic type.

In the prescription of HRT, some doctors still ignore the family history of women patients. A number of women told their doctors that they had a family history of heart disease, strokes and high blood pressure. Despite HRT being contra-indicated in these circumstances, they were told specifically that there was no problem with taking it.

My mother died of breast cancer but I was refused a mammogram by my GP and put on HRT over a seven-year period. I later contracted both breast cancer and osteoporosis.

I had had phlebitis in both legs, my mother had experienced a stroke while her father had heart attacks, coronary thrombosis and a stroke, nearly all my family had high blood pressure, yet I was still prescribed HRT.

After explaining the family history of strokes, and some discussion with my GP, I was told that an implant had minimal side effects.

Some male doctors seemed to have jumped readily to the conclusion that women were suffering from menopausal problems, and to have prescribed HRT without taking into account physical and emotional conditions that had nothing to do with the menopause.

I regret ever agreeing to take HRT, but it was almost as if I had no choice, even though my GP knew that I was a very healthy and active person with no symptoms of the menopause.

The woman below whom I interviewed had not had any ill health over the 30 years prior to the visit to her doctor. She had been very active, doing a lot of cycling and walking. The first visit to her doctor followed her marriage break-up.

The reasons for my depression had nothing to do with any medical condition and everything to do with the fact that I was now having to cope with a difficult divorce. By the time of my divorce, when I was in my forties, my son had moved away, my eldest daughter was at university, and my younger daughter had gone to live with her boyfriend. I was living alone in a five-bedroom house, which I couldn't afford to heat. Then my mother died.

It was during this period that I went to my GP for the first time in many years. I went for depression. I can remember no discussion with the doctor about my depression, but can remember that he latched on to my having missed a period. I have the clearest idea, looking back, that I was given HRT for depression.

Whether my recollection is correct or not, one thing is crystal clear: there was no discussion about HRT or its side effects. I was asked no questions about the medical history of my family, and I was given no tests for oestrogen levels or anything else, before being prescribed it.

In the cases of women who had their wombs and ovaries removed at an early age, some glimmering of a reason can be seen for the prescription of HRT, at least in the primary post-operative stages of their recovery.

A comprehensive discussion with such women is, however, imperative, especially as, now lacking the physical ability to have children, they may settle for an early menopause and be willing to go through the readjustment of the body to new hormone levels. Yet some consultants have taken for granted women's agreement to take HRT following operations. A number of women were surprised to come round from the anaesthetic to find that their consultant had injected implants into them, which could not be controlled or removed.

I had a total hysterectomy and was given an implant. I needed more and more of these over a period of three-and-a-half years, feeling worse and worse each time. Eventually, my oestrogen blood levels reached 2,000 [five times the normally quoted maximum]. I then took myself off the implants and tried patches, to no avail. I still felt terrible. In the end, I went to a Menopause Research Clinic and they told me that I had to come off HRT completely, although they did not explain what the problem was.

At the age of 31, I went into hospital for a laparoscopy because there was the suspicion that I was suffering from polycystic ovary disease. I went down for the procedure on Tuesday morning, and by lunchtime, to my shock and horror, I awoke with a subtotal hysterectomy [removal of the uterus but not the cervix] and bilateral salpingo-oophorectomy [removal of the fallopian tubes and ovaries]. Mind you, no one actually told me what I'd had done. When my husband and parents came to visit that evening, they queried why I had two drains, only to be told that I'd had a hysterectomy, etc. Apparently, I must have signed a consent form, but no one mentioned the possibility of such drastic surgery beforehand, or its implications, eg, instant surgical menopause. I was later put on HRT.

Besides constituting a crime against the woman concerned, the implanting of HRT without permission, perhaps more than any other fact, illustrates the imperfect assumptions upon which some physicians base their prescription of HRT. Science is not a crystal ball; no physician should automatically prescribe a drug on the basis of a guess about the patient's condition or her desire following an operation.

Two years ago I underwent surgery for a full hysterectomy and the removal of my ovaries and cervix. I was 40 years of age. I was placed on HRT, but since my operation I have never felt well. I have a fuzzy feeling in my head and morning dizziness as though I have had a heavy night of drinking the night before. I have increased bouts of depression; my metabolism has gone haywire. I have gained over two stone in weight, despite going to the gym four times a week and trying various diets. I also suffer from a lack of sexual desire, dry hair and extremely dry scalp.

In October 1987, during a hysterectomy operation, I was given a 100mg HRT implant without my consent. I was only told about the implant at my first check-up after six weeks. My consultant said, 'I have given you an implant, you will need one every six months.' No explanation or warning of side effects was given, and I took his advice without question because I trusted him. I felt ill quite soon after the operation, but was told I had a virus. I had lots of health problems over the next two years, but was always told that it was a virus. In 1991, I became very ill and was in and out of hospital. I eventually found out that my oestradiol levels were massively too high and that I had been overdosed on oestrogen. I have asked repeatedly to have the implants removed, but have been refused.

I have experienced many side effects from HRT implants, which were inserted during an operation to remove my ovaries. Although I was not happy about being given HRT, I was told not to worry about the implant and that it would make me feel like a new woman.

The sudden plunging of the body into an altered state following an operation to remove a woman's ovaries, whether or not it is necessary, appears to indicate to most physicians that they should try to restore oestrogen levels. Doctors who turn immediately to hormone replacement therapy, however, rather than take time to consider all the alternatives, are often doing their patients no favours.

I had a hysterectomy nearly ten years ago. I did not want my ovaries removed, and went into hospital with a clear idea of what was ahead. Just before my operation, the surgeon chatted to me and said I would not need my ovaries for much longer and it was wiser for me, to avoid ovarian cancer, to have them removed. I can't tell you how sorry I am to have agreed. I have five children, which I now know reduces my chances of ovarian cancer anyway. I suffered terrible depression after the operation. My then doctor did not believe in HRT and she had me on a very low dose. Eventually, I changed my doctor, was given more HRT and my health improved. However, when I have tried to lower the dose with the intention of coming off, the serious depression returns. If I had not had my ovaries removed, the symptoms would not have been so severe. In fact, I am now sure my original symptoms were of an early menopause at 45 and I did not need the operation anyway.

The medical and scientific 'rules of thumb' that govern the length of time that HRT should be prescribed to women have frequently changed. Generally speaking, drug companies want to prescribe the largest number of drugs to the largest number of patients for the longest possible time, a lifetime course being the ideal. When HRT was marketed for cosmetic/menopausal reasons, at its height in the 1960s and 1970s, the pharmaceutical companies did their best to convince women that taking it over very long periods would ensure perpetual youth and beauty. But since the 1960s it has become more evident that HRT can cause terminal illnesses if taken over long periods, and the marketing life of the drug has diminished.

Knowing that patients would eventually find out that prolonged use of HRT for menopausal conditions would mean only, and inevitably, that they would go through a menopause when they came off the treatment, the drug companies began looking around for another, more substantial reason why, despite the risks, women should take HRT over many years. Osteoporosis was just such a reason. Because oestrogen promotes the production of growth hormone, which in turn helps bones to grow, it could be plausibly argued that HRT should be taken as a prophylactic. And because osteoporosis does not usually set in until women are some years past their menopause, the ongoing prescription of HRT throughout and after the menopause can be argued for, never mind that it introduces all the life-threatening and accumulating risks with which the drug has always been associated. An increased risk of breast cancer, deep-vein thrombosis, coronary heart disease and stroke, with the menopause always and ineluctably in prospect at the end of treatment, seems a poor trade-off for a therapy that is not, after all, the top-quality promoter of bone density that it has been held to be.

Those doctors who proselytise HRT have done their best in the past, and are no doubt doing their best at present, to covertly stretch out the prescription time of the treatment. The letters from distressed women sent to the MHL pointed clearly to this. Some women had unaccountably been taking HRT for anything up to 18 years.

Signs and Symptoms of Imbalance

Once women have passed through the menopause, they can find themselves thankfully free of the disturbing mood swings and depression that have previously accompanied their periods. Any increase in oestrogen levels, however, can bring on serious depression.

The depression suffered by some women on HRT has been so terrible that it has driven them to take antidepressants over long periods, to seek the help of psychiatrists and even to consider or to attempt suicide. Some end up in psychiatric hospitals.[2]

One renowned case of suicide as a consequence of HRT came to light while Maggie was running the MHL: that of the wife of a solicitor, the assistant deputy coroner for North-East Cumbria, Sheena Osborne. Mrs Osborne killed herself after taking HRT for the second time to control osteoporosis. She was prescribed the drug despite having quite specifically told her doctor that she had become suicidally depressed when taking it before. On her second course of it, she descended into a deep depression within days of beginning, and killed herself with a massive drugs overdose.

I successfully took one make of HRT for eight years. Then I switched to another product, which contained progestogen. After starting on this, I started getting depressed, but never associated this with HRT. As my depression deepened over the next two

---

2 In her paper 'Increased risk of mental illness and suicide in oral contraceptive and hormone replacement therapy studies' (*J Nutr Environ Med* 1998;8:121-7), Elizabeth Price cites the results of a long-term study of mortality and cancer and its updated analysis, carried out in 1987 and 1990 (Hunt K, Vessey M, McPherson K, Coleman M. Long-term surveillance of mortality and cancer incidence in women receiving hormone replacement therapy. *Br J Obstet Gynaecol* 1987;94:620-35, and Hunt K, Vessey M, McPherson K. Mortality in a cohort of long-term users of hormone replacement therapy: an updated analysis. *Br J Obstet Gynaecol* 1990;97:1080-6.) This study of over 4,000 women and its update, she says, showed that the actual number of suicides was more than double the statistically expected, while in the extended study the incidence was nearer three times the expected number. Price's interest in depression, suicide and hormones came after a personal experience of her own. 'Some years ago, shortly after starting HRT, I developed abnormal mood swings, which I had to be careful to keep under control. Ten months later, within a week of stopping HRT, all symptoms ceased.'

years, I had counselling and was on antidepressants. Up until this happened I had no medical history of depression.

After two years on the new HRT, I was involved in an accident and was taken to hospital as a trauma patient. As I was taking no medication apart from painkillers, I miraculously started to feel better and the depression began to lift. Consulting my GP, he said that *HRT had definitely not been the cause* of the depression. Unconvinced, I went to a consultant, who said that HRT certainly could be the cause and that I was probably intolerant to manufactured progestogen. In the end, I was weaned off HRT over a period of six months by a medical herbalist, who also helped me with my menopausal symptoms. My depression has now gone.

Cases of adverse reactions caused by the incorrect prescription of implants, and the gradual overdosing of the patient, display all the classic adverse side effects.

I had been receiving an implant of 100mg over eight years. When I changed my doctor, I found that I had levels of 1,800 of oestrogen – between 200 and 400 is the recommended level. I had to wait three years before it came down to normal. I had dreadful mood swings, awful panic attacks. I took myself to see a psychiatrist because I thought that I was as mad as a brush. He said, yes, it was caused by a total imbalance of hormones.

Many women taking HRT had problems with the condition of their eyes and eyesight.[3] A number suffered from blurring and mistiness and deteriorating vision, as well as dry eyes. Others had the frightening consequences of haemorrhaging from the eye, while still others developed ulcers around the eye, as well as the more common ulcers in the mouth.

Since I started using oestrogen cream for vaginal soreness and splitting, my eyes and ears have become increasingly painful.

---

3 A paper in the *Archive of Ophthalmology* reported a connection between the production of ovarian hormones and the amount and stability of liquid produced in the eye. Smith JA, Vitale S, Reed GF, Grieshaber SA, Goodman LA, Vanderhoof VH, et al. Dry eye signs and symptoms in women with premature ovarian failure. *Arch Ophthalmol* 2004;122:151-6.

Headaches often accompany menstruation and are affected by sex hormone levels, so it would be expected that they may be a side effect of taking HRT, which can increase the incidence of migraine and other headaches because it causes an overreaction in the arteries and veins.[4] Some headaches experienced with HRT are worse than severe migraines. They can completely destroy quality of life, particularly for women who have not previously experienced headaches of any kind. Some have reduced their incidence of headaches tenfold when they stopped both smoking and taking hormones.[5]

On occasion, headaches turn into blackouts and periods of apparent unconsciousness. Sometimes the headaches get progressively worse. A number of women commented that they felt as if their heads were 'in a vice', or 'being crushed'. The headaches experienced were rarely straightforward, and many described terrible pressure in their heads. One woman related how it felt as if her brain would blow out of her ears.

One of the most common symptoms of oestrogen overdose, reported by a number of women, was dizziness. These women had difficulty in lying down, and had to stay awake at night, sitting or standing upright. A number commented that, during dizzy spells at any time, they would fall or veer sideways.

Consultants who proselytise HRT as a prophylactic for osteoporosis never draw attention to the fact that, while osteoporosis can lead to bone fractures and breaks in elderly women, many women report that dizziness induced by HRT can lead to more falls than they might otherwise have. Added to this is the fact that women who stop taking HRT after using it as a prophylactic against osteoporosis, can find that the condition of bone thinning becomes rapidly more pronounced.

> I came off HRT in late 1998. In 2001, it took orthopaedic consultants to give me an MRI scan, which revealed four collapsed vertebrae and the fact that I had severe osteoporosis. My status of minus 4.4 put me in the bottom 2 per cent of the worst cases. But

---

4 Cited in McTaggart (op. cit.). Kaiser HJ, Meienberg O. Deterioration or onset of migraine under oestrogen replacement therapy in the menopause. *J Neurol* 1993;240:195-6.

5 Cited in McTaggart (op. cit.). Klijn JG, Lamberts SW, Birkenhager JC. TRH test for prolactinoma. *The Lancet* 1979;2:581-2.

I had been taking HRT for ten years prior to 1998 and it was supposed to have prevented osteoporosis!

A large number of women who wrote to the Menopausal Helpline had suffered serious weight gain, completely against the natural order of their lives. The gain was usually around two stone and appeared shortly after treatment began.

I have had a weight gain of over two stone over the years I have been taking HRT.

I gained two-and-a-half stone in weight.

I have put on a stone in weight, I feel physically so bloated, my abdomen feels like a rock and I look about five months pregnant. I suffer from moderate night and day sweats and generally feel below par in mood, energy, memory, etc.

Most of the effects produced by HRT are not absolutes, but vary between extreme loss and extreme gain. Because general practitioners do not have the sophisticated equipment necessary to measure the quantity of hormones each individual patient might in theory need, any of the advertised positive effects of HRT can also actually be reversed on prescription.

For instance, blood pressure goes up and down depending on levels of oestrogen. While some women did say that their blood pressure became 'lower and lower' to an unhealthy degree, other women reported serious rises – which could ultimately have led to strokes or heart attacks. These 'reverse' results can be dependent upon a variety of factors, which doctors had failed to examine.

Unwanted hair on the face and failing hair on the head can be a serious problem for many women. Loss of hair was a special problem to a number of women, as they had previously considered their hair to be an important factor in their looks, personality and identity.

After taking HRT, some women complained of the growth of facial hair so severe that they had to shave their chins. Such growth did not stop some of the same women from suffering from male pattern baldness, which involves losing hair at the temples and on the crown of the head. Some women suffered such serious baldness that they had to wear wigs.

My body hair ran riot, while I developed male pattern baldness, losing about 70 per cent of my head hair. The hospital suggested that the oestrogen dosage of my HRT should be increased, but my hair loss accelerated.

When I first started on HRT I noticed hair loss around my hairline and went to see the doctor. I was told that it was not the HRT that was causing it.

After seven years of taking HRT, and now being on the one which is said to suit me best, my hair has started to thin all over and has gone from a thick mop to sparsely covered, which has upset me dreadfully. Nor do I like the fact that I have to shave my chin almost every day.

The effects of HRT on the function of the thyroid are described in the next section, which looks in detail at one woman's problems. Thyroid irregularities were often brought up in letters from women to the MHL.

After the effects of HRT implants, which my consultant had first put in without my consent, over a period of four years I became increasingly ill. In 1991, it was found that my thyroid had enlarged. It had grown so large that it had wrapped around my windpipe. I had difficulty in swallowing and breathing. I had to have a thyroidectomy in which all of the right hand side was removed. I was very ill after the operation and could not speak for three months. The consultant described the thyroidectomy as the most difficult he had ever done.

A number of women reported burning sensations, particularly on the back and the fleshy part of the legs. This 'burning' was one of the most unpleasant and painful sensations experienced by women on HRT. It could be either on the outside or the inside of the body. A similar feeling of burning, as if the skin were on fire or had been badly burnt, is sometimes associated with allergy and chemical sensitivity.

I experienced swelling of the legs, particularly about the knees, together with a tingling/burning sensation, like sunburn, and, indeed, I was applying 'after sun' to reduce the pain. Sleeping was, at times, a nightmare, as I could not bear the bedclothes touching my legs, likewise wearing tights.

There were also more permanent changes in the skin. While some women suffered complaints such as dermatitis and psoriasis, others developed discoloured patches. Yet other women reported changes in their skin tone, which they found unpleasant; their skin turned either greasy or very dry.

I have been taking HRT for five years now. I have been taking it to combat a 40 per cent bone density loss. About two years ago, my scalp became very dry and sore. Gradually, I have also developed dry patches of skin on my back and upper chest, and in the past couple of months this has spread to my upper arms and stomach, lower back, and now completely covers my upper back. The whole texture of my skin has changed to feel rough and unpleasant, and the patches now seem to erupt and become sorer.

I have yellow skin patches over the lower jaw line.

When I first started on HRT I developed vitiligo, which is an uneven skin pigmentation and which got worse and worse over the years.

I began my course of HRT in May 1993. Over five years, until 1998, despite constant visits to doctors and hospitals, I had developed: swollen eyes, burning cheeks, terrific heat burning through my body and shoulders, very red arms like bad sunburn, occasionally being covered from head to toe in septic spots, whole body itching, brown, discoloured tongue, bad eczema and psoriasis on my scalp, mental confusion, lumps in my breast and armpits. After allergy tests at a private London clinic in June 1998, and having been told that I should be on a lactose-free diet, I read the ingredients in my HRT and found that they contained lactose. I decided to stop taking the HRT. By September 1998 I had returned to almost complete health.

Some women, especially elderly ones, who wrote to the MHL, complained of general feelings of unwellness. The adverse reactions referred to in the following paragraphs had to have occurred more than once for me to note them, whilst any mention of conditions already referred to above has been omitted from the following section.

Often mentioned amongst feelings of general unwellness were gall bladder problems: 'I also have slight gall bladder tenderness.' The allopathic 'treatment' for this, the removal of the gall bladder, often created further imbalances. It has been recognised for many years that increased levels of oestrogen can cause gall bladder problems.

After experiencing initial headaches, which my doctor said would eventually go, I started to feel quite unwell in myself but unable to find a cause. I was fatigued, dizzy, had stomach cramps, etc. After six months, I was rushed to hospital with severe pancreatitis, I had another two bouts of this and then had my gall bladder removed.

The information sheets for some brands of HRT tell the user that it can create carbohydrate intolerance. This led to many women having not only allergic responses but also digestive problems. Despite their being quoted on the data sheet, many doctors fail to accept reports of these and many other side effects as adverse reactions. Carbohydrate intolerance and food allergies produced common complaints of gastroenteritis and diarrhoea. For most doctors, the problem of food allergy or intolerance is an untrodden path. It is unlikely that they will recognise it, still less attribute it to HRT.[6]

Many women experienced mouth ulcers, and while their doctors denied these could be related to HRT, some of the women's dentists were quick to point out that such ulcers could commonly be caused by oestrogen imbalance.

Women on HRT suffer a long list of minor ailments, which they are often unable to dovetail together into one condition. Individual women can experience multiple problems such as: breathlessness, palpitations, feeling faint, nightmares, blurred vision and impaired memory. Many reported changes to their breasts, which became very tender, enlarged or developed lumps, while others described their breasts as becoming solid, which is consistent with the finding that HRT can make breast tissue denser, and tumours more difficult to detect in consequence.

---

6 Royal College of Physicians. *Allergy, the Unmet Need: A blueprint for better patient care.* London: RCP; 2003.

Some women complained that adverse reactions to the treatment continued long after they had stopped taking HRT.

> I was on HRT for almost five years. I stopped taking it in 1993. Now, in 1998, five years on, my problems of reaction to the treatment are still as profound. They are: a burning sensation in my mouth, my lips, my head, chest, stomach and between my shoulder blades. Bleeding from my lips and occasional blood in my mucous. I have pressure headaches in the top of my head, cramps in my fingers and legs, regular sleep disturbance, and increased production of thicker saliva.

Because HRT, if given in the wrong quantities, can create even stronger menopausal symptoms, some women find themselves going through a kind of super-menopause while taking the treatment. Again, this may continue after they have stopped the treatment.

> *I only used HRT for one month, but had such terrible side effects, cramps in my legs and hot sweats much worse than the ones I had before I began taking it.*

> *Other symptoms include the most horrendous hot flushes, lasting up to five minutes. Accompanying these are: severe sweats, heart racing, tingling in my limbs such that my fingertips throb. The hot flushes are followed by cold flushes, leaving me totally debilitated. Between the hot and cold sweats and the leg pain, I am waking up around six times per night and this broken sleep is, obviously, taking its toll.*

Although long, detailed studies have shown an increased risk of breast cancer, thrombosis and stroke in women taking HRT, the great majority of the women who sought advice from the MHL had a wide variety of less deadly reactions. Some women did, however, write to the helpline expressing fears of deadly reactions or recounting very serious experiences, which they were convinced were related to HRT.

Deadly Reactions

Sometimes adverse reactions can only be measured and labelled by virtue of where the patient ends up in the medical pyramid. A general practitioner can further distance himself from the side effects of HRT, for instance, by referring a patient to a heart specialist, so seeming to move the problem away from any menopausal treatments the patient has received.

Despite having had serious problems with the Pill in the late Sixties, this woman began taking HRT in the late Nineties, because she thought that it would strengthen her pelvic floor, which had been weakened during a number of births. She was prescribed an oestrogen-progestogen form of HRT. No oestrogen levels were checked.

After five months, during the progesterone phase, I experienced constant palpitations and piercing downward pains in the upper body. I had also gained two stone in weight by the end of six months. I decided at the end of the first six months to discontinue the prescription. However, during withdrawal I suffered increased discomfort, including: palpitations night and day increasing in ferocity, intense heat in upper body, constant facial flushes, pain on eating, substantial elevation of my blood pressure, blurred vision and lack of sleep. These symptoms are still with me, though declining, a year after withdrawal from HRT. I have never felt so ill and frightened for so long in my life. As a consequence of my visits to the doctor, I was prescribed Losec [for gastro-oesophagal reflux disease, or GERD – what we used to call heartburn until the pharmas decided to dignify it with a new illness label], beta-blockers, sleeping tablets, and have taken many bottles of Gaviscon [for heartburn, again]. I was put under the care of a cardiologist.

I had a heart attack in 1991 aged 48, caused by HRT. Even in hospital the HRT was added to my medication regime. Later, back at the menopause clinic, they continued to prescribe HRT, saying that without it I could have had a 'worse' heart attack!

Women who contracted cancer after taking HRT, and who wrote to the MHL, frequently felt bitter about not having been told the full story when

97

it was prescribed to them. Although it cannot be proved that the cancer these women experienced was solely or even mainly due to HRT, they felt certain that HRT had played a part.

In 2001, after having been on HRT for around 18 years – and told it was safe – I developed cancer and had a left breast mastectomy.

I took HRT for two years from 1995. Within three months of taking a new type of HRT, I got blurred vision in one eye. It was a horrendous task to try to persuade the medical profession that I had something wrong. After a year's investigation I was told that I had a tumour, the growth of which had been precipitated by hormonal changes. I had to have a four-and-a-half-hour operation to remove the benign tumour from my optic nerve. I was told not to take HRT anymore, but no one would commit themselves to saying that HRT was responsible.

I have cancer of the neck after being overdosed over a four-year period from HRT implants.

Sometimes, it is specialist consultants in areas other than endocrinology who are the first to broach the subject with the patient of HRT and its damaging effects. Despite this, these consultants have done little over the years to bring the matter of adverse reactions and deaths to the notice of regulatory bodies, nor are they eager to offer themselves as expert witnesses in court.

I then had a number of scans, which proved that I had had a pulmonary embolism. The consultant advised that I stop the HRT treatment, although nobody would admit that this was the cause.

In late May of 1999, I began to feel ill, and by early June I was in dreadful pain, coughing up blood and unable to breathe. I was admitted to hospital, where I was diagnosed as suffering from multiple pulmonary embolisms. When this condition was stabilised, I was discharged and told that I would have to take warfarin [originally developed as a rat poison] to thin the blood for the remainder of my life.

In late August of 1999, I was advised at my HRT clinic to discontinue taking HRT until December, when it would be safe to continue. In March 2000, I was eventually told by a specialist that the cause of my pulmonary embolism must be HRT and that it would, perhaps, be safer if I refrained from taking it.

Dialogue with the Deaf

Talking to the doctor was like talking to the wall.

What is most worrying is that doctors don't believe you or they don't want to believe you.

The great majority of women who wrote the thousands of letters to the MHL did not appear to have any criticism of doctors or the medical profession prior to going on to HRT. In fact, the unquestioning trust that they placed in their doctors was, in the main, what led them to take, and then to persist with, HRT.

This trust, however, began to evaporate when the women returned to their doctors' surgeries with a multitude of adverse reactions. Although hardly any of the women initially understood their 'new illnesses' as adverse reactions, in the main they educated themselves after facing an implacable lack of understanding or diagnostic skill from their doctors. Numbers of these women became radicalised during this protracted process of condescension.

I have been and am treated, as a lot of women are, like a neurotic hypochondriac, and it isn't right. I want to prove to these doctors that these very debilitating side effects do exist. I am sick to death of the dismissive attitude of some of the medical profession, and I believe it's time us women put them straight.

The stock phrase used to me on several occasions was 'HRT doesn't do that' – well, HRT certainly does do that, and in some cases it seems downright dangerous.

I recently saw my GP and told him that I had taken myself off HRT because of the side effects. I related to him how many women were suffering side effects. You would not believe this man's attitude! He thinks HRT is a good product and more or less said that it was all in my mind. He said that there is always someone with an axe to grind, and any adverse reports were purely conjecture. I was so angry that I told him that if 10,000 women all ground their axes at the same time, the noise would be deafening.

One woman told me the story of the months leading up to her hospital admission, when it was found that she had a large number of blood clots above her groin, which her consultant told her had been caused by HRT.

The doctor, who had prescribed HRT, had over the previous three months suggested phlebitis, gout, sprained muscle and sprained ankle for the terrible pains and the evident symptoms of illness I was suffering. The pain was so severe that I rang my doctor complaining that I couldn't stand it. I was now desperately searching for any reason for the pain, and asked the doctor if it could be one of the drugs he had recently prescribed. He considered it, told me to come off the drug I had just been given, and then to come to see him in a week's time. No mention was made of my continuing HRT prescription.

When I got to the surgery a week later, I had hardly finished explaining how terrible was the pain in my toes, and showing the doctor not just the swollen veins but the splashing of red dots around the veins covering my foot, than he was ringing the hospital asking for an emergency admission.

An angiogram showed that the veins in my foot had closed up and were no longer carrying any blood. The results of further x-rays showed numbers of blood clots, which had accumulated in the veins at the top of my leg. When I was told that I would have to have a whole leg amputation immediately, I demanded a second opinion. The consultant I chose was everything a good doctor should be and he managed to save the majority of my leg. When I asked him what had caused the build-up of blood clots, although later he was to record 'a coagulant', he replied without hesitation, 'HRT'.

The treatment of women who have reported adverse reactions to HRT by their mainly male doctors, exposes the terrifying limitations of a practice of medicine that is based upon pharmaceutical drugs about which the general practitioner knows next to nothing. It also shows how many men are quite unsuitable to be doctors. On this crucial issue of women's health, many of them appear to be mired over their heads in a quicksand of insensitivity, ignorance and chauvinism.

The doctors of a large number of women who wrote to the MHL had refused to entertain the idea that HRT could have caused adverse reactions. In reporting this, women repeated such expressions, as 'all in my mind', my doctor was 'adamant' and 'doctors are not prepared to listen'. In some instances, doctors referred their patients to psychiatrists when they insisted that their illnesses were adverse reactions to HRT.

The consistency with which many doctors fail to grasp the problems of adverse reactions would lead even the most naive of spectators to imagine that these doctors are involved in a conspiracy. I have summarised below a number of the much longer accounts given by women about their doctors in their letters to the MHL.

A well-known HRT consultant gave me the feeling that I was being neurotic. When I reported to him depression, lethargy, bloated feelings, a gain of two stone in weight and hair loss, and suggested that this might be caused by HRT, he 'would have none of it'.

When I went to my GP with all the classic adverse reactions to high oestrogen levels, including high blood pressure and aching legs, my doctor told me, 'Forget the leg pains and get on with your life.' My new doctor gave me Prozac. After almost 12 years on HRT my doctor hinted that my high blood pressure might be related to HRT, so I came off and all my adverse effects ceased. I then had to face the menopause in my early sixties.

Since taking HRT I have suffered from a fuzzy feeling in my head, morning dizziness, increased bouts of depression. I have gained over two stone in weight. I also suffer from a lack of sexual desire, dry hair and extremely dry scalp. I have spoken with my GP and he says that there is no connection.

When I told my doctor that HRT was making me feel so ill that I had to stop work, he told me that, in fact, it could do me nothing but good.

When I went to my male doctor following a wide variety of adverse reactions, which I linked to HRT, he accused me of talking 'rubbish' and told me that I should stay on it for at least five years. Eventually, I contracted cancer and was told by the consultant that it had been caused by increased oestrogen.

After a couple of months of taking HRT I began to feel generally ill. By accident I forgot to take the tablets on holiday and began to feel better again. I wanted to test this, so I went back on and, yes, I felt ill again, so I stopped. Since then, I have tried to find out exactly why I felt ill. Three doctors have told me without examination that my symptoms were all due to a 'kink' in my spine. When I asked my GP – the first to say there was a kink in my spine – to point it out to me, he admitted that there was nothing wrong with my spine.

After having a succession of implants, after one had been given to me without my consent during an operation to remove my ovaries, I began to suffer a series of side effects. Excessive weight gain of approximately three stone, painful breasts plus an increase in their size, bloating, fluid retention in my legs and feet. I also suffered severe depression; I am epileptic and my condition worsened. I explained all this to my gynaecologist time and time again, but was told not to be silly and that these symptoms could not possibly have anything to do with this drug. Three years after my first implant, when I attended the hospital for a further implant, my gynaecologist told me that he had attended a conference on HRT and that the implants were not suitable for all women. Not only did some women suffer adverse reactions, but, in my case, there was a great risk of thrombosis, as my legs were so swollen. I used patches for 12 months but the side effects were still very bad. Five years after beginning HRT, I decided to stop taking it. I have to admit that this was one of the best decisions I have ever made.

When considering coming off the treatment, a number of women took straightforward, pragmatic approaches that put their doctors to shame. Many women voted with their bodies and came off HRT regardless of their doctors' advice. Some women surprised themselves by simply stopping taking HRT, and some, at the same time, vowed never to visit their doctors again. Many women realised after their ordeals that they should have trusted their instincts in the first place rather than trust their doctors.

> After reading the small print in the HRT tablet packet, the penny dropped, and I asked my doctor about HRT causing the illnesses I had suffered. This was pooh-poohed by him totally. I was still convinced, however, and tried taking the treatment again, just in order to see if my symptoms returned. They did, and I have never taken it since that time. My doctor, however, still thinks that it is unconnected.

My doctor is adamant that HRT is not responsible for my skin problems. I have always had a dry skin, yet I have never suffered any rashes or problems at all until recently. I have carefully examined my diet and lifestyle for any changes which could explain this radical change to my skin. But after reading the leaflet issued with the HRT, which suggests that skin rashes can be caused by this form of HRT, I am drawn to the conclusion that the HRT may well be causing the problem through a long-term build up of one or more of the ingredients.

> The question I ask is, do GPs fully understand and connect to HRT the many and varied symptoms women report? Why don't GPs tell women that, whatever age a woman comes off HRT, she will have menopausal symptoms, ie., hot flushes, night sweats, etc.

No doctor in the land will ever, ever, ever persuade me to go back on any form of HRT. I will slowly piece my life back together, knowing that I, and I alone, really know my own body, and that body does not need poisoning by HRT. I am not disputing that HRT has probably helped many thousands of women, but all women are different, and doctors must not take the blanket view that HRT is the be-all and end-all panacea for all womankind and prescribe it automatically.

Some women point to the difficulties of giving up HRT, and a few women suggested that the treatment was addictive.[7,8]

---

7 A number of papers over the past decade have argued that both oestrogen and progesterone are addictive. See White M, Grant ECG. Addiction to oestrogen and progesterone. *J Nutr Environ Med*, 1998;8:117-20.

When I had to give it up, I was on the point of collapsing. When I look back now I realise how ill I was. But you just keep trying to carry on as normal. The point I am trying to make is, I was hooked.

I am now completely finished with any form of HRT and well rid of it. I have had the worst four years of my life in coming off HRT plus the awful three-and-a-half years on it.

Many women come away from their adverse experiences of HRT with good questions about their treatment, the NHS and the attitude of doctors, but with insufficient power to change things.

The Official Record

With respect to all hormone replacement therapeutic products, there have been a total of 6,451 reported adverse reactions received by the MCA (now the MHRA) via the Yellow Card Scheme.[9]

The Yellow Card Scheme was introduced in 1964. A communication from the Medicines Control Agency (MCA) to Maggie Tuttle says the following:

'It is important to bear in mind that the reporting of a *suspected* adverse reaction does not necessarily mean that the drug has caused the problem. Many factors have to be taken into account in assessing causal relationships, including the possible contribution of other medication and illness. At the present time, the MCA does not accept reports directly from patients, as medical interpretation of the suspected reaction is considered vital. Patients who suspect they have suffered an adverse reaction to their medicines are instead encouraged to report these to their doctor or pharmacist, who may then report it to the Scheme.'

8 In 1995, the *Sunday Times* ran a story by Lois Rogers, which said that 'Thousands of women are addicted to HRT'. The article was based on a study by Susan Bewley, women's health specialist at St. Thomas' Hospital. *Sunday Times*, 6 August 1995.

9 Maggie Tuttle claimed that within the space of six years, she received over 11,000 letters of complaint from women who had had adverse reactions to HRT. These letters were mainly sent following her appearances on TV or her having appeared in newspaper articles.

This is typical MCA (now MHRA) distortion, which fails to give the other side of the story, because neither the MCA nor any other independent body accepts accounts from women who are seriously affected by hormonal therapies. As we have seen, doctors often reject reports of side effects out of hand.

The regulators have recently piloted patient reporting, and yellow cards are now accepted from the public (visit: www.mhra.gov.uk), although how much weight they carry, we cannot know. One would not have to be an out-and-out cynic to suspect that patient reports carry less weight with the regulator than those from doctors, who are reckoned to submit yellow cards in, at most, just ten per cent of cases of those adverse drug reactions that they are willing to countenance.

The adverse reactions complaint system depends very heavily upon doctors and other healthcare workers first acknowledging adverse reactions, and then taking the time and trouble to fill in and submit a yellow card. As is shown from the reactions of doctors above, and as has been suggested by a number of authorities, official figures released by the MCA reflect a very, very small fraction of the actual number of adverse reactions to many drugs.

It has been said that, in both Britain and North America, there has for years been a plan to cut down on the reports of adverse reactions. Joseph Hassleburger, on his Health Supreme website, has this to say about the FDA:

> While aspartame, for instance, has brought great profits to the industry, the FDA plainly refuses to look at the numerous adverse reaction reports. FDA field agents are reported to block people from even reporting events, because aspartame 'could not cause such a reaction'. The same is true for cholesterol-lowering statin drugs, where apparently widespread reports of muscle pains, memory loss and other side effects just don't seem to make it into the FDA's system.' [10]

The MHRA is directly and almost completely funded by the pharmaceutical industry, which pays for the Agency to license and service the licensing of their drugs. And to a great extent the pharmaceutical companies

---

10 Joseph Hasselberger, Health Supreme website, 1/1/2005.

still manage and manipulate media coverage and regulatory interest in adverse reactions. The lesser side effects of HRT are brushed aside with such bland statements as: 'Some women experience side effects when taking some forms of HRT. This is because they have not found the right dose or combination.' Or, 'HRT is identical to natural hormones and very rarely has side effects or adverse reactions.' And, of course, there is always the old chestnut : 'This is just anecdotal evidence.'

None of this is to say that the lesser adverse reactions to HRT have been ignored by writers, researchers and doctors. From the beginning of the introduction of hormones to the body, and certainly from the advent of the Pill, both minor and major side effects of hormone supplements have been reported. But while science has argued about the major side effects, such as cancer and thrombosis, it was left to the doctor and the patient to come to terms with the lesser ones. Of these two protagonists, it is, of course, the patient who has had to suffer the actual effects and summon the words and the energy to convince the doctor of their experience.

Chapter Four

Limited but
Spectacular Victories

The chance that the average patient will get the right drug in the right amount, at the right time, is in the order of 50 per cent.

Dale Console[1]

She wouldn't move for me. I was a lawyer, subtler than a policeman, as treacherous as a doctor.

Ross MacDonald[2]

Because of the inadequacies of the English rail system on the Sunday in September when I first visited Shirley, I ended up having to record her story, initially at least, in an hour-and-a-half in the middle of almost nine hours of travelling. Although I knew that I would see her a second and, maybe, even a third time, I was sure that what had happened must qualify for the damning definition which an anthropologist friend of mine had once levelled at a sociologist also of my acquaintance. The sociologist's attempt to understand the homeless by staying in a Salvation Army hostel for a couple of nights, had been described by her as 'voyeuristic' and 'the worst kind of empiricism'.

---

1 Dale Console to Congress in 1969.
2 Ross MacDonald. *The Ferguson Affair.* New York: Bantam; 1963.

I was embarrassed at my stupidity and lack of planning that had led to a situation where I would hardly be able to scrape the surface of Shirley's case, let alone get any understanding of her personality. Writers' subjects, although usually very grateful that someone is taking an interest in them, quite rightly also feel that they are about to be treated with respect, and more especially given time and understanding.

As it happened, my poor scheduling gave me an insight into Shirley's personality that I might never have gained, had I had an abundance of time for that first meeting. Talking to people about conflicts, whether they are legal or medical, is always difficult; an occupation akin to doing a huge jigsaw puzzle. Rarely do all the pieces simply assemble themselves, and more often than not you are left scrambling after fragments as the picture recurrently falls off the table; most times you know there will be bits missing.

Listening to Shirley's story, and despite her apology for the untidy papers scattered about her house, it was easy to see how she had made the headway she had against a pharmaceutical company. During those first 90 minutes, she behaved as interviewees rarely do. With her folded arms resting on her crossed knees, she looked at her fingers and maintained a constant mental focus. Shirley is a concentrated person, small and compact; she has a way of speaking from her inner self, which struck me as not at all English. As she rolled out her story, I rarely needed to interrupt her, as the picture took shape smoothly and logically.

My fears about basing my view of Shirley on a quick visit was finally allayed when the book took two further years to finish. During this time, I was able to visit her again and she was able to add her own writing and corrections to her chapter. She proved to be a necessarily exacting task-mistress, wanting me to tell in 'real time' the story of her journey. For any writer this can be a daunting problem, and for any subject inevitably frustrating.

To some extent, it must be the case that people idealise their lives before the onset of illness. The mind refuses to see gradations or slow sinking processes, which denote the onset of ill health. Instead, the sick person sees a line over which they step from reasonable contentment to extreme illness. This is not, of course, to suggest that there are not cases where the decline from good health to bad is not sudden or steep; it is only to argue that when one is sick, it is easy to bracket states prior to this as healthy.

One of the first questions that I asked Shirley was what kind of life she had led, what kind of woman she had been, before she suffered the adverse reactions to HRT. She replied immediately, 'A happy, contented, fit, healthy life,' then added 'taking 100 micrograms of thyroxine for the previous 30 years.'

Shirley was diagnosed with hypothyroidism when she was 21 in 1964; between then and 1994, she saw no doctors, had no blood tests, and remained fit and healthy, the treatment completely disposing of the symptoms she had suffered from 1963 to 1964.

Having left school at 16, Shirley began work in her hometown of Plymouth. When she was 20, however, she began to gain weight, and to feel sluggish and tired. Her GP had no understanding of what might be wrong with her, but at the local hospital she was immediately diagnosed by the registrar as having an underactive thyroid.

The thyroid gland excretes thyroxine, a vital hormone. When the thyroid ceases to work properly, the heart rate and the metabolism slow. Hypothyroidism is an autoimmune response in which the immune system begins slowly to attack the thyroid gland. The condition is much more prevalent in women than in men. One in 50 women will find that they need thyroid replacement therapy at some time in their lives.

Shirley was soon convinced of the benefit of the 100 microgram thyroxine supplementation, because, as she now points out, had such a supplement been given to someone who had a fully-functioning thyroid, they would quickly lose an inordinate amount of weight and develop other medical problems, with the heart for example. Within a year, Shirley was back down to what she considered her normal weight, she had regained her energy and started working again.

It was almost 30 years later that Shirley was prescribed HRT by her general practitioner. Following the death of her partner two years previously, she had moved house to live with only her dog for company. Just after her 52nd birthday, she went to her doctor's to collect a repeat prescription for thyroxine.

There was absolutely nothing wrong with me when I called at the doctor's surgery; out of the blue, he said, 'You're small, you might get osteoporosis when you get older, I think that we should prescribe you HRT.' I was given HRT for absolutely no reason at all.

Unlike many other women, Shirley had done some reading about HRT, so she asked her doctor a series of questions about its dangers. He countered these by saying that HRT now had progesterone in it, implying that it had been made safe.

Unfortunately, at that time, Shirley didn't know to ask what, in her case, was the most important question – that of the relationship between oestrogen and thyroxine. Her doctor, of course, should have known that it would interfere with thyroid activity. The fact that Shirley had a very real thyroid condition, militated absolutely against the prescription of HRT for her purely putative osteoporosis.

The way in which HRT was explained to her by her doctor led Shirley to understand that the form of HRT he was giving her had been specifically developed for increasing bone density and was to be used by people in danger of osteoporosis. She accepted the prescription for Prempac C,[3] but found that when she got the product, the patient information leaflet referred only to problems of the menopause.

Symptoms of the effect of HRT on her already underactive thyroid, appeared quite soon after she began taking it. She developed huge blotches on her face, and slowly, 'insidiously' she says, she began to lose her energy.

When she went to see her GP, he told her that she was fine and there was nothing to worry about. Two years later, in October 1996, Shirley could see that she was far from fine. She was a different person, no longer fit or healthy. During that winter, she would be freezing cold after the shortest walk outside. Although crucial blood tests for thyroid function ought to have been done at least once a year, and although she was now attending her doctors every couple of months, in two years Shirley had had no blood tests, either for thyroxine levels or for oestrogen.

During 1997, Shirley experienced fatigue and what she describes as woolly-headedness, dizziness, a feeling of heaviness in her head, which

3 Made by Wyeth.

she says was 'akin to wearing a crash helmet with the visor down'. Her vision had become blurred. She suspected that her ill health was due to the HRT, but when her doctor insisted that she continue taking it, she didn't argue with him.

Finally, however, she simply informed him that she was going to stop it. Shirley's determination was such that her doctor could raise no objection; she 'threw the packet away and went on holiday'. Stopping HRT did not, however, end her ill health, and, indeed, over the autumn of 1997, she became more unwell.

The HRT Shirley had taken, she now knows, having blocked even further her production of thyroxine, had caused knock-on adrenal insufficiency, her metabolism had slowed, and this had sabotaged her well being.

After years of patient work, throughout her suffering, Shirley has discovered that when she was prescribed the HRT, she should have had her thyroxine supplementation increased, and that on coming off HRT, because of the previous thyroxine deficiency, she should have taken steroids to prevent an adrenal crisis. In November 1997, ill and deprived of energy by lack of adrenalin, she collapsed. This collapse and the conditions that followed were indicative of an autoimmune disease.

By 1998, Shirley was bed-bound, and she was to be in this condition for the next 18 months. When she later managed to get hold of her medical records, she saw that on her notes during 1995, her doctor had written: 'Personality the largest part of the problem.' She clearly remembers when this remark was written, a few months after she began taking HRT, when she was becoming concerned about her health and attending the doctors more frequently. At this time, she can remember his reluctance to speak to her or even to look her in the eye.

Despite the fact that a thyroid test, taken in the middle of 1998, came back as grossly abnormal, she was told by the doctors that the results were normal. 'I am convinced now that there was a conspiracy to withhold treatment,' she says, the word 'conspiracy' dovetailing into her speech as if it was a concept she entertained every day. She looked hard at me, almost daring me to disagree, but also knowing that she was speaking a language that I would probably understand.

At this time in 1998, her hair was falling out, and she became completely bald. She had lost considerable weight, her hands were dead from the wrist down and her feet and legs were numb. The muscles in her throat had stopped working properly, her gums had receded, her mouth was full of ulcers and she was producing little or no saliva. All of these things made it almost impossible for her to swallow; she found it harder and harder to eat. This was all due to an autoimmune disease that was out of control. Her weight dropped to five-and-a-half stone.

She was also subject to frequent blackouts and collapses. Following her reporting these symptoms, her GP sent her to see a counsellor. She received a letter from the practice arranging an appointment with someone whom she understood to be medically qualified. Later, Shirley found that the counsellor had no medical training at all. She formed the opinion that the referral was part of the conspiracy that prevented her from receiving vital medical care from the endocrinologist and saw her branded as a patient with a personality problem. Of course, the counsellor was not there to get involved in the physical or biological side of Shirley's illness.

> You could have knocked me down with a feather. How could a person with no medical training be employed with the medical profession, seeing patients who were known to be taking certain medications for definite physical conditions.

It took Shirley almost ten years of serious illness and study to accumulate all the information she could about the interactive effect of thyroxine and oestrogen.

Oestrogen supplementation dramatically increases blood levels of thyroxine-binding globulin, the substance to which thyroxine binds in order to be transported round the body. The process, which also occurs in pregnancy, leaves less of the free-acting thyroxine in the blood to be used to create energy. In women who have a normally-working thyroid, or in a healthy woman who is pregnant, thyroid function is adjusted by the body. In Shirley's case, however, her new dose of oestrogen had nullified the thyroxine supplement which she had been taking for the past 30 years, exacerbating the autoimmune disease that had first taken her to the doctor, aged 21.

Now her adrenal gland had been targeted by her own immune system. She found out that it had been known since the 1960s that oestrogens exacerbated or even caused lupus, one of the best-recognised autoimmune diseases.

Shirley maintained that her doctor should have known this as a simple rule of practice, because when women with thyroid problems become pregnant and produce more oestrogen, doctors are warned to take special care with them. These women have their thyroxine supplements increased and they are put under the care of a consultant endocrinologist and specialised gynaecologist.

Now that Shirley has access to her medical records, she can see that during 1995, when she first began to be ill, the blood test she did have showed the clear need for an increase in her thyroxine supplementation.

In October 1998, after a visit to her doctor's, during which he had got up from behind his desk and shown her the door, her repeated visits came to an abrupt conclusion. In 1999, she saw another doctor, who sent her to hospital for tests. There, despite having been told her medical history and having discussed the problems she had had with her doctors, her attendant physicians suggested that she had liver disease. HRT was prescribed again, but withdrawn some months later.

Shirley was kept in hospital over three days, during which period she felt a growing hostility towards her from the doctors and nurses. Medical notes since gained from the hospital and her GP, show that the figures for thyroid stimulating hormone (TSH) had gone up from the normal lower level of 0.01 to 47.22. She thinks that she was not told about this result because it would have reflected badly on her doctor, who as she had yet to discover, had received a blood test result showing a level of 17.81 the previous year.

Following her stay in hospital, Shirley was seen by a dietician who, concerned about her condition, wrote to her GP suggesting that Shirley, especially because of her difficulties in eating, might usefully be prescribed nutrient-rich formula drinks.

The letter that came back to the hospital, now in Shirley's possession, is a study in the carelessness and arrogance of a physician who, despite having made serious mistakes, had come to be utterly cynical about a female patient. He declined to prescribe vitamins to Shirley, stating:

> On considering the contents (of your letter) I am firmly of the opinion that *Shirley* has no medical reason to bring her within the scope of borderline substances (vitamins) and, therefore, strongly feel that it is inappropriate to issue her with NHS prescriptions for these supplements. On the information I have on *Shirley*, it would be entirely appropriate for her to take food of her choosing and prepare it through a liquidizer to achieve the same effect. (author's italics).

> I am sorry to be unhelpful (sic) but I rather feel, particularly in her case, that this would have an additional damaging effect of confirming her view that she has some kind of diagnosis which, in fact, does not exist.[4]

Shirley's case and the conflict into which she was precipitated over a six-year period, describes an important mode of lamentable patient-doctor relations. Essentially, Shirley's male doctor had concluded that she was mentally unstable and a fantasist. Unable to change his mind in any rational manner, especially when test results were being withheld from her, Shirley was forced to investigate the science of her condition herself.

In November 1999, Shirley made a complaint against her GP's practice to her area health authority. As a consequence of the complaint, she was called to attend a 'reconciliation meeting'[5] with two of the doctors from her medical centre. The coordinator of this meeting evidently didn't spend long pondering its outcome, because, on the same day, she sent an ill-considered ballpoint-written letter to Shirley, which contained the following 'decision'.

> Following our meeting with the GP's to-day, I write to confirm that although you do not agree with the doctor's explanation regarding your complaint of 'failure to diagnose' there will be no further action taken. I trust you continue to feel better and that the future is good to you.[6]

Following the complaint about her GPs at the end of 1999, Shirley was struck off the patient list of her local medical centre.

---

4 Letter from Shirley's medical centre to the senior dietician at her local hospital. 2 July 1999.

5 It is unclear as to whether such meetings are held to 'reconcile' patients to their lack of power or to 'reconcile' everyone to the idea that doctors should be encouraged not to admit mistakes.

6 Hand written letter from South & West Devon Health Authority to Shirley, November 22 1999.

SHIRLEY

In March 2000, the Community Health Council (CHC) dismissed her complaint against her GP practice, saying that, after a number of enquiries and investigations, it concluded that there was a lack of evidence. These enquiries cannot have delved too deeply, because the all-important blood test results remained buried in her medical records.

In October 2000, after a long struggle with the health authority, Shirley had a meeting with a health authority doctor, who listened to an account of the past three years of ill health. This doctor at last unearthed from GP records, where they had been interred for two-and-a-half years, the grossly abnormal blood test result from March 1998, revealing thyroid stimulating hormone (TSH) of 17.81. This result should have been within the reference range of 0.01 to 5.5. These test results and one produced by the hospital where she had stayed in January 1999, had not been produced at any investigations held at the CHC or PCT during the previous year, 1999-2000. When the 'independent' doctor found these results, he himself assured Shirley that she did have, previously and presently, a genuine complaint.

Sight of these test results by any impartial person would have shown a massive and damaging rise in TSH between 1997, when it had stood at 3.48, through 1998, when it was recorded at 17.81, to a reading in 1999 of 47.22. These readings were, of course, highly germane to Shirley's case; had the doctor pointed out to her the early rises, with their health-damaging consequences, and had this condition been discussed with her, both she and her doctors might have plotted a course to a recovery.

In late 2000, a new GP picked up the pieces of Shirley's shattered life. Her health began to improve, although she was still taking only nutritional liquids and very soft foods.

During 1999 and 2000, when she had felt well enough, Shirley had written letters to the Medicines Control Agency (MCA – now reorganised as the MHRA) and the manufacturers of the HRT she had taken. Letters that Shirley wrote to the MCA in May and August 2000 provoked the blandest of replies, which gave no information on the specific problem suffered by Shirley, relating to thyroxine and HRT. But in a February 2000 letter,

Louise Kerr of the Pharmacovigilance Group, Post Licensing Division of the MCA, says, quite simply:

> Oestrogen therapy may lead to a reduction in levels of thyroxine. This is because oestrogen is known to increase levels of a thyroxine-binding protein. An increase in this binding protein will result in a reduction in the level of circulating thyroid hormone, possibly resulting in hypothyroidism.

So here, in a nutshell, was a complete analysis of Shirley's serious medical condition, which she had suffered since 1995 and which her general practitioners had failed to diagnose, while accusing her of being a fantasist.

Unfortunately, Louise Kerr at the MCA knew nothing more about the condition or its prevalence, and suggested, reasonably, that Shirley 'contact your local library as they should be able to conduct a relevant literature search for you'. Shirley, inevitably, wondered why a research follow-up to this serious adverse reaction was not the job of the MCA, and why she, as the injured party, should have to conduct such important research.

Through September 2002 to May 2003, Shirley wrote a number of letters to Wyeth. The company avoided sharing any information about their product with her by suggesting that she should contact her doctor about her problems and giving her the address of the Amarant Trust. In September 2002, Wyeth wrote that there was no recognised interaction between HRT and thyroxine. This statement came as a surprise to Shirley, who, deeply engaged in researching her condition, had found many references in the literature about the various interactions between HRT and thyroxine and the thyroid – perhaps the key word, here, was *recognised*.

When her letters to Wyeth got her nowhere, Shirley began writing to the MHRA in earnest, pursuing her idea that the product literature and GPs should be educated about the presently 'not recognised' relationship between HRT and thyroxine.

Over the period of eight months in which Shirley was writing to Wyeth and the MHRA, she finally elicited a more senior-level admission from the MHRA that women taking thyroxine should be very careful when using HRT. Then, in the last months of 2003, when the company updated its patient information sheet, which has by law to be given with prescriptions, a reference to thyroid disease and oestrogen was inserted.

In August 2003, Shirley had received a personal letter from the MHRA, which informed her that the results of her investigations would be included in product and prescribing literature in the future.

> The Expert Working Group (EWG) of the Committee of the Safety of Medicines (CSM) on hormone replacement therapy (HRT) recently met to discuss various aspects of the safety of HRT, including the effect on thyroxine requirement in women with hypothyroidism. I apologise for the delay in replying to you, but I wanted to let you know the outcome of their decision.
>
> After careful consideration of the issue, the EWG advised that there was a theoretical basis for an increased thyroxine dose requirement in some women with hypothyroidism who take HRT and that adding a warning about this possible effect to the product information for HRT preparations would be justified.[7]

In anyone's terms this constituted a substantial victory, although one that had cost Shirley dear. It was also a victory that had been achieved *in spite of* the NHS, to which Shirley had also written, and not *because* of it.

Jane Woolley's letter, quoted above, also answered some other questions which Shirley had put to the MHRA. The answer to one of these was simple, although, on reflection, very interesting. Shirley had asked why the effects of HRT on the thyroid or on the use of thyroxine had not been a matter of issue in any of the trials through which HRT had been put. Jane Woolley answered that, 'Since it is not possible to conduct clinical trials that are relevant for all potential users of a medicine prior to licensing, *the safety profile of a medicine in routine clinical practice can only be truly evaluated after licensing,* when health professionals use it to treat a more diverse group of patients.'

One wonders if most patients know that they are part of an ongoing clinical trial, during which they will be experimental subjects in the post-marketing surveillance and safety of drugs. The matter is particularly frightening in relation to HRT, because here is a case in which the drug in question affects a large number of other connective parts of the body's system and has been prescribed at least since 1945.

---

7 Letter from Jane Woolley of the Medicines Control Agency, Post Licensing Division, 11th August 2003.

Following the complaints procedure against her GP, Shirley wrote frequent letters to the GMC and the Health Service Ombudsman (the Health Service Commissioner for England). Like many women, when Shirley began her campaign, she did not have focused objectives. However, she became increasingly aware that the NHS dealt very badly with endocrinology cases. She also became aware that there are other low-level, less publicised conditions, which GPs regularly seem to miss. Apart from getting involved in campaigning on those issues, she also wanted some kind of justice in her own case.

In March 2003, she attended a meeting with two members of the Plymouth NHS Primary Care Trust (PCT), during which it was said that her doctors could sue her.

The first letter following this meeting showed how low the Trust and her former medical centre were prepared to stoop. The letter of 30 April 2003, stated baldly:

> The practice in question have indicated that they would consider taking legal action regarding harassment if they feel the original complaint is being made against them once again. *This is in light of the fact that all previous investigations have cleared them of any neglect or responsibility.* (author's italics).

This last sentence was not completely true, and might have been better worded: *this is in light of the fact that all previous rulings, which were arrived at without proper investigation or adjudication, dismissed your complaint.*

Still, threats of legal action didn't worry Shirley, who had been out of her corner with the gloves on for some time now; in fact, at this stage, she would have welcomed a court case. There then followed, during May and August of 2003, and then up to May 2004, further exchanges with the Plymouth NHS Primary Care Trust. Her letters to them were principally concerned with getting her general practitioners to accept responsibility for failing to diagnose her very serious condition. One might have thought that, after having dragged the MCA into her corner, and having stood up to Wyeth, one of the world's largest pharmaceutical companies, and seen them amend their drug safety data sheet, wringing even a subdued admission from her GPs would not have been that difficult.

During these exchanges, the PCT stuck doggedly to its case that Shirley's complaints against her practitioners had been rigorously investigated, using fair procedures, and found unproven. In the final letter of May 2004, the PCT fell back on threats again, saying: '… this matter is now fully closed and any further complaints with regard to this issue would be considered under the PCT's Vexatious Complaints Policy'.

❦   ❦   ❦

Shirley had been consulting solicitors since 2001. The first company she approached in her hometown wanted nothing to do with the case. The second company followed the case until Shirley fell out with them. With her help, the lawyers had found a consultant supportive of her case from 1998. The expert and the solicitors were in agreement that wrongdoing could be proved from this time – the time when her doctor had failed to inform her of the grossly abnormal blood results. Shirley, however, was insistent that the case should be pursued from the time she first collapsed at home in 1997. Up until the time it was dropped, the case had cost Shirley £2,000.

With 'expert' witnesses, solicitors will often try to limit the duration of liability, so making it easier for the other side to settle. Inevitably, a client like Shirley, as honest, principled and determined as the day is long, presents serious problems for such pragmatists.

In 2003, at a meeting with a consultant, Shirley was informed that her serious ill health, in the form of autoimmune illness from 1997, could have been avoided by appropriate treatment – the administration of steroids.

Shirley approached her third firm of solicitors in June 2003, with her additional knowledge. Over a year after she began her 'case' with the solicitors, she received a bill for an additional £1,275.56. In the same envelope, the solicitor sent a copy of the 'expert witness' statement that he had 'commissioned'. The statement agreed completely with the defendants and so ended Shirley's case. Shirley contested the new bill, claiming that she had paid the solicitors £1,000 in 2003, and this amount adequately covered the work which had been done on her behalf.

In August 2004, she received a letter from her solicitors telling her that enforcement action would be taken against her if she continued to refuse to pay the bill. Not a person to be easily bettered in an argument with professionals intent on ripping her off, Shirley 'saw red' and tried to begin an action against the solicitors for failing to properly carry out her instructions.

Failing to get very far with this case, Shirley was faced with an enforcement action served against her by the solicitors to be heard at Plymouth Small Claims Court.

Although the judge began the hearing by insisting that the court would not consider the medical issues, and that the case was entirely about money owed to the lawyers, he ended it by commenting on the employment of the expert witness by the solicitors. Apparently with no medical knowledge, and seemingly unaware of the ongoing debate about the role of expert medical witnesses in contentious contemporary cases, the judge said that the solicitors – who told the court that they had obtained the name of the expert witness from a data base – were not to know that he had little knowledge of Shirley's condition or how a thyroid function test might be evaluated. The adjudicator in this case gave the green light to a new form of expert witness – the 'inexpert expert' witness.

Having given £1,000 to the solicitors at the start of the case, Shirley asked the court that the solicitors account for both this provisional amount and then for the further £1,275 that they were now demanding. They told the court that the first £1,000 had been used in obtaining Shirley's medical records and in paying the expert witness. The further £1,275 was accounted for by the work that they had done in analysing those records.

Ironically, this analysis had led them to concur with the expert witness that Shirley had never had autoimmune disease brought on by an excess of oestrogen and a lowering of her thyroxine levels. In effect, the lawyers were arguing that Shirley owed them £1,275 for work which they had done for the defendants, completely contrary to her instructions. With claiming solicitors like this, defendants clearly have no need for counsel!

Shirley is now working with two consultants who are in complete agreement with her when she talks about her condition. Her thyroid function has remained stable with low TSH, and letters are exchanged with her consultant and regular blood tests ensured. The tests and their results are communicated and discussed with her by both general practitioner and consultant.

❦   ❦   ❦

Shirley's central issue throughout her one-woman campaign was that, even if her doctor had been ignorant of a connection between HRT and thyroxine, when she became seriously ill he should have done his homework. He might then have treated her properly for the adverse consequences of the HRT prescription on her earlier diagnosis and prescription of thyroxine. This abdication of responsibility for prescribed drugs, especially HRT, is one of the central themes of this book. The idea of an ongoing trial of prescription drugs, which might produce *unrecognised* adverse reactions over 50 years after they were first introduced, should be anathema to scientific medicine. And, as is the case with HRT generally, the continuous revelation of previously *unrecognised* adverse reactions is a minefield for the patient.

Shirley's case gives us hope for the tenacity and enduring nature of lay women forced into wars with professionals. Stated crudely, at the core of the case is the obvious moral bankruptcy of professionals who fail to admit their mistakes and then draw together to defend themselves when faced with someone who stands up to them.

The tragedy is that Shirley endured almost 10 years of illness and agony before she herself, with minimal help, sorted out a treatment programme. Almost unbelievably in this case, the HRT-producing company and the MHRA acted *relatively* quickly and without hubris to correct faulty and missing information. The NHS and medical professionals, meanwhile, chose to remain ignorant of the information, consistently challenging the veracity of Shirley's complaint and threatening her with legal action. The doctors involved in this case should feel humbled by the fact that one woman, with no medical training, argued through the science of her case, while they wallowed in their ignorance.

PART THREE

Chapter Five

A Vanishing History and Disposable Science

I Discovery

All these scientists are the same, they say that they want to work for us but really all they want is to rule the world.

Mel Brooks, Young Frankenstein[1]

One should doubt the sanity of conceiving of scientific research as the ticket to eternity for a minority of over-nourished and bored people, and start doing something to stop billions of people from starving in hopeless misery.

Marco Mamone Capria[2]

When Henry Ford quipped about the Model-T cars produced by his company from 1909, that 'you can have any colour you want – so long as it's black', he pointed up a serious question that would face manufacturing capitalism as it entered the modern period. This period and

---

1 *Young Frankenstein* (Twentieth Century Fox, 1974), directed by Mel Brooks.

2 Mamone Capria M. Is science worth pursuing? In: Dumontet S, Grimme H, eds. *Biology, Biologists and Bioethics: Concerns for scientists, politicians and consumers.* Naples: Foxwell & Davies Italia; 2004.

Ford's type of production were, half a century later, to become known as 'Fordism'. Fordism was the apotheosis of conveyor-belt capitalism. It involved the use of standard parts, manufactured by standard machines, which were assembled by workers engaged for long periods at repetitive tasks.

The question, which only came to be addressed after the 'passing' of European fascism at the end of the Second World War, was whether or not it would be possible for a scientific form of production, ushered in by growing individualism at the end of the 18th century, to create productive techniques that reflected this human individualism. Ford's statement was a reluctant admission that, in the first decades of the 20th century, engineering science could produce only a standard, one-coloured motor vehicle.

Not surprisingly, Henry Ford was a supporter of fascism. His conveyor-belt capitalism massively influenced the social relationships of the working class and the culture that surrounded them. As Fordism created new manufacturing processes in Europe and North America, it also had a considerable effect upon all social institutions; citizens increasingly came to see themselves as part of a machine.

In the period prior to the Second World War, the machine became transcendent, and while the human body was expected to echo its virtues, European society as a whole, aided by an insistent militarism, was supposed to act collectively. Everything that was an impediment to the uniform forward march of society, and particularly to scientific logic, was to be eradicated; everything that differed from the 'norm' was to be dispensed with.

The 'discovery' of the realities of fascism at the end of the war, and an understanding of the mistakes of communism, led liberal western society to a new analysis of the productive mass. Not only had Fordism become notorious for reducing workers to machine parts, but it had consolidated a class that could now create industrial mayhem by withdrawing one of the parts in the machine – its labour. Capitalists searched for a way in which it was possible to separate the worlds of mass, standardised production from the organisation of marketing and consumption; to separate the machinery of production from the individuality of the consumer.

The question of whether or not it might be possible to make the product more individual, and thereby divide up the mass while satisfying the consumer more exactly, became paramount – not simply as a philosophical quandary but also as a question of governance.

Over the next half-century, the manufacturing process, while adhering to the basic economic laws that the system had created, geared up to producing goods that appeared to reflect the individualism of a society, the unity of which was disintegrating. This was facilitated by competition, advances in science and the production of more individual machines. On the whole, the individuation of products was achieved by changing little more than the colour and the shape of things, so that they might appeal to different consumers.

In the 1950s, Henry Ford's words might still have been almost true for the colour of men's jackets, but by the end of the 1960s, a man could choose from a thousand colours and shades in all items of clothing, and the same was almost true of the motor car. If consumers could not find what they wanted on the market, had they had the money, they could turn to a craft producer for an item made to exact personal specifications or with individuality.

With many different consumer products, capitalism fulfilled much of its early promise, and the system came to generate a diversity that was wide enough to suit most pockets and tastes. In relation to the consumption of clothes, at least, European individuals in the post-industrial age were happy knowing that they could express their uniqueness through what they wore, and it was unlikely that, on any particular day, they would meet someone dressed exactly like themselves.

Later generations, after the 1960s, came to understand that the matter of uniqueness and individuality, the whole question of identity, ran much deeper than the choice of colour and shape of consumer items. None of this analysis about the progress of capitalism in accommodating the individual, however, applied even vaguely to the development of pharmaceutical medicines or the therapeutic approaches of the modern allopathic physician. At the beginning of the 21st century, society in both Britain and North America is still completely locked into pharmaceutical Fordism and the monopoly production and distribution of its wares. But while the limitation in choice of car colour or the standardisation of clothing was never likely to cause the consumer physical harm, the consumption of standardised scientific medicine is gradually placing consumers in increasingly grave danger.

There are a number of reasons why pharmaceutical manufacture has remained unable to address the matter of human biological diversity. One reason, however, dominates, and it is the rationale that dictates the whole model of scientific medicine. All pharmaceutical medicines, although many of them are tested on animals,[3] are explored, developed and produced for a common standard human organism.

This is despite the fact that old, as well as new scientific discoveries, ranging from fingerprints to DNA and from human thought to the creation of ideas, increasingly point to the uniqueness of the individual. And despite the fact that we know more than we ever have before about the sensitivities of different people to different substances, medicine unbendingly refuses to admit the importance of divining and analysing the biological differences between people.

The rise of 'alternative' medicine over the past 20 years is clearly rooted in the realisation by the post-industrial individual that we are all biologically unique and that the treatment of ill health has to be predicated upon that uniqueness.

♦ ♦ ♦

Although 'scientific medicine' had its beginning in the 18th century, it came of age in the first half of the 20th with the rise of the modern pharmaceutical company. The medicine of the compressed 'pill', or the 'Tabloid' as Wellcome's original version was called, was to be the cornerstone of medicine throughout the 20th century.

In the 1920s, the 'medical' properties of radium were 'discovered', and for the first time in Europe and North America, physicians had a universal 'cure' to offer cancer sufferers. The medical and political establishments bought into radium in a big way, investing millions in the sub-

---

3 This is one of the simple facts that makes a nonsense of 'scientific' medicine. Most medicines are tested on organisms that are constructed quite differently from humans and can display completely different reactions. Nothing could, in fact, be less scientific in relation to human medicine, than vivisection or drug-testing on animals.

stance which they believed would literally rid society of cancer. This first 'cure-all' was followed by hundreds of others, in the form of pills, powders and surgical procedures. In the 50-year period between 1920 and 1970, doctors began to gain the notional stature of priests. In the main, they forged a position as far beyond criticism as previous divine representatives.

To some degree, the greatness of the physicians' power grew from the fact that during this period they appeared to hold the reins of science and, therefore, the secrets of apparently universal cures. In the early days of the 1920s, scientific medicine was so crude that it mattered little that individualism did not play a part in diagnosis, prognosis or treatment. If you had radium stuffed up one or other of your body's orifices in 1929, it would undoubtedly, whoever you were, destroy a great swath of tissue. More pointedly, perhaps, the laity was relieved that science had 'conquered' cancer. It didn't matter that treatments failed to take their individuality into account, or that their doctor failed to address them as individuals.

Inevitably, the reliance upon medical Fordism had a number of apparently beneficial effects. Crisis medicine, which depends upon conveyor-belt techniques and uses common medical technology to mend, to resuscitate or to rebuild human life, is one of the great achievements of modern medical science. It might even be said, laying aside ethical questions, that spare-part surgery, a massive step forward for medicine, was achievable because medicine conceived of all human bodies as essentially standard issue.

In respect of pharmaceutical medicine, however, Fordism has largely been a failure, mostly because it relies upon the idea that the body is a machine and that all bodies are the same. The more complex the medicine becomes, the higher the chance of adverse reactions or failing responses in different bodies.

By the end of the 1960s, and with the damage that thalidomide wrought, the gilt was beginning to wear off the physician. The laity began to realise that scientific medicine had an immense capacity to damage; it was the beginning of a period of enquiry and regulation, which attempted to bring doctors and hospitals under scrutiny. Because doctors were the individuals who treated patients, the spotlight was consistently played on their mistakes and their faults. However, by this time, doctors had become little more than ciphers for the drug companies, who were running far in front of the medical field with their experimentation and scientific research, now funded by self-generating private finance.

While the pharmaceutical companies and their scientific domination of medicine are mainly to blame for the lack of any system of integrated health care in advanced societies, doctors are the principal agents of pharmaceutical Fordism.

Massive changes have taken place in the craft of medicine since the beginning of the 20th century. Perhaps the most considerable of these changes has been the battle fought by the professional medical bodies against empiricism. Empiricism, in relation to medicine, involves observation by physicians of the patient. It involves the recognition of what doctors feel through experience about the signs they observe. Empiricism also inevitably involves listening to the patient's description of his or her condition, even if this articulation is not acted upon.

Any intelligent person would assume that empiricism might forever form the basis of the practice of medicine. This would be as wrong as assuming that the modern police detective is trained in the intuitive practices of Sherlock Holmes.

From the middle of the 19th century until the present day, orthodox medicine has fought an unceasing war against empiricism, and pharmaceuticals have gradually supplanted the experience of the practitioner, deterring any subjective involvement of either the patient or the doctor in the individual's treatment. While the personal, observational skills of doctors have been eroded, their assumed knowledge of life sciences has been massively extended, and a biological test carried out by a technician now exists for almost every condition of difference from the norm. The doctor has turned from being a creative healer with considerable knowledge of his individual patients, to a sorcerer's apprentice in the service of technicians and drug producers, a pit-stop mechanic tinkering with bodies on their common life science journey to the scrapheap.

The battle against empiricism was waged by professional physicians not just to defend science, but partly because the alternative forms of medicine, particularly herbalism and, later on, homeopathy, based their treatments on an analysis of empirical information gained from the patient. Both these practices eschewed the facility of modern science in favour of the empirically-based wisdom of the healer.

Diagnosis, in homeopathy especially, is based almost entirely upon empirical observation of even the smallest parts of the patient's uniqueness, daily routine, thoughts, body posture or facial expressions. Homeopathy is a patient-centred medicine. Diagnosis in early forms of osteopathy and bone-setting would be drawn from the most intricate observations by the healer of the patient's posture. Inevitably, these therapies also pay some respect to the use, diagnostically, of the relationship between the healer and the subject.

To scientific medicine it is irrelevant that, as in the cases of both herbalism and of homeopathy, empirical information is related to a broader constitutional system before a diagnosis is made and treatment given, thus reinforcing the practices with a rational structure. Because scientific medicine does not allow for individual idiosyncrasies, there is no point in empirical observation. Listening to and observing the patient has, therefore, quickly become a misdemeanour.

After the 1920s, physicians became separated from chemists and biologists, and drugs began to be profitable entities produced by industrial companies rather than entities directly related to patients' health and physicians' experience. Sharon Batt, in her book *Patient No More*, speaking specifically about oestrogen-based drugs, quotes Pierre Blais, a Canadian drugs researcher expelled from the Canadian 'health protection' bureaucracy after criticising silicone breast implants, as saying: 'Good drug design ceased, unfortunately, in the 1930s.'[4]

Even in a post-modern society, where every aspect of intellectual and commodity production is reviewed and critiqued, the ground plan of science and the links between the individual endeavours of scientists is difficult to discover. Research into hormones, the production of the birth control pill (which uses oestrogen to block ovulation), the production of hormone replacement therapy – which shores up oestrogen supply

---

4 Batt S. *Patient No More: The politics of breast cancer*. London: Scarlet Press; 1994.

when nature or surgical intervention depletes it – and, more recently, the synthesis and consumption of hormonal supplements such as human growth hormone, all entail a scientific assault on the natural parameters of human life.

While some scientists stick doggedly to the most common ethical rationale that research into the make-up of the human body will, in time, lead to the conquest of disease, others clearly have a more shadowy purpose. Since the introduction of moving-part machinery during the Industrial Revolution of the late 18th and early 19th centuries, scientists and cultural thinkers have been obsessed with transcending the historical life-cycle and life condition of the human body.

Scientific exploration in this field has wavered from the most exactly focused (the idea of organ transplants), to the widely speculative (the idea that it might be possible to live for ever). Because developed society holds no audit of science, its directions or motivations, experimentation in many of these areas could be called secret or conspiratorial. While many forms of culture, ranging from comics to the fiction of Oscar Wilde, Mary Shelley, H.G. Wells and Robert Louis Stevenson,[5] explore the social consequences of changing the human body and consciousness, scientists remain silent in public about where their work is taking them.

Consideration of this area of social and scientific development is impeded by the increasing separation between the regulatory and policy-making aspects of government and the entirely private institutions of science. While it was relatively easy to understand the motive and direction of mechanical science in, say, the 1950s, with its focus on domestic labour-saving devices, in the 21st century it is almost impossible to disentangle the aims and directions of private medical science, beyond the obvious fact that it is fundamentally commercial, and the rather bland and usually untruthful statement that it is 'trying to find cures for illness'.

Clearly, experiments with and research into hormones, especially in women, are related to a number of general ideas. At the top of this hierarchy of goals must be the centuries-old aspiration to reproduce human

---

5 Mary Shelley, *Frankenstein*. H.G. Wells, *The Island of Dr Moreau*. Oscar Wilde, *A Picture of Dorian Gray*. R.L. Stevenson, *Dr Jekyll and Mr Hyde*. This tradition continued with a number of superheros in the *Marvel* comics and, into the present, with films such as *Robocop*.

life, now in bio-robotic form. Perhaps one rung down the hierarchy is the idea that science might create immortality or, at least, halt the ageing process. In relation to women, this later idea is associated with concepts that might ultimately determine the regulation and control of human life on earth: the advent of artificial human reproduction. And, of course, there is the flip side to the research: creating infertility and selectively halting population growth, or ridding the world of what Henry Kissinger once charmingly referred to as 'useless eaters'.

When we discuss the advent and the continuance of the use of hormone replacement therapy, we have to keep these general ideas in mind. Knowing what we now know about the human radiation experiments that were carried out in almost complete secrecy on many individuals and groups between 1948 and 1980,[6] we must remind ourselves that doctors can have hidden motives and might be directed by invisible hands.

It might be best if we suggested that these general directions are founded in commercial curiosity, because further examination of the motives of scientists inevitably leads into the murky waters of conspiracy. It can, however, be said simply and with some certainty that, for the most part, these projects are part of a wider political and commercial design, and that they inevitably produce spin-offs that affect the lives of the population. It could also be said that *the great task of medical science* is not to enhance and to support being human but to *transcend* being human.

The Industrial Revolution began in the second half of the 18th century. The end of the Middle Ages released a spectacular diversity of inquiry into the nature of the natural world and the possibilities of reconstructing the man-made world. Humanity was no longer to be a subjected victim of the world, but could begin to dictate its own pace, even change the direction of human, social and industrial development. For the first time, the individual began to emerge as a person who could develop wholly original ideas beyond the realm of God's determination.

---

6 Advisory Committee on Human Radiation Experiments. Final Report. Washington, DC: U S Government Printing Office; 1995.

Discoveries came slowly at first, and then, with an incredible explosion, ideas rushed through the 19th century, gaining material shape. Inquiries into what shaped males and females, and into what might prevent ageing, had been made in many civilisations, going back to the ancient Egyptians. In the latter part of the 18th century, physicians and others began injecting themselves and others with crushed animal testes and ovaries. Using fresh or dried preparations of cows' ovaries, Austrian and German gynaecologists began experimenting with early hormone therapy for women with menopausal symptoms. The point of these tests was often to see whether or not sex characteristics and various aspects of ageing could be changed.

Throughout the 19th century, scientists worked on the ideas of both male rejuvenation and contraception, while trying to isolate the hormones that controlled sexual identity. In 1849, in one of the first ever endocrine experiments, the researcher Arnold Berthold had transplanted a rooster's testes into a castrated bird and restored the rooster's comb, which had atrophied after neutering.

In 1889, some 71 years after Mary Shelley had written her famous novel, *Frankenstein*, Charles Edouard Brown-Séquard[7] sat down, rolled up his sleeve and intravenously injected himself with canine testicular extracts.[8] These injections, he was later to claim, reversed his signs of ageing. At the same time, in his writing, he suggested that the intravenous injection of ovarian extracts would have the same effect upon women. Brown-Séquard had studied with Claude Bernard, the infamous vivisector and father of endocrinology.

In 1919, Ludwig Haberlandt, an Austrian physiologist, rendered female deer infertile by injecting subcutaneous implants of ovaries from pregnant rabbits.[9]

---

7 French physician and physiologist, born April 8, 1817, Port Louis, Mauritius; died April 1, 1894, Paris.

8 Barbara Seaman (op. cit.) reveals that Brown-Séquard actually injected himself in a more sensitive part of his body than his arm, but I was so pleased with my phrase, '... sat down and rolled up his sleeve,' against saying '... stood up and let his trousers down', that I left it less historically accurate.

9 Common L. Great balls of fire. *Medical Post*, 26 April 2000. Volume 36, Issue 16.

In the 1920s, a Russian, Dr Serge Voronoff, popularised 'monkey-gland' implants at his clinic in Algiers. Dr Voronoff transplanted ape and chimpanzee tissue into his patients. Besides restoring virility, Dr Voronoff said, these glands also reversed senility, a claim made previously by Brown-Séquard.[10]

In the mid-1930s, Ernest Laqueur in Amsterdam finally succeeded in extracting pure testosterone from ground-up bulls' testicles. Later, George Rosenkrantz synthesised the same hormone from Mexican yams.

Just after the Second World War, Dr L.L. Stanley, of San Quentin, California, used gonadal tissue from executed convicts to help patients who had lost their own testes through trauma or disease.

The discovery and then the synthesis of the hormone oestrogen was one of the many scientific breakthroughs that coincided with the birth of the modern scientific world after the First World War. When scientists had isolated the 'female principle', they called it oestrogen, from the Greek words oistros, meaning frenzy or desire, and gennein, meaning to beget or procreate.

Scientists began research into sex hormones at Schering, the German drug and chemical company, in 1923. In the same year, Edgar Allen and Edward Doisy treated mice and rats that had undergone oophorectomy with follicular fluid isolated from hogs' ovaries, and found that this restored the animals oestrous cycles, suggesting that the oestrous hormone was produced in the ovarian follicle.

In 1926, German chemists S. Loewe and F. Lange detected oestrogenic hormones in human urine, and in, 1927, Selmar Aschheim reported greater concentrations in the urine of pregnant women. Doisy then isolated oestrone in crystalline form from human pregnancy urine. A few months later, in 1928, Adolf Butenandt, a Nazi sympathizer working for Schering, isolated the same compound. (Continuing his research up to and throughout the war, Butenandt succeeded in isolating a number of hormones, particularly testosterone in 1935.) 'Theelin', as Allen and Doisy named their hormone, was protected by a university-held patent.

---

10 Seaman B. *The Greatest Experiment Ever Performed On Women: Exploding the estrogen myth.* New York: Hyperion; 2003.

A. S. Parkes and C. W. Bellerby subsequently coined the word 'oestrin' (now oestrone) for the hormone(s) responsible for oestrus.

In 1930, Guy Marriam isolated oestriol, a relatively weak oxidation product of oestradiol and oestrone, from pregnant women's urine. This was later isolated from the human placenta. In 1931, pregnant mares' urine was found to be a rich source of oestrogen, and this remained one of the main sources of oestrogen for the next 70 years.

Oestriol was the first oestrogen manufactured on a mass scale. It was patented in 1934 and marketed as Estriol.[11] For the period of its first patent (July 1934-1951), Estriol was produced under licence from St Louis University. The university patented a number of other oestrogens, most particularly oestrone, which was found in the urine of pregnant women and mares, in follicular liquor of many animals, in the human placenta, in bulls' and stallions' urine and in palm kernel oil.

In 1934, two English doctors, J.W. Cook and Charles Dodds, showed oestrogen activity in at least eight different forms of stilbene preparation (stilbene is a crystalline compound used in the manufacture of dye).[12] In 1938, Dodds went on to formulate diethylstilbestrol (DES), the first orally active synthetic oestrogen. Some five times more potent than oestradiol, and the most potent naturally-occurring oestrogen in mammals, this synthetic (non-steroidal) oestrogen would, for the next 25 years, be the basis of most oestrogen replacement therapy, with the disastrous and continuing consequences described in the Introduction and in more detail below. Dodds, who would be knighted for his achievement, did not take out a patent on the drug, but published his research in the journal *Nature* of February 15, suggesting that this should be a gift to mankind.[13]

This decision was not simply philanthropic: with the war edging closer, and with fears that German scientists such as Buntenandt were themselves on the verge of synthesising oestrogen as well as trying to

---

11 Butenandt A. Über "Progynon" ein krystallisiertes weibliches sexualhormon. *Naturwissenschaften,* 1929; 17:879.

12 Clorfene-Casten L. *Breast Cancer: Poisons, profits and prevention.* Monroe, ME: Common Courage Press; 1996.

13 John Robbins, *Reclaiming Our Health.* Tiburon, California: H J Kramer; 1996. Citing Mokhiber R. *Corporate Crime and Violence: Big business power and the abuse of the public trust.* San Francisco, CA: Sierra Club Books; 1988.

patent oestradiol, a natural substance, Dodds wanted to ensure that the intellectual property did not lie in German hands alone.

Later in 1938, however, scientists working for Berlin-based Schering, synthesised and applied for a patent for ethinyl oestradiol. Inevitably, other pharmaceutical companies took out their own patents and rushed to market.[14] Nor would Dodds's gesture stop the demented scientists of the Third Reich carrying out enforced hormone experimentation on concentration camp victims, as detailed below.

Dodds was particularly responsible for raising the question of oestrogen and cancer, after male lab technicians handling stilbestrol powder started to grow breasts. He sent the powder to cancer specialists for testing, and the results of the research, published in 1940, showed that stilbestrol did indeed cause reproductive cancers in both male and female mice. Large numbers of concerned scientists added their voices to Dodds's, in protesting against the general use of DES, and tried hard to persuade the FDA not to let it become freely available, but to ensure it was reserved for cases of compelling need.[15]

Yet again we find that inconvenient findings from animal studies can be set aside by the very bodies that most stridently defend vivisection. Careless of the known cancer risk, in a pattern that would repeat itself over and over, in 1939 and 1940, major drug companies made applications to the FDA for licence to market diethylstilbestrol. They formed a cartel to campaign for the marketing rights, and, throughout 1940, using lobbyists and physicians, they battled to get the FDA to give it the green light.[16] In 1941, the FDA agreed to the licensing of DES.

The American Medical Association (AMA) backed the patent and the commercial distribution of DES, saying that it could 'mitigate suffering for millions of women over 40.' [17] Although the chemical was to be

---

14 John Robbins citing Susan Bell, *The Synthetic Compound Diethylstilbestrol (DES)*, 1938-1941: 'The social construction of a medical treatment' (Dissertation). Waltham, MA: Brandeis University; 1980.

15 Barbara Seaman, op. cit.

16 Barbara Seaman, op. cit.

17 John Robbins citing Haberman, H. Help for women over 40. *Hygeia* 1941;19:898-9. Also condensed in Readers Digest, Nov. 1941. Cited in Diana Dutton, *Worse Than the Disease: Pitfalls of medical progress.* Cambridge: Cambridge University Press; 1988.

used on women, from the beginning it was also 'designed' to be fed to intensively-reared livestock to fatten the animals up prior to slaughter.

Hormone Experimentation and the Second World War

With oestrogen being produced before the outbreak of the Second World War, and progesterone available as the war began, German scientists and doctors working in concentration camps took full advantage of their captives to carry out crude experiments.

Scientists seem to have been centrally concerned with ways of sterilising populations. Selective sterilisation could be used to create coming slave labour, and minorities inside the new German empire might also be wiped out.

Wolfgang Eckhart, the Professor of Historical Medicine at Heidelberg University, says about Auschwitz and other camps: 'The concentration camps were used as a huge laboratory for human experimentation. We have to look upon the camps as outposts of pharmacological research. The Nazis wanted to sterilise the population of the east, especially Russian people, but enable them to continue to be useful as workers.'

The German chemical combine IG Farben ran a plant inside Auschwitz. At least 30,000 slave workers died in medical experiments in the plant, where scientists and doctors carried out continuous experimentation on inmates. A subsidiary of IG Farben, Degesch, produced the Zyklon B gas which killed millions of experimental subjects in Auschwitz after they had served their purpose.[18]

The experiments at Auschwitz ranged from the most general, in which large numbers of female inmates were fed on progesterone-laced meals in the hope that they would become infertile, to the more sophisticated.[19] Plant extracts that contained progesterone were injected into

---

18 Coalition against BAYER-dangers (Germany), www.CBGnetwork.org

19 While these and other experiments were roundly condemned by the Allies after the war, the data and observation from them continued to be used by manufacturing scientists and academics in developed European countries in peacetime. See Marco Mamone Capria, op. cit.

women's vaginas. These plant juices were extremely toxic and painful, and the experiments resulted in the deaths of many women. Doctors and scientists paid the guards at Auschwitz to send women to the IG Farben plant.

One Auschwitz prisoner, interviewed in 2004 by Mark Handscomb, BBC Radio 4 reporter, for *It's My Story*, was Zoe Polanska Palmer. Like thousands of other children, she had been destined to be gassed once her usefulness to Nazi science had ceased. During her two years at Auschwitz, Zoe, then aged 13-14, was forced to take tablets and pills as part of a series of pharmacological experiments believed to be early birth-control tests.

Zoe was saved by a Russian doctor who evacuated her to Dachau, where she recovered from the experiments before eventually settling in Scotland. Eyewitness testimonies held in the Auschwitz camp archive claim the doctor who force-fed her pills worked for Bayer when it was part of the IG Farben conglomerate.

Zoe was part of Dr Mengele's genetic research, and was experimented on by Dr Victor Capesius. In 1959, Capesius was imprisoned and charged as a defendant for war crimes in the Auschwitz trials, which lasted until December 1963. He was sentenced to nine years and released 10 months early, in 1968. Other Bayer employees worked as SS doctors at Auschwitz.

In present-day Germany, Bayer is one of the most successful pharmaceutical companies, and, says the Alliance For Human Research Protection, 'a growing number of people do not understand that IG Farben's successors, Bayer, BASF and Hoechst still refuse to apologise for their misdeeds'. Nor is it widely known that, just before the war, in order to protect US imports of chemicals and pharmaceuticals, much of Farben was subsumed by those great US philanthropists, the Rockefellers. After the war, the Rockefeller-owned companies were allowed to keep IG Farben's entire property, whereas the surviving slave workers received nothing. Until today, Bayer, BASF and Hoechst have paid neither wages nor compensation to their former camp inmate workers.

Problems, Problems, Problems

In the unseemly rush to the market that followed the war, synthetic oestrogens were pushed mainly for replacement therapy in cases of apparent oestrogen deficiency. Under a range of trade names, including Femidyn, Follidrin and Ovifollin, these preparations were prescribed from the late 1940s for menopausal problems and always for short-term use. The Merck Index on Chemicals and Drugs for 1952[20] states that the medical use of diethylstilbestrol is as an oestrogen replacement therapy, which should be used with caution on any patients who have a history of breast or genital cancer or liver disease. Limited side effects of the chemical were, even in 1952, recognised as nausea, vomiting, headache, oedema and uterine bleeding.

As early as 1939, Nobel laureate Dr Hans Selye had written of the work on stilbene: 'It is well for the physician to realise that oestrogens do not only affect the sex organs *but have general systemic effects*, and that weight per weight diethylstilbestrol proved more toxic in the majority of our experiments than the natural oestrogens.' [21]

The fact that synthesised hormones were extremely toxic obscured for many years the effects of the administration of 'natural' hormones. To this day, Wyeth Pharmaceuticals still insists on calling the oestrogen used in Premarin 'natural' because it is derived from the urine of pregnant mares. The logic, in any case, that the administration of 'natural' oestrogen to women is inevitably 'natural' is clearly faulty. As is the idea that, while synthetic hormones are toxic, 'natural' ones, administered unnaturally to women, are not.

From the beginning, Charles Dodds, who had synthesised the first synthetic oestrogen, was convinced that it could be a serious danger to women's health. As time went by, he became an increasingly vociferous campaigner on the subject.[22]

---

20 *The Merck Index of Chemicals and Drugs.* 6th ed. Rahway, NJ: Merck; 1952.

21 Selye H. On the toxicity of oestrogens with special reference to diethylstilboestrol. *Can Med Ass J* 1939;41:48-9.

22 Barbara Seaman, op. cit.

It was also clearly recognised that other synthetic hormones had toxic effects. By 1945 it was known that the administration of synthetic progestogens could create sensitivities resulting in anaphylaxis, a sudden, severe, sometimes fatal allergic reaction. Synthetic progestogens, which were 500 to 1,000 times more potent than natural progesterone, were first produced commercially in the 1950s.

In 1943, Kharasch and Kleiman wrote up their synthesis of diethylstilbestrol in the *Journal of the American Chemical Society*. [23] This preparation had activity 400 times greater than any natural oestrogen.

Soon after DES had been licensed, Drs George and Olive Smith at the Free Hospital in Boston began using the therapy for their women patients who appeared to be in danger of a miscarriage. They had noted that those most at risk had lower oestrogen levels. Two studies that the Smiths carried out seemed to suggest that women who took DES not only did not have miscarriages but had very healthy babies.[24] Studies conducted in the 1950s, however, came to the opposite conclusion, that women who took DES had more miscarriages. Around two million women took DES in North America between the late 1940s and the early Sixties.

Throughout the 1950s, there was increasing evidence that DES was not only ineffective, but had terrible side effects, including uterine disease in women treated with it after giving birth. Despite continuous reports of adverse reactions throughout the 1960s, around one million pregnant women were given DES in North America, mainly for the prophylactic prevention of miscarriage and various 'female problems', including postmenopausal 'complications'. Before the end of the Sixties, it was being dished out like sweets, for headaches, dizziness, nervousness, depression, 'frigidity', insomnia, muscle and joint pains and infertility.[25]

The earliest cases of endometrial cancer associated with DES were reported in 1966. A 14-fold increase of the disease among postmenopausal women who had undertaken oestrogen replacement therapy

---

23 Kharasch MS, Kleiman M. Synthesis of polyenes. III. A new synthesis of diethylstilbestrol. *J Am Chem Soc*, 1943; 65:11-5.

24 Smith OW, Smith GV. Use of diethylstilbestrol to prevent fetal loss from complications of late pregnancy. *N Engl J Med*, 1949; 241:562-8.

25 Liane Clorfene-Casten, op. cit.

for over seven years was reported. As is common, when evidence of adverse reactions and deaths begin to accumulate, the producing company moved the goalposts. The manufacturers of DES began to suggest it as a contraceptive and for the suppression of lactation for women who did not breastfeed their babies.[26]

In 1971, two studies linked cancer in daughters to the administration of DES to their pregnant mothers. Later in 1971, the FDA was being accused of having side-stepped, for four-and-a-half months, a decision to ban DES for use with pregnant women. In November it announced that DES should not be given in pregnancy.

In April 1977, three women filed a $77 million class action against Eli Lilly & Co, after discovering that, during their pregnancies in 1951 and 1952, they had been unwitting guinea pigs in a trial of DES at the University of Chicago Lying-In Hospital. The women believed that the tablets they were prescribed were some kind of special supplement to ensure a 'healthy baby'. Not until 25 years later did they learn the truth from an advisory warning letter from the university. Under their action, 1,078 women charged that they had all been given DES while pregnant without being told about it. A federal judge dismissed their claims, but allowed a claim of 'battery' for an 'offensive invasion' of their persons. In February 1982, the three women accepted an out-of-court settlement of $225,000 and the promise of health monitoring for the children exposed to DES in the experiment.

May 1977 saw the rejection of a damages suit filed in 1974 by 144 women and 40 of their husbands, who had sued on the grounds that the women had contracted cancer after having taken DES during their pregnancy. The judge ruled that the action had failed to note brand names (DES was only sold under its generic chemical name, anyway) and manufacturers, and to link these to specific illnesses. Lawyers in this case argued before the courts that there should be an industry-wide liability. They said that all the companies that had marketed DES had known that it contained carcinogenic chemicals.

It was eventually found that between 60 and 90 per cent of daughters born to women who took DES during pregnancy had abnormalities

---

26 Ibid.

in their vagina or cervix. DES daughters stand a substantially higher risk of miscarriage, stillbirth, ectopic pregnancies and other poor pregnancy outcomes.[27] DES sons have highly increased rates of sterility and testicular abnormalities,[28] while DES mothers have a 40 per cent greater chance of developing breast cancer.[29] It has been estimated that 60,000 North American women will eventually die of breast cancer as a consequence of taking DES.[30]

DES in Food

To get rid of DES in the food chain was to prove even more difficult than getting it withdrawn from human prescription. By the 1950s, DES had become a major food additive, despite the fact that a knock-on effect had been demonstrated in women who ate poultry treated with it.[31]

In November 1971, Senator William Proxmire submitted legislation to ban the use of DES in cattle and sheep feed. The US Agricultural Department, however, argued that a ban on DES would increase the price of beef by three-and-a-half cents a pound, to which Proxmire replied, 'Cheap beef or lamb is a very bad bargain indeed if it brings with it the threat of poor health.'

Despite other attempts to bring in legislation, it was not until 1972 that the Agriculture Department announced new and restricting regulations for the use of DES as a growth hormone in food animals. Even stricter regulations were brought in a short time later, when it was found that the residue levels of DES in meat were twice the regulatory maximum.[32]

---

27 Robbins J. *Reclaiming Our Health: Exploding the medical myth and embracing the source of true healing.* Tiburon, CA: H J Kramer; 1996.

28 Ibid.

29 Ibid.

30 Diana Dutton, *Worse Than the Disease: Pitfalls of medical progress.* Cambridge: Cambridge University Press; 1988. Cited in John Robbins, op. cit.

31 Bird, *Endocrinology*, 1947. Cited in Liane Clorfene-Casten.

32 Sobel LA, ed. *Cancer and the Environment.* New York: Facts on File; 1979.

In 1973, during a US Congress hearing which was trying to ban DES contaminated food, it became clear that the FDA had previously rejected the advice of its own advisory panel on carcinogenesis. Despite announcements of support for DES from its officials and those of its manufacturers, the agency now, at last, announced an actual ban on DES. This ban was, however, overturned by the US Court of Appeal, which said that previous bans had been illegal and that DES could be used freely again until special hearings were conducted, which must include the users and manufacturers. The FDA, the court said, had used 'scare tactics'. The judgement went as far as to suggest that the FDA should not consider banning DES, but should work out a scheme that was also good for the meat producers.

In June 1979, the FDA finally banned DES as a growth stimulator fed to cattle. Although DES is now banned in North America and Britain, its potential contribution to cancer in women still lingers on, with a disease that can have a 20-year latency period.[33]

From the beginning, the production of sex-hormone-based therapies has been governed by ideological considerations. Their widest use outside hormone replacement therapy has been in the birth control pill, where they are used to create infertility. Just as with male and female rejuvenation ideas, the idea of enforced infertility was always backed by powerful industrial interests.

Ideas about using hormones to suppress fertility date back to the 19th century. Such ideas really came to prominence with the Eugenics movement, which began in England at the end of the 1800s. In the 1930s, both the North American and German Governments were involved in eugenics programmes of sterilisation. Guided by ideological purposes of controlling and purifying populations, the birth control movement and its search for a chemical or biological agent to control reproduction, inevitably pushed health considerations into the background.

---

33 For a fuller story of DES and meat see: Schell, O. *Modern Meat: Antibiotics, hormones and the pharmaceutical farm.* USA: Random House; 1984.

In North America, Rockefeller-dominated industries that had spent millions of dollars on research into oestrogen and its commercial production and were deeply involved in the development of hormone-based contraception. In 1933, major financial support for the two German institutes responsible for eugenics, the Kaiser-Wilhelm Institute for Eugenics and Anthropology in Berlin, and the Kaiser Wilhelm Institute for Psychiatry in Munich, came from a Rockefeller fund.[34]

In 1951, Margaret Sanger, a eugenicist deeply committed to the sterilisation of the 'unfit',[35] created the International Planned Parenthood Association. Its first funding came from the US Government, the World Bank, and the Ford and Rockefeller Foundations. The Board of IPPA was made up of representatives from multinational chemical, pharmaceutical and oil companies.[36]

Sanger persuaded Dr Gregory Pincus and his colleague, Dr Min-Cheuh Chang, at the Worcester Foundation in Massachusetts, to embark on research into oestrogen-based birth control. The contraceptive pill, which was based upon the ability of oestrogen to suppress ovulation, was developed by Pincus and Rock.

The first trial for the oral contraceptive pill (OCP) was carried out on 6,000 women in Puerto Rico and Haiti by Searle in 1956. This was mainly because, in the majority of states in North America, contraceptives were outlawed. Women in the Puerto Rico trial suffered serious side effects – nearly 20 per cent suffered dizziness, stomach pains, headaches and diarrhoea. The researchers conveniently put the complaints down to 'suggestibility'. This is more than they did in relation to the three women who died: study leaders asked for no autopsies[37] or examination of the women's bodies.

During the trials, it transpired that the progestogen pill was contaminated with oestrogen. When, however, the oestrogen was taken out, women experienced breakthrough bleeding. Pincus and Rock put back

---

34 Trombley T. *The Right to Reproduce: A history of coercive sterilization*. London: Weidenfeld and Nicolson; 1988.

35 Ibid.

36 Ibid.

37 Batt, op. cit.

the oestrogen. The first Pill was Enovid, 10mg of the progestogen norethynodrel, and 0.15mg mestranol, a synthetic oestrogen.

The Pill was licensed by the FDA in 1960,[38] despite the fact that, although hundreds of women had participated in trials of Enovid, only 132 had taken it continuously for a year or more.[39] Enovid was licensed for use in the USA in 1960 and in the UK in 1961, and within two years, more than a million women were using the Pill. This was despite the fact that numerous studies had shown a link between oestrogen and cancer. Other studies, from the beginning, linked the Pill to heart attacks and blood clots. Neither the FDA nor the authorities in Britain backed any further research into the oral contraceptive, until the matter of blood clots and thrombosis began to hit the headlines much later.

More or less the same arguments relating to adverse effects have followed hormone-based contraceptives since they were first produced in the 1960s. Sharon Batt, in her extensive and precise book *Patient no More*, traced Rose Kushner,[40] a fellow breast cancer patient, after finding an odd volume of hers in a library. Kushner had found that, despite studies showing that there were an alarming number of women under 30 contracting breast cancer, there was no warning about this with the Pill.

Batt quotes Kushner as saying that she finally found an official text which explained that organised medicine objected to label warnings on the Pill about cancer because package inserts would 'confuse the patient' and 'interfere with the physician-patient relationship'. 'In short, doctors wanted to retain their power over patients,' says Batt.

---

38 Seaman B, Seaman G. *Women and the Crisis in Sex Hormones.* New York: Rawson Associates; 1977.

39 Since the licensing of the Pill, by the FDA in 1960, the FDA and pharmaceutical companies had frequently broadcast the story that trials for the pill had involved thousands of women. The Seamans, however, point out that at a Senate investigation in 1963, it was revealed that 'approval of Enovid' was based on clinical studies of only 132 women who had taken it continuously for a year or longer. The Seamans make the small point in their fabulous book that Pincus and Rock also tested the formulation for the pill on men to find whether or not it made men infertile – it did, but for some reason the FDA only continued to develop, license and market it for women.

40 Kushner R. *Breast Cancer: A personal history and investigative report.* New York: Harcourt, Brace Jovanovich; 1975.

In 1984, trials of an implanted hormone device were carried out in Brazil by Rockefeller's chemical and pharmaceutical companies and the US-based Population Council. The result was Norplant, a contraceptive that has been dogged by controversy and disastrous adverse health reactions. The implants, which have been used in enforced sterilisation programmes in developing countries, have caused menstrual chaos and presented serious problems of removal.[41]

In the 1960s, there was a suspicion that the Pill might cause cardiovascular problems in women.[42] This link between the OCP and cardiovascular disease was actually established during the 1960s and 1970s.[43] In 1969, Britain's Committee on the Safety of Drugs recommended that doctors no longer prescribe pills containing more than 50µg of oestrogen, since these were associated with a higher risk of blood clots.

A study by Pike in 1981 suggested that one year on the Pill for a woman under 35, boosted her chance of breast cancer by 30 per cent; eight years almost quadrupled it.[44] In 1985, the US National Technical Program's Fourth Annual Report on Carcinogens, stated that all synthetic oestrogen products were carcinogenic.

❦ ❦ ❦

Throughout the Sixties, marketing of oestrogen replacement therapy boomed in North America. Based as it was on gimcrack science, it was not

---

41 Farmer A. *Prophets and Priests: The hidden face of the birth control movement.* London: Saint Austin Press; 2002.

42 See Dr Ellen Grant, 1968; Grant 1969; Bloemenkamp KW, Rosendal FR, Helmerhorst FM, Bauller HR, Vandenbroche JP. Enhancement by factor V Leiden mutation of deep vein thrombosis associated with oral contraceptives containing third generation progestogen. 43 *The Lancet,* 1995; 346: 1593-6; Chasen-Taber L, Stampfer MJ. Epidemiology of oral contraceptives and cardiovascular disease. *Ann Intern Med,* 1998; 128: 467-77.

43 Venous thromboembolic disease and combined oral contraceptives: results of international multicentre case-control study. World Health Organization Collaborative Study of Cardiovascular Disease and Steroid Hormone Contraception. *The Lancet,* 1995; 346: 1575-82. Further analyses of mortality in oral contraceptive users. Royal College of General Practitioners' Oral Contraception Study. *The Lancet,* 1981;1:541-6.

44 Pike MC, Henderson BE, Casagrande JT, Rosario I, Gray GE. Oral contraceptive use and early abortion as risk factors for breast cancer. *Br J Cancer,* 1981; 43:72-6.

scientific information or a sound basis in health care that was used to sell oestrogen replacement therapy (ERT), it was fear and the promise of a fictional Utopia. In an article in *Look* magazine in 1966, Richard Wilson,[45] the great and fraudulent proselytiser of ERT, wrote: 'While not all women are affected by menopause to this extreme degree, no woman can be sure of escaping the horrors of this living decay.'[46]

From the very beginning of mass marketing of hormone replacement therapies, there was always an alternative and usually more correct scientific medical view on ERT. Robert Hoover, an epidemiologist with the National Cancer Institute, conducted a study of one practitioner's patients prescribed ERT between 1939 and 1972. This study looked at 1,891 menopausal women in Kentucky who had been prescribed oestrogen. Results published in 1976[47] showed an increase in breast cancer related to both dose and length of prescription. Other factors included family history and whether or not oestrogen was taken during, rather than after, menopause.

By 1975, when the taking of oestrogen for menopausal problems and 'to stay young and feminine' was well underway,[48] study results were beginning to show a link between ERT and endometrial (uterine) cancer. By June 1976, the evidence was mounting against ERT; one study had found that cancers of the uterus increased as much as 150 per cent between 1969 and 1973, among women taking oestrogen after the onset of the menopause. The doctor in charge of this study, Noel S. Weiss, commented: 'The important point is that it is unlikely the disease is due to some characteristic of the women rather than the medicine ...'[49] And Dr Thomas M. Mack of the University of California, who directed another

---

45 See following chapter.

46 Wilson RA. A key to staying young. *Look*, 11 January 1966. See Chapter Eight for more on Wilson. Wilson advocated the use of HRT from 9 to 90 years of age.

47 Hoover R, Gray LA, Cole P, MacMahon B. Menopausal estrogens and breast cancer. *N Engl J Med,* 1976; 295:401-5.

48 25 million prescriptions were being written annually.

49 Weiss NS, Szekely DR, Austin DF. Increasing incidence of endometrial cancer in the United States. *N Engl J Med,* 1976; 294:1259-62.

study, said, 'There is a high level of statistical significance that oestrogen causes cancer of the uterus.'[50]

By the mid-1970s, a clear link between ERT and uterine cancer – up to a ten-fold increase – had been proven. Responding to this, thousands of North American women had their uteruses removed so they could continue to take oestrogen replacement therapy. Next, in order to capture slipping markets, companies added synthetic progesterone, progestogen, to their oestrogen therapy, so making it apparently safe.

In 1976,[51] a new study warned that there was 'a definite possibility' of a cause-and-effect link between ERT and breast cancer. One of the long-standing selling points of oestrogen therapy had been that it warded off breast cancer. Researchers found that after 15 years of taking ERT, the probability of a woman developing cancer doubled.[52]

Also in 1976, in one of the rare public admissions in medicine, Dr Robert W. Kistner, professor of obstetrics and gynaecology at Harvard Medical School, who had previously defended the Pill and oestrogen replacement, told the *Washington Post* that he retracted all his earlier statements. The medical use of oestrogen in menopause could, he said, 'not be substantiated'.[53]

In 1979, there was even more evidence of the link between oestrogen and uterine cancer.[54] In the largest study ever of women taking oestrogen, it was found that such women were six times more likely to have cancer of the uterus than those not taking it.

For the next decade and a half, the link between oestrogen and breast cancer was simply forgotten by scientists and drug dealers. The most likely reason for this is that it looked as if Wyeth (at that time,

---

50 Mack TM, Pike MC, Henderson BE, et al. Estrogens and endometrial cancer in a retirement community. *N Engl J Med,* 1976; 294:1262-7.

51 Hoover R, Gray LA, Cole P, MacMahon B. Menopausal estrogens and breast cancer. *N Engl J Med,* 1976;295:401-5.

52 The number of women in the study who might have been expected to develop breast cancer was 39.1, but 49 women, or 25% more than expected actually developed it.

53 *Washington Post,* 19 August 1976.

54 Antunes CM, Strolley PD, Rosenshein NB, Davies JL, Tonascia JA, Brown C, et al. Endometrial cancer and estrogen use. Report of a large case-control study. *N Engl J Med,* 1979; 300:9-13.

American Home Products), by adding progestogen, to the oestrogen, had solved the 'cancer problem'. In fact, they had only appeared to have 'solved' the uterine cancer problem. There was no way of knowing what this new, quickly cooked up recipe might do to women.

The other reason why the cancer scare appeared to have been forgotten was that the producers of HRT, especially Wyeth, stepped up their 'good news' propaganda offensive. In the 1970s and 1980s there was a steady stream of reported benefits apparently associated with long-term use of HRT.

In the 1990s, adverse data again emerged when a meta-analysis of 19 studies published in April 1991 concluded that ERT was a risk for breast cancer.[55] Over the following ten years, there were increasing reports that HRT caused breast cancer.

Liane Clorfene-Casten cites Dr Julian Whitaker, editor of *Health & Healing*, saying that by 1995 there were at least 30 studies confirming an increased risk of breast cancer in women using oestrogen. One study suggested that women who used HRT over a five-to-nine-year period, risk a 59 per cent increase of breast cancer with an additional risk for older women.[56]

By 1995, the packet literature issued with Premarin, although trumpeting in bold print in an accompanying booklet the low risk of breast cancer if taken at low doses , stated in the small print: 'Some studies have suggested a possible increased incidence of breast cancer in those women on oestrogen therapy taking high doses for prolonged periods of time (five years or more) ...'[57] Wyeth directors just crossed their fingers, hopeful that no one would make much fuss, and watched the dollars pour in.

55 Steinberg KK, Thacker SB, Smith SJ, Stroup DF, Zack MM, Flanders WD, et al. A meta-analysis of the effect of estrogen replacement therapy on the risk of breast cancer. *JAMA*, 1991;265:1985-90.

56 14-year follow-up study on nurses health conducted at Harvard Medical School and reported in *Oncology News*, April 1994. Cited in Liane Clorfene-Casten, op.cit.

57 Booklet produced by Wyeth-Ayerst, which accompanies Premarin, quoted in Liane Clorfene-Casten.

This is not a story of science moving sedately forward, carefully adding pieces to a puzzle before making recommendations to patients. This is a story of the corruption of the scientific and medical community. The belief that hormones are good preventive medicine has been a triumph of marketing over science.[58]

In English law, the average and common-sense person is referred to as 'the man' – or more recently 'person' – 'on the Clapham omnibus'. The expression is, of course, on the one hand, a rather slighting observation about the British class system, and, on the other, fairly flattering of the independent, commonsensical thinking of the *ordinary* English person. Anyone on a Clapham omnibus, be they male, female or child, keeping up with the medical news in the early part of the 21st century, might have sensibly concluded that it had been found, quite suddenly, that hormone replacement therapy caused cancer.

Following the story, the omnibus passenger would probably think that all would be made right by the regulatory agencies and the drug companies concerned. The man or woman on the Clapham omnibus would have been very wrong on both points.

Throughout the 1980s and 1990s, as we have seen, the producers of HRT introduced new and more medical arguments in its favour. And while thousands of women still took the drug in order to give themselves everlasting youth, millions more were prescribed it by physicians for apparently serious medical reasons.

It is worth reprising, here, the evidence that had been mounting against HRT, particularly in the matter of breast cancer (as described in the Introduction to this text), up until 2004, when one would have thought there was no barge pole long enough with which to touch hormone therapy.

There was the recommendation from the US Government's scientific advisory panel, in the year 2000, that synthetic oestrogen used in HRT be listed as a cancer-causing agent. (The fact was that hormone therapy was not only predisposing women to breast cancer, but was making it more difficult to detect.) The Women's Health Initiative in the USA had, by July 2002, concluded that women taking combination HRT increased

---

58 Executive Director of National Women's Health Network. Quoted in: The ten worst corporations of 2002. *Multinational Monitor*, 2002; 23(12).

their risk of breast cancer by 25 per cent, as well as running an increased risk of deep-vein thrombosis and stroke.[59]

At the end of 2002, in the States, steroidal oestrogen was labelled a 'known carcinogen', and in August 2003, one strand of the British Million Women study was called off amid breast cancer fears. It was said that, over a decade in the UK, an estimated 20,000 cases of breast cancer among women aged 50-64 could be attributable to HRT – 15,000 of these among women on combination therapy.[60] A North American research paper estimated that cases of breast cancer in the US caused by HRT could be 120,000.[61]

In March 2004, the Women's Health Initiative study found that the use of oestrogen supplementation increased the risk of strokes, while showing no signs of averting heart attacks as its manufacturers and prescribing physicians had claimed. Somehow, however, against this appalling background, the manufacturers of HRT, and Wyeth in particular, managed to keep talking up the therapy, insisting that it not only relieved menopause symptoms, but was actually a *defence* against osteoporosis, deep-vein thrombosis, stroke and coronary heart disease and Alzheimer's. And, despite the fact that hormone replacement was not licensed for anything other than menopausal difficulties and, despite the fact that it was contraindicated in a wide range of cases, HRT continued to be prescribed 'at the drop of a hat'.

In the wake of the aborted Million Women study, with drug company PRs spinning like tops, and with the national press providing a vehicle for HRT's proponents, the Department of Health had little choice but to declare that HRT should be given only in small doses on short prescriptions. The beginning of this shift in opinion at the DoH brought the underlying battle for HRT marketing out into the open, and there was hand-to-hand fighting between drug company loyalists and more independent physicians and policy makers.

---

59 Writing Group for the Women's Health Initiative Investigators. Risks and benefits of estrogen plus progestin in healthy postmenopausal women: principal results from the Women's Health Initiative randomized controlled trial. *JAMA,* 2002; 288:321-33.

60 Beral V; Million Women Study Collaborators. Breast cancer and hormone-replacement therapy in the Million Women Study. *Lancet* 2003;362:419-27.

61 Null G, Dean C, Feldman M, Rasio D, Smith D. Death by medicine. *Life Extension Magazine,* March 2004.

In North America, Wyeth, after more than half a century of peddling Premarin, told women using HRT not to worry, they would soon have a low-dose course of treatment available. And, anyway, as one doctor suggested, the type of cancer that HRT caused was not a serious one. Cardiovascular disease was also causing the drug corporations a little local difficulty, with the WHI reporting a 2.11 times increased risk of venous thrombosis, based on 5.2 years of follow-up. (The current study incorporates data through July 7, 2002, with an average follow-up of 5.6 years.)

In the wake of two halted Swedish studies in 2004, Professor Michael Baum,[62] visiting Professor of Medical Humanities at University College Hospital, London, claimed that, while it might be time to look for an alternative to HRT, this was necessary, not because HRT caused breast cancer, but because 'Women have overreacted because of all the scare stories.'[63] Such a response, from a founding member of the Campaign Against Health Fraud, was to be expected. This organisation has always failed to rail against or to draw to public attention the side effects of drugs, preferring to smear alternative medicine and its practitioners. Like many other medical professionals since the year 2000, what Baum was suggesting was that the evidence being placed before the public was not actually scientific information, but scaremongering by opponents of HRT.

In calling off the Million Women study and urging more care in the prescription of HRT, the British Government contrived to give the impression that, while doctors had hitherto been circumspect in their prescribing, they would now be positively stringent.

The reality, however, was quite different. At a later date, Dr Maureen Baker, honorary secretary of the Royal College of General Practitioners and a supporter of HRT, speaking of the number of women using HRT over lengthy periods, said 'I understand that about 20 per cent of women have stopped taking HRT, but that is likely to include many who have been on it for years and did not really know *why they were still taking it.*'[64] This statement, perhaps more than any other made during 'the

---

62 Walker, Martin J. *Dirty Medicine: Science, big business and the assault on natural health care.* London: Slingshot Publications; 1993.

63 *Daily Telegraph,* 17 February 2004.

64 *Daily Telegraph,* 17 February 2004. 'Time to replace HRT, says cancer expert'. February 17 2004. Dr Baker also suggested that HRT prescription was *'an individual decision to be made by a woman in consultation with her doctor.'*

HRT crisis' at the start of the new millennium, speaks volumes about the attitude of physicians towards their patients and towards pharmaceuticals.

Dr Philip Sarrel, Emeritus Professor of Obstetrics and Gynaecology and Psychiatry at Yale University School of Medicine,[65] reacting to findings of the Women's Health Initiative, was similarly relaxed about the dangers of hormone therapy, taking the view that new study results did not mean that women should give up on HRT. 'The paper does help guide women and their physicians in being selective in a choice of hormone therapy,' he said.[66]

The scientific evidence announced between 2000 and 2004 was the making of a massive battle between the drug companies, their loyal physicians and medical researchers, worthy scientists and concerned consumers. But apart from tweaking the system, neither the regulatory authorities nor the major producers of the 'therapy' did anything of any significance to protect the future health of women taking hormones.

Not only this, but everyone who was anyone in both the regulatory authorities and the drug companies was suddenly struck dumb about the fact that the history of the use of exogenous hormones is fraught with the constantly observed link between hormones and cancer and other serious diseases.

In fact, the sex hormone therapy producers had been between this rock and a hard place on many occasions over the past two decades, drawing class actions, arguing that the scientific evidence against HRT was flawed and suggesting that the chances of women contracting cancer from their products was minimal.

Behind the scenes, a massive, trundling propaganda machine had been manoeuvred into place. Across North America and Britain, whole industrial sectors had been working continually to shore up the consumption of HRT and to defeat the critical scientific and popular opposition to it.

---

65   Philip M. Sarrel, MD, Emeritus Professor of Obstetrics and Gynaecology and of Psychiatry, Yale University School of Medicine, New Haven, Conn.

66 'HRT's link to higher blood clot risk confirmed. Study also finds odds higher in older, heavier women'. By Amanda Gardner, HealthDay reporter, Oct. 5 (HealthDayNews) 2004 ScoutNews.

Throughout 2004 and 2005, ever-mounting numbers of studies were reported, the results of which rolled back history. Articles planted in the press led women to believe that the reported dangers were simply report blips and nothing real. The corporate-backed lobby groups repeatedly publicised consensus statements which reassured women about the use of HRT.

In December 2005, James Meikle, health correspondent of the *Guardian*, reported on the research carried out on monkeys in North America. From this work, Jay Kaplan, from Wake Forest University Baptist Medical Centre in North Carolina, was publicising the fact that 'Women may need to boost their oestrogen levels up to 10 years before the menopause to ward off heart and bone disease.'[67]

And in February 2006, the Society of Obstetricians and Gynaecologists of Canada, as if consigning to the waste bin of history a vast body of research, issued a reassuring report which claimed that 'after years of confusion about its safety as a treatment for symptoms of menopause, hormone replacement therapy received the green light'.[68] In this report, doctors claimed that taking HRT was a lifestyle choice, such as delaying childbirth, smoking or not taking exercise – all personal decisions in which the physician should have no say – just push the drugs, nothing but the drugs.

In the first months of 2006, Wyeth, those long-term purveyors of 'natural' mares'-urine-based concoctions, were busy pressing the FDA to outlaw all natural, plant-based, bio-identical hormone products. The eradication of this competition would give HRT some protection in a falling market.

---

67 James Meikle, the *Guardian*, December 6, 2005.
68 Canadian Press, Feb 7, 2006. 'MDs back HRT for menopause symptoms'.

Chapter Six

A Vanishing History and Disposable Science

II Production

If our scientists and medical colleges would put forth the same effort in finding the virtues in the 'true remedies' as found in nature for the use of the human race, then poisonous drugs and chemicals would be eliminated and sickness would be rare indeed.

Jethro Kloss[1]

The production of medicines in the modern world, like the production of many other commodities, began, after the 1920s, to assume a life of its own. Once the umbilical cord of need was broken, and the local intimacy of raw materials was lost, production drifted off, first to the big metropolitan cities, and then to other countries. Production in the post-modern world became like no other in the history of civilisation: products came to be imagined, researched and then produced within the hermetically-sealed society of the company or the industry. The lack of local originality of production based on need, necessitated advertising and marketing to assure distribution.

---

1 Kloss J. *Back to Eden*. Loma Linda, CA: Back to Eden Books Publishing Company; 1988.

It is for this reason more than any other that such a long controversy has dogged the production and marketing of HRT. It was always the product of corporately-orientated, mainly male scientists. It was never, at any time, and despite the fact that women were dragooned, bribed and fooled into aiding its marketing, a product that grew directly from the collective needs of women.

The oestrogen research developed at the University of St Louis in the 1920s and 1930s, was partially funded by the Rockefeller Foundation, which, says Maurice Bealle, during the first 44 years of its existence, gave 'large, sometimes huge, sums of money to medical colleges and universities'.[2]

Between 1913 and 1956, the Foundation gave the Washington University of St Louis $2,842,132.45. The great majority of this money was for drugs development, for trade-named pharmaceuticals, which were then sold through the many pharmaceutical companies that Rockefeller had come to control.[3]

The Rockefeller family came to control substantial pharmaceutical interests when, just before the Second World War, Rockefeller used Standard Oil to buy out a number of the companies linked to IG Farben, the German-based chemical cartel responsible for human experimentation in the death camps (see previous section).

Fearful that Rockefeller interests in IG Farben in Germany would be seized by the Allies at the end of the war, American IG, a company set up by Standard Oil, purchased a controlling interest in many of the IG Farben pharmaceutical companies. These included Sterling Products Company, Schering, Monsanto, Dow and Hoffman-LaRoche. American IG then quickly changed its name to General Aniline and Film Corporation, thus protecting its now global pharmaceutical interests.

Following the war, during which, some say, Rockefeller managed to gain protection from bombing for all the IG Farben capital and plant, IG Farben remnants, despite having been involved in aiding Nazi genocide,

---

2 Bealle M. A. *House of Rockefeller: How a shoestring was run into 200 million dollars in two generations*. Washington, DC: All America House; 1959.

3 Morris A. Bealle, ibid.

were consolidated into Bayer, Hoechst and BASF and integrated into the Rockefeller empire.[4] In the USA, Rockefeller also took over Squibb and then Merck, which by the 1950s had 20 subsidiaries, including Sharpe and Dohme, while consolidating its holdings in American Cynamid and Charles Pfizer. In 1946, American Cynamid took over Lederle, one of the biggest biological manufacturers, dealing in such things as vaccines. Sterling became the largest holding company in the Rockefeller drugs empire, having 66 subsidiaries and being worth almost $130 million in 1957.

Later, both American Cynamid and Lederle, along with Wyeth, came under the control of American Home Products (AHP). Wyeth had been incorporated in 1860 and AHP founded in 1926. In 1931, AHP bought Wyeth from Harvard University where the controlling interest had been held.[5] In 1943, AHP also bought Ayerst. In 1987, Wyeth and Ayerst joined to become Wyeth-Ayerst.

In March 2002, American Home Products was stripped of all its non-pharmaceutical subsidiaries and, after 76 years, relaunched simply as Wyeth Pharmaceuticals, a global, research-based pharmaceutical company.[6] The name of Wyeth was chosen because the new company said it stood for scientific excellence and the integrity of healthcare. This was not actually true, as Jonathan Liebenau points out in *Medical Science and Medical Industry*. Even in its early days, the Wyeth company 'aimed less at being science-based than science-associated. It developed a scientific style of rhetoric with little investment in accompanying hardware.'[7]

In July 2003, Wyeth Pharmaceuticals reported a net income for the second quarter of $864.4 million, an increase of 44 per cent on the previous year's earnings.

---

4 This was done, principally, by Allen Dulles, who was Rockefeller's lawyer and oil company business manager, and who, in 1948, was to become the CIA's first director.

5 Seaman B. *The Greatest Experiment Ever Performed On Women: Exploding the estrogen myth*. New York: Hyperion; 2003.

6 While this was clearly a restructuring for economic reasons, it was also, in all probability, an attempt to ditch the image of AHP, which over the previous twenty years had become associated with agro-chemicals, veterinary products and household pesticides.

7 Liebenau J. *Medical Science and Medical Industry: The formation of the American pharmaceutical industry*. London: Macmillan; 1987.

Wyeth Pharmaceuticals, for the past three decades, has controlled a 70 per cent market share of hormone replacement products.[8] Wyeth is a quintessentially Rockefeller company; its past, present and future echo the establishment and exercise of power that exude from the Rockefeller construct. Wyeth combines the brave new world of bio-pharmaceuticals with country-crippling financial power and a global political agenda.

Premarin, Wyeth's best-selling oestrogen supplement, made from pregnant mares' urine, was first developed by biochemist James Bertram Collip, who, while at the Canadian McGill University in 1928, was approached by William Mckenna, head of the recently-established Ayerst Laboratories. In 1942, Premarin was approved by the FDA for menopausal symptoms.[9] It was produced by Wyeth under the control of AHP, until Wyeth and Ayerst became Wyeth-Ayerst.

Within American Home Products, Wyeth-Ayerst produced Alesse, Premarin (conjugated oestrogen tablets), Premphase (conjugated oestrogen/medroxyprogesterone acetate tablets) and Prempro (conjugated oestrogen/medroxyprogesterone acetate tablets).

There is an almost unbridgeable gulf between the theories of medical science and the practice of corporate drug pushing, between human communities and pharmaceutical corporations. Rather than researching, treating and curing long-established illnesses, pharmaceutical companies – 'inadvertently' aided by the processed food industry's manufacture of junk foods, and by other environmentally toxic industries, together with their own manufacture of adverse reactions – now create new illnesses and markets, which their drug development divisions can research.

For complex reasons, modern drug companies have been able to avoid the scandals that have surrounded the tobacco and asbestos industries. One of the reasons, which is perfectly evident, is that pharmaceuti-

---

8 Their patent on the oestrogen replacement drug Premarin was owned by Wyeth until three years ago, for 60 years. Time and again, the company managed to re-establish its patent and stop other companies from manufacturing generics.

9 Seaman B. *The Greatest Experiment Ever Performed On Women: Exploding the estrogen myth.* Op. cit.

cal drug producers have hidden behind physicians. Physicians, although equally responsible for the iatrogenic nightmare called scientific medicine, are much closer to the patient and more clearly responsible, while pharmaceutical company directors and agents have become somehow lost in the background.

Contemporary definitions of power are much more personal than they were half a century ago. While earlier portrayals of power concentrated on groups or their symbols, today's definitions look closely at individuals. Of interest to the women's movement, in particular, has been the sometimes hidden culture of power that exists between men and women in professional specialisations, such as the very personal imbalance of power that exists between doctors and female patients and psychoanalysts and psychiatrists and female patients. With respect to HRT, it seems essential that women view the treatment offered to them in relation to the power that executives of pharmaceutical companies and doctors hold over female patients. In this case, the male establishment, from scientists through pharmaceutical executives to doctors and journalists, has worked concertedly to enforce its power over women and to sell women a product that will reshape them in men's terms.

HRT was perhaps the first mass-distributed drug for which pharmaceutical companies and their executives created medical conditions as its market blossomed. Almost entirely, these 'medical' conditions played on the vulnerability of women in relation to their looks, their sexuality and their ability to be happy in later life. This assault on the vulnerability of women in the third age was simply an extension of the cultural markers put down by consumer capitalism throughout the rest of women's lives. Women are consistently undermined by a power culture created by men, which lays the emphasis on motherhood, adherence to the family rather than economic earning capacity, youth and sexuality. At the same time, concepts of deeper human worth, such as sensuousness, intellectual achievement and political identity, are abandoned.

We live in a world that is completely out of kilter, where executives of multinational pharmaceutical corporations live in luxury, often on the other side of the world from the women – in the case of HRT – who get ill and die consuming their products. These senior executives and board directors are personally beyond ethical discourse and beyond any legal accountability. Women who are offered HRT by their doctors should ask themselves whether or not they agree with the moral values of the men who produce it. Both female and male patients should familiarise themselves with the power of pharmaceutical companies, before they get involved in any of the treatments offered to them by their doctors.

What does it mean that HRT is produced by companies that are part of the Rockefeller global economic and political interests? And how does the powerful sphere of influence that emanates from the companies producing HRT affect their marketing? Do these things make a substantial difference to the survival of a particular drug or treatment?

With the involvement of Wyeth in Rockefeller interests, and Organon one of the other main HRT producers in another European network of power, and with both these companies proximity to the popular media, the lines between science, news, marketing and entertainment become impossibly blurred. In fact, science becomes meaningless because it is dressed up or dressed down by the popular media to suit commercial interests.[10]

All of this is important in the case of HRT, because when an HRT product gets into trouble, producers are able to draw not only upon the Chase Manhattan Bank, the major financial pillar in the Rockefeller empire, on senior politicians,[11] and a great clutch of vulturous aged lawyers, but also on countless powerful public relations, media, advertising and communications groups, which have ready and global access to thousands of media outlets.

---

10 A survey in 1978 by the Columbia Journalism Review failed to find a single comprehensive article about the dangers of smoking in the previous seven years in any major magazine accepting cigarette advertising.
http://www.trunkerton.fsnet.co.uk/pharmaceutical_drug_racket.htm

11 Dana Marie Kennedy, Director of Seniors Outreach for the Democratic National Committee, in her article 'Bush and the Pharmaceutical Companies,' 2000, published during the last North American presidential election, reckoned that Bush took over $300,000 from pharmaceutical companies for his presidential campaign. Kennedy explains how this will affect seniors with the cost of the 50 most frequently used drugs by seniors having risen by almost twice the rate of inflation since 1999. She also points out that the top Bush health care policy adviser, Deborah Steelman, who argued against any regulation of drug prices, had also represented a number of major drug companies and their professional association, Pharmaceutical Research and Manufacturers of America.   (cont.)

Using all these devices, directors are able to avoid any personal or corporate litigation that might find them or their companies responsible for manslaughter, murder or human rights violations. At the same time, a company such as Wyeth can keep its products afloat through storms of the most serious protests from consumers and scientists.

There are a number of ways in which big companies keep a consolidated power in the hands of a concentrated group of individuals. The most obvious is to have one central company holding power over a number of smaller subsidiaries. In an age when fields of business tend to be dominated by cartels of large companies, 'groups' of associate companies are now more usual.

Looking at interlocking directorial boards is one of the simplest ways of recognising that the power of whole industries is in the hands of a small number of people. Although this might be boring to read about, it is the only way that we have of understanding how commercial power works in the real world. How do we understand, for instance, why a particular person advocates the use of HRT, except by trying to uncover the links between that person, and those who employ him or her, and who ultimately controls these people?

Frank A. Bennack Jr, one of the highest-placed board members of Wyeth, was, until recently, president of the Hearst Corporation. The Hearst newspaper empire was bought up by Rockefeller interests in the 1930s. Today it is one of the largest media organisations in the world. It

11 (*cont.*) In June 2002, Say No to Drugs reported on Bush's launch of the new plan for prescription drugs (which involves senior citizens signing up with insurance companies to obtain drugs). Under this plan there would be no extension of Medicare to senior citizens. Often, of course, the insurance companies are linked anyway to the drug companies. Twenty-one company donors, mainly pharmaceutical companies, paid $250,000 each for a place at the dinner, which launched the policy and which it was hoped would raise $30 million for the Republican Party. Every company giving money to the event had business before Congress. This article ends with a list of direct pharmaceutical company contributions to politicians in 2000, which shows that 20 Democrat and Republican representatives, including George W. Bush, received sums of between $75,800 and $477,633 (the latter figure being taken by Bush). "http://www.flara.org/bushandpharm20sepoo.htm"

owns 12 newspapers, 17 magazines, 27 television stations, a large number of other media outlets, as well as some consumer product dot.com outlets. The magazines that Hearst controls include the major popular magazines read by women in Britain and North America:[12] *Cosmopolitan, Country Living, Good Housekeeping, Harper's, House Beautiful, Marie Claire, Seventeen,* and *Town and Country.*

Under Bennack's leadership, the Hearst Corporation acquired ten of its 12 newspapers, including two of North America's biggest – the *Houston Chronicle* and the *San Francisco Chronicle,* two major consumer magazines and multiple television stations. Bennack is still the chairman of the National Magazine Company Limited of Great Britain,[13] a subsidiary of the Hearst Corporation.

Bennack is also a director of JP Morgan Chase and Company, a part of the Rockefeller Chase Manhattan Bank, which is joined with the financial interests of JP Morgan, which Rockefeller took over after Morgan's death in the 1930s. One other director of Wyeth, Walter V. Shipley, is also a retired chairman of the Chase Manhattan Bank.

Another Rockefeller luminary, highly-placed on the board of Wyeth, is the 71-year-old Clifford L. Alexander. Alexander is president of Alexander and Associates, one of North America's biggest private personnel consultancies. Alexander advised four consecutive US presidents, Kennedy, Johnson, Nixon and Carter, principally on labour matters. Under the Kennedy administration, Alexander was part of the White House staff, serving as foreign affairs officer of the National Security Council. In 2003, Alexander retired from the board of Moody's Corporation, the parent company of Moody's Investors Service, a leading provider of credit ratings, research and analysis, covering debt instruments and securities in the global capital markets. Moody's separated from Dun & Bradstreet in the year 2000. Alexander had also served as chairman and chief executive officer at Dun & Bradstreet from 1999-2000.

The previous chairman of the board of Wyeth, John R. Stafford, who retired in January 2003 but who remains as a director, was also a director

---

12 Walker, Martin J. *Dirty Medicine: Science, big business and the assault on natural health care,* pp 269-271. London: Slingshot Publications; 1993.

13 The National Magazine Company publishes *Harper's* and *Cosmopolitan* in Britain.

of JP Morgan Chase. Stafford was chairman of the board of Wyeth from 1986, and chief executive officer from 1986 until May 2001. Stafford is also a director of Verizon Communications and Honeywell International, both of which have Rockefeller links. A number of the directors of Wyeth are also directors of Exxon Mobil, the Rockefeller oil group.

The biggest Rockefeller holding is Time Warner, which, since a merger with America Online in 2001, has been called Time Warner AOL. The present chairman of the board and chief executive of Time Warner is Richard D. Parsons, a lawyer. In the past, Parsons was lawyer to Nelson Rockefeller and a senior White House aide under President Gerald Ford. The board includes a past chairman of tobacco giant Philip Morris Inc. and present chairman of Colgate-Palmolive.

Time Warner AOL owns most of the major media outlets in the developed world, and apart from Murdoch-owned interests, all the major outlets in North America. It owns the Time-Life group, CNN and all its subsidiary news companies, all the Warner Brothers interests, including the film studios and companies, as well as their television outlets, and somewhere in the region of 80 magazines. The magazines include a number that deal with women, health and medicine, including, specifically: *Parenting, Baby Talk, Health, Hippocrates, Weight Watchers, Popular Science, Food and Wine*. Now, following the merger with AOL, Time Warner has at its fingertips a swath of web outlets.

One of the senior executive officers in the Time Warner complex is Norman Pearlstine, the editor-in-chief of Time Inc. Pearlstine oversees the editorial content of Time Inc.'s magazines, including *Time, Life, Fortune, People*, etc. Prior to joining Time, Pearlstine was with Dow Jones and Co and was a managing editor of the *Wall Street Journal*. He is a member of the Council on Foreign Relations, the Rockefeller think-tank – the philosophy of which reflects and informs US Government foreign policy.

While the Rockefeller-backed Wyeth Pharmaceutical company controls a large part of the market in HRT, one of the most dangerous products prescribed in Britain, an HRT implant called Riselle, is produced by Organon. Organon is joined with Rockefeller interests, especially in relation to HRT, through its 2003 linkage to Pfizer. Organon does, however, have enormous power within its own multinational global environment, which protects it and ensures the defence of its products when they come under attack.

In just the same way that pharmaceutical companies infiltrate voluntary organisations in order to increase market share, they also use every method they can to influence government. With a socialised health care system, the government or the National Health Service are the core organisations that have to be influenced. Beyond the individual government is the 'local' international trade organisation; for Britain this is the European Union.

In the next chapter, I show how Wyeth joined with the British Government and with the Association of the British Pharmaceutical Industry (ABPI), to maintain – if not increase – its guarantee of drugs sales to the British socialised health care system. Some of this work is done by playing a part in the socialised health care system by, for example, funding nurses to administer vaccines in community health practices. There is, however, one more conventional way of influencing governments. This does not demand hard work and intervention in primary health care by selling drugs to doctors, but depends upon ensuring that your company is as near as can be, close to or part of government.

The classic historical example of this in the UK was the influence of the Wellcome Foundation, the drug company that made the money for the Wellcome Trust up until the mid-1990s. The Foundation and the Trust split up and, while the manufacturing side was taken over by Glaxo, the Trust is now one of the biggest medical funders in the world, and gives as much money to medical research in Britain as the Medical Research Council does.

If, in the late 1980s, the Wellcome Foundation had manufactured a drug to make people's noses smaller, Her Majesty's Government and the NHS would have sold it to the population as being the greatest breakthrough in medical and psychiatric care since the advent of the hospital. This was principally because, from the 1920s onwards, the Wellcome Foundation and its Trust virtually constituted the medical aspect of the British Government.[14]

One of the outstanding contemporary examples of drug pushing involvement in government, is the position on the board of Gilead Sciences Inc., the Californian biotech company, of Donald H. Rumsfeld,

---

14 Walker, Martin J. Op. cit.

US Government Defense Secretary. Rumsfeld took up his position with Gilead in 1997 and joined the Bush Administration in 2001. Reportedly, Rumsfeld still holds an unspecified stake in Gilead, valued at between $5 and $25 million. Since Rumsfeld has held his dual positions, the Homeland Securities Act has given protection against legal liability to vaccine and other drug manufacturers, while also introducing measures for military control over compulsory vaccination during a state of emergency. More recently, Gilead developed and now owns the rights to Tamiflu, the untested avian influenza treatment, the development of which has secured millions of dollars in research support from the US Government.

Organon has ridden all criticism of its implant treatment in Britain. It has done this almost entirely by exercising the powerful links with its parent company and its friends in the corridors of power. Organon is served and protected by some of the most powerful business interests and directors in the developed world. When you see who Organon knows, its ability to keep Riselle alive in Britain when even the FDA would not give it a licence for North America, falls into place.

Organon, a Dutch company in origin, which took over a German company in 1925, set up a base in England in 1923, and in 1926 standardised the world's first oestrogen extract, oestrone. In 1962, Organon manufactured its first contraceptive pill. Today, the company, whose headquarters are in New Jersey, has national bases in many parts of the world and is owned by Akzo Nobel, one of the most powerful and influential chemical companies in the world.

Organon produces the following hormone replacement products: Livial, Ovestin, Riselle and Adriole. Organon's approach to marketing the menopause is subtler than that of Wyeth. The change in only a few words in its publicity signals it as an apparently more humane and intellectually aware corporation. Unlike Wyeth, which has frequently suggested that the menopause is an inevitably poor state of health, Organon makes a point of saying: 'Although the transition from a fertile to a non-fertile state is an entirely natural process, it has become increasingly obvious that the decline in oestrogen production that characterises the menopause has serious early and long-term health implications.'

Organon produces Livial as a treatment for osteoporosis. Livial was first manufactured in 1991, and it is at the forefront of Organon's campaigning, now that HRT is being directed more specifically at the osteoporosis market.[15]

Ovestin contains the oestrogen oestriol, and is used for general urinogenital symptoms, that might accompany menopause. It apparently does not cause any kind of endometrial cancer and is, therefore, not conjugated with progesterone and can be used by women with an intact uterus.

Riselle contains oestrogen in the form of oestradiol, and is marketed by Organon as especially useful for women after hysterectomy. Each implant lasts for six months.

Organon's latest treatment is a testosterone supplement for men, Andriol. This makes men behave as men should. More recently, Organon has got into the booming area of psychiatric drugs, mainly antidepressants.

Organon has a particular relationship with Pfizer. In June 2003, Akzo Nobel's Diosynth business signed a multi-year contract with Pfizer Inc. The deal involves supplying Pfizer with the active pharmaceutical ingredient for the commercial production of their growth hormone disorder drug. The agreement was broader than this, because it entailed agreements on marketing and PR.

Between them, the two companies fund ObgynWorld.com and the magazine *Obgyn*. ObgynWorld is also sponsored by FIGO, the International Federation of Gynaecology and Obstetrics.[16] In fact, FIGO, the main international organisation representing obstetricians and gynae-

---

15 The data sheet for Livial quotes the following adverse reactions: 'Occasionally, vaginal bleeding or spotting may occur, mainly during the first months of treatment. Other adverse events that have been occasionally observed include: headache and migraine, oedema, dizziness, pruritus, increase in body weight, nausea, abdominal pain, rash and depression.' Data Sheet for Livial (Tibolone 2.5mg tablets), indicated for complaints resulting from the natural or surgical menopause and prevention of postmenopausal stress.

16 FIGO says about itself on its website: 'Over the last half century, FIGO has grown into a worldwide organization representing more than 150,000 obstetricians and gynaecologists in 102 countries. Through the work of four Committees and 21 Advisory Panels, FIGO's work embraces many aspects of obstetrics and gynaecology. Through its official relationships with such international bodies as the World Health Organization, the International Planned Parenthood Federation, the International Federation of Fertility Societies, *(cont.)*

cologists worldwide, founded in 1954, now funnels its professional information through the web portal of ObgynWorld – that is, through Organon and Pfizer. This is despite the fact that there is an obvious conflict of interests between the drug companies and the stated goal of FIGO, 'To promote the well-being of women and to raise the standard of practice in obstetrics and gynaecology.'

Pfizer is another pre-eminent Rockefeller drugs company. Its directors, who are linked to Rockefeller institutions, include: William H. Gray III, who was a congressman[17] from 1979 to 1991 and is now a director of the Rockefeller J.P. Morgan Chase & Co; Constance J. Horner, who served as assistant to President George H. W. Bush from 1991 to 1993, and who, prior to this, was deputy secretary for the US Department of Health and Human Services; William R. Howell, a director of both Exxon Mobil, the Rockefeller oil company, and the Halliburton Company; Henry A. McKinnell, another director of Exxon Mobil and a director of the Trilateral Commission; and Ruth J. Simmons, who as well as being a trustee of the Carnegie Corporation, which belongs to Rockefeller, is also on the Council on Foreign Relations.

Michael V. Novinski, now the president of Organon USA and a vice-president of Organon International, began with Organon in 1979, before going to Wyeth for ten years from 1982 to 1992. In 1992, he returned to Organon, to become its US president in 2003. In strategic moves, which he probably learnt at Wyeth, Novinski got involved in the New Jersey Cystic Fibrosis Association and the Society for the Advancement of Women's Health Research.

Organon owner, Akzo Nobel, is the world's biggest paint manufacturer, and one of the world's largest chemical manufacturers, as well as being one of the major salt producers. It has had its present name since 1994, and the company is the product of a number of mergers and takeovers, most especially with aspects of both Hoechst and Bayer pharmaceuticals, the dregs of I. G. Farben.

---

16 (*cont.*) the UNFPA and others, FIGO has been able to work in a collaborative way to develop projects and programmes that have been and continue to be effective in addressing the problems women face as a result of inadequate health care and social inequality.'

17 Or Lawmaker, as the North Americans began to call representatives just before the invasion of Iraq.

An overview of Akzo Nobel's three business lines gives an immediate and startling insight into the industrial base of contemporary medicine.

The company's coating group makes paints, mainly automotive finishes. Its chemical unit produces pulp and paper chemicals, functional chemicals such as flame retardants, crop 'nutrients', and chemicals for use in detergents and cosmetics, while its pharmaceutical unit produces contraceptives, fertility treatments and antidepressants.

The supervisory board of Akzo Nobel has linking directorships with Royal Dutch Petroleum/Shell, Corus Group (born of a merger in October 1999, between British Steel and Koninklijke Hoogovens), ABN AMRO (a Dutch bank), Unilever (which is a partly Dutch company following the merger in 1930 between soap makers Lever Brothers and Margarine Unie), and Bayer. It also has on the board, Abraham E. Cohen, the president of Merck Sharp & Dohme International. Karel Vuursteen, who moved on to the Board in 2002, has been a member of the Trilateral Commission for a number of years. Cees J.A. van Lede, who retired in 2002, was also on the International Advisory Council of JP Morgan.

A. A. Loudon, the last chairman of the supervisory board of Akzo Nobel, was also a member of the Dutch parliament between 1995 and 1999 and a director of ABN AMRO bank.[18] Hans Wijers, chairman of the board of Akzo Nobel since 2003, was minister for economic affairs in the Dutch government from 1994 until 1998. Maarten van Veen is a director of ABN AMRO, Akzo Nobel and Corus.[19] The Akzo Nobel board also includes: Virginia Bottomley, former secretary of state for health and cabinet member; Paul Bremer III, a former US Ambassador to the Netherlands and chairman of the US National Commission on Terrorism, and chairman of Marsh Crisis Consulting.

The Unilever board has on it Lord Brittan, a member of the Thatcher government from 1979 until 1986, member and then president of the

---

18 W. Dik, also on the Board of ABN-AMRO, worked for Unilever between 1964 and 1988, and for a year in the 1980s he was Secretary of State for Foreign Trade in the Dutch Government. A. Burgman, a director of ABN-AMRO, has since 1999 been chairman of Unilever. Also on the board of ABN-AMRO is D.R.J. de Rothschild.

19 Another director of Corus, Dr Kurt Lauk, is a trustee of the International Institute of Strategic Studies, which is close to the RIIA and to the UK and US intelligence services.

European Commission in the Eighties. Claudio X González, also on the Unilever board, was special advisor to the president of Mexico between 1988 and 1994, as well as being a member of the International Advisory Council of the JP Morgan Chase bank. Then there is Senator George J. Mitchell, who was a member of the US Senate from 1980 to 1995 and chairman of the Northern Ireland Peace Initiative from 1995 to 1999. Lord Simon of Highbury is European advisor to the Board of Morgan Stanley, and was a UK Government minister between 1997 and 1999, chairman of BP from 1995 to 1997. Jeroen van der Veer is president of Royal Dutch Petroleum.

The board of Royal Dutch Shell, under Van der Veer, reflects the same mixture of banking, government, defence and chemical/pharmaceutical interests. Shell UK chairman, Lord Oxburgh, was at one time chief scientific advisor to the Ministry of Defence. Luis Giusti is a senior advisor at the Center for Strategic and International Studies in Washington DC. Sir John Kerr, the UK permanent representative to the EU, was British Ambassador to the USA and Foreign Office permanent under secretary of state, while also being a non-executive director of Rio Tinto and a Trustee of the Rhodes Trust.

Wyeth Pharmaceuticals – An Iatrogenic History

Pharmaceutical production and marketing is a bear pit. The industry has settled into a number of massive companies, which control pharmaceutical medicine from the early research through to the marketing. One of the essential and most critical challenges to have faced these companies in relation to marketing over the past decades has been to find every possible means, other than direct advertising, to gain access to the putative patient. As production markets have outrun the capability of doctors to prescribe drugs, and as the relentless search for profit has meant having to manufacture new markets, bypassing the physician, the dealers in medical drugs have searched desperately for new ways of drawing in gullible consumers.[20,21]

---

20 I say gullible because quite often these medicines simply do no work. As Allen Roses, worldwide vice-president of genetics at UK GlaxoSmithKline (GSK) said in December 2003, more than 90 per cent of drugs work in only 30 or 50 per cent of the people they're prescribed for. Richard Ley, for the British pharmaceutical industry, commented, 'It's not (cont.)

The worldwide web has helped companies in their creation of markets. While 'quackbusters' rail against alternative views on cancer treatments on the Internet, in contravention of national laws it is now possible to buy many drugs directly on the Internet.[22] Apart from HRT, the classic example of how drug companies are managing and growing new markets is Viagra. The drug has achieved a popular – almost cult – status and spawned a number of charities and other organisations that purport to help people with 'sexual dysfunction'. Although it is against UK law to advertise pharmaceutical prescription products to the public, everyone knows about Viagra, which has become, without the help of doctors, one of the most popular drugs in the history of medicine.

While the use of the Internet is a fairly transparent strategy, others might slip your notice. The drug companies, in the guise of conducting research, now control almost all the 'specific illness' charities. What better way to sell drugs could there be than drawing together all the patients with a particular illness – or perceived illness – and then suggesting that they can help by joining drug trials? The time has long since passed when any of these charities and volunteer organisations gave independent and researched help with conditions or medical problems.

Culture is another area that has been colonised by the drug companies. Most pharmaceutical companies had cottoned on to brand-name

---

20 (cont.) really news to anyone that not all medicines work in all the people all of the time. What is certainly true is that we often don't know why.'

21 In North America, where direct-to-consumer advertising of prescription drugs has been legal for some years, since the mid-1990s pharmaceutical companies have trebled the amount of money they spend on advertising these drugs to consumers. From 1996 to 2000 spending on ads rose from $791 million to nearly $2.5 billion. See:

Rosenthal MB, Berndt ER, Donohue JM, Frank RG, Epstein AM. Promotion of prescription drugs to consumers. *N Engl J Med,* 2002;346:498-505.

Lee TH, Brennan TA. Direct-to-consumer marketing of high-technology screening tests. *N Engl J Med,* 2002;346:529-31.

Holmer AF. Direct-to-consumer advertising: strengthening our health care system. *N Engl J Med,* 2002;346:526-8.

Wolfe SM. Direct-to-consumer advertising: education or emotion promotion? *N Engl J Med,* 2002;346:524-6.

22 Whether or not pharmaceutical companies are involved in this avoidance of law and regulation, as the tobacco companies have proven to be with the illegal transport and distribution of cigarettes, remains an unanswered question.

advertising through culture, long before it became fashionable to write novels at the behest of States, perfume houses and jewellers. For the first years of AZT prescription, Wellcome was able to use the ongoing drama of AIDS to promote the only anti-viral 'remedy' on the market. One of the biggest areas of direct-to-public marketing is through the position of the new 'culture' doctors and popular commentators, who use their positions as television and newspaper pundits to marshal people towards certain treatments.

The other resources that the contemporary drug company need are risk liability advice, and product liability advice and recovery. When drug companies are hit by PR disasters – for instance, if one of their drugs kills 10,000 people – they need countless people to pick them up, to argue their case and, if at all possible, simply to hide the problem. Throughout the Eighties and Nineties, disaster followed disaster, and in North America product liability cases were taken against a large number of drugs. Pharmaceutical marketing strategies became as secret as spy games in the Cold War. Hundreds of marketing, media and communications companies specialising in marketing drugs, science and the realities of illness and its treatment, have been involved in intense, large-scale, marketing battles.[23]

Whatever the pretence of pharmaceutical companies to be at the cutting edge of science or to be leading contributors to public health care, above almost all other industries apart from politics, weapons procurement and chemicals, the pharmaceutical industry is concerned about preserving a positive image that generates continuing profit. It is now no longer possible to talk about allopathic treatments or their delivery, separate from the commercial infrastructure of capitalist society. Health and health care are mediated by armies of organisations and individuals who have no knowledge about, or interest in, human health, but are interested only in profit and spin.

Over the past few years, Wyeth has needed all the help it can muster to keep out of trouble, or, rather, to get out of the trouble it has got into. The company has faced frequent class actions over Norplant and HRT,

---

23 During the year 2000, more than $13.2 billion were spent on pharmaceutical marketing in the US alone (Disease Mongering, Bob Burton and Andy Rowell.)

and most recently a settlement of $13 billion over the Wyeth-produced slimming aids fenfluramine-phentermine, popularly known as fen-phen and marketed as Pondimin, and dexfenfluramine, marketed as Redux. The 'treatments', approved as appetite-suppressants, were withdrawn in 1997, after they were determined to be dangerous. Fen-phen was hyped by the media when it came on the market in the mid-1990s.

Pondimin (dexfenfluramine and levofenfluramine, licensed in 1989) and Redux (dexfenfluramine, licensed in 1996), were used in a regimen catchily dubbed 'fen-phen', based on the prescription of fenfluramine alongside phentermine. Phentermine and fenfluramine were approved by the FDA for short-term use as appetite suppressants in 1959 and 1973 respectively, then someone had the bright idea of yoking the two together. In May 1992, in the USA, the journal *Clinical Pharmacology and Therapeutics* published the results of a four-year clinical study, which suggested that the drugs used in combination over a considerable length of time – ie., not according to the FDA approved label – could achieve significant weight loss.

Off went the latest bandwagon, with the delighted media on board. Wyeth spent $2.3 million on an ad blitz in medical journals, according to *Forbes* magazine, and a slimming craze was born. An estimated six million North Americans had taken Pondimin or Redux when, in 1997, the 'treatments' were withdrawn after they were determined to be dangerous. Studies linked fen-phen to potentially fatal heart valve damage and lung disease; publicity and settlements followed.

The problem with legal settlements is that they are not enforceable, as ethical rules, on the pharmaceutical companies concerned, nor do they create a new moral climate within the company. As with HRT, after the settlements, however, Wyeth tried hard to resurrect the preparations and to publish papers written by 'opinion leaders' whom they had paid.[24] It spent $80 million on payments to scientists, whose research might call into question the side effects of its drugs. Declining to co-author one such study, in a letter of January 1999, cardiologist Katherine Otto

---

24 Zuckerman D. Hype in health reporting: "checkbook science" buys distortion of medical news. Extra! September/October 2002. www.fair.org/

accused Wyeth of a lack of candour and of failing to allow investigators full access to data.[25]

Wyeth Pharmaceuticals is a most favoured company in relation to the New Labour government. The first US drugs company to be chosen to work with the government Public Health Service Laboratory manufacturing vaccines, it is deeply involved in helping to 'modernise' the NHS.[26] Wyeth's track record, however, is little different from that of most large pharmaceutical companies.

Two disconcerting phrases in the 2003 Wyeth Annual Report demonstrate how lacking in concern about health, and how bereft of culture, intellect and literary sophistication, the modern multinational business is.

One section of the report profiles Wyeth's four one-billion-dollar-selling drugs during 2002. Each drug is introduced with a full-page colour photograph of a grateful consumer.[27] Protonix is a drug manufactured by Wyeth, which, they claim, heals the damage caused by acid reflux – or heartburn. The page about it shows the portrait of moderately handsome Victor Madrigal, from Laredo, Texas, wearing a jazzy shirt and eating tacos. Beneath this portrait is the following: 'Victor Madrigal of Laredo, Texas, began taking Protonix in 2003 after being diagnosed with erosive oesophagitis. Victor had been suffering from severe heartburn during the day. At night, acid reflux interfered with his sleep. Protonix relieved these symptoms, allowing Victor to sleep throughout the night *and resume eating his favorite foods*.' (author's italics).

---

25 'The $22 billion gold rush' by Robert Lenzner & Michael Maiello was dated April 10 2006. *Forbes* magazine.

26 See the essay 'The Ghost Lobby, New Labour and the Pharmaceutical Industry' by the author.

27 Perhaps more than any other type of multinational company, pharmaceutical giants are adherents to strict political correctness. It is almost as if, knowing they are going to damage a large number of people's lives, they have to stress that this damage is shared out equitably. Every photograph in Wyeth's Annual Report can be clearly read. There are young men and young women in equal number, there is ethnic diversity – not simply black individuals – with Asian and Oriental people, and there is a good selection of apparently lone mothers and silver-haired oldies, just to show that Wyeth does not have a discriminatory employment policy. The fact that poor and elderly ethnic populations in North America find it difficult to gain access to medical care is not a subject which is dealt with in the Annual Report.

What is so frightening about these sentences is that the highly-paid media consultants used by Wyeth, or their own in–house department, failed to understand that in these two sentences they summed up so cogently the principle argument against the use of palliative pharmaceuticals. In pharmaceutical company promotion, cynicism has turned into beguiling naivety to the point where one would not be shocked to read the slogan: 'We'll make you feel better while you continue to make yourself ill.'

The second turn of phrase in Wyeth's 2003 Annual Report is also frighteningly honest and, oddly, beyond cynicism. Opening the section of the Report that deals with what companies call 'contingencies', ie., a chance occurrence that might affect the finances of the company in the future, you will read:

> The Company is involved in various legal proceedings, including product liability and environmental matters of a nature considered *normal* to its business. (author's italics.)

The surrealism implicit in this statement becomes clear only when you go on to read about claims on the company in the matter of Pondimin and Redux, which are still being dealt with, and numbered initially 111,700.[28] Of these, at the time of writing, 11,200 claims have been processed to completion. The 2003 report suggests that claims will continue to be brought until the year 2015. The amount of money set aside in trust to pay these claims is presently $3.75 billion, although some expect claims ultimately to exceed this amount.

Had this been the Annual Report of the US Armed Forces, news of 11,200 (at its absolute lowest) civilian casualties might be reckoned to be expensive but unavoidable collateral damage. How, though, can a health care business shrug off as 'normal' critical health damage of between 11,000 and 600,000 people? Perhaps, more pointedly, why are society at large and the regulatory agencies falling for this immense confidence trick?

---

28 The report breaks these down into those which are plausible and those which, for whatever reason, appear unsuitable for payment. Wyeth took legal action against some doctors who had helped lawyers to gather evidence of the drugs damage.

The marketing goal of pharmaceutical companies is not health; it is making maximum profit from its products. Strategies for achieving their marketing goals can be broken down: First, to produce drugs that individuals take for long periods of – or, better still, for all of – their lives; second, to discover or to manufacture large universal populations to which drugs can be sold; and third, to find easily-manipulated populations in which the previous factors are present, for example, the workforce and the families of multinational companies or patients tied to national systems of socialised medicine.

All products of pharmaceutical companies cause either long-term or short-term adverse reactions in many of their consumers. However, because of the refusal of physicians to acknowledge the damage done by pharmaceuticals, many of these adverse reactions lead to the prescription of even more drugs, to treat the undiagnosed symptoms of adverse reactions.[29]

The last section of this chapter looks at the health, social and regulatory problems that Wyeth has encountered over the past few decades. It is necessary to raise these issues because, encouraged by free market tendencies and New Labour, Wyeth has gained access to the British Parliament, the NHS and parts of the voluntary sector, without any kind of regulatory audit.

Diazepines

Wyeth was one of the companies responsible for the introduction to Britain of the benzodiazepine tranquilliser range of drugs during the 1960s and 1970s. Wyeth manufactured Ativan.

Benzodiazepines turned out to be highly addictive and very toxic. In their submission to the Home Office Advisory Council on Drugs, Michael Behan and Barry Haslam charged that the drugs were never properly tested for safety, and that only poor-quality, short-term trials were carried out. They accused both Hoffman LaRoche (makers of Librium) and

---

29 The Medicines Control Agency has itself admitted to a ninety per cent under–reporting of adverse reactions.

Wyeth of having withheld clinical trial information on adverse reactions and of using exaggerated and false claims to promote their drugs.

When introduced into Britain prior to the 1968 Medicines Act, the benzodiazepines were given a Licence of Right, without any assessment of their safety. Licences continued to be granted without any assessment until the mid-1980s. When data sheets were issued for the drugs, Wyeth withheld information in various countries. In the UK, with desultory monitoring by the MCA, information about side effects was left out, and only weak warnings against taking the drugs during pregnancy and about the possibilities of addiction were included. Wyeth particularly withheld evidence of seizures during withdrawal from Ativan. It took the actions of two whistleblowers, Thomas Harry and Dipak Malhorta, former medical directors of Wyeth, to bring Wyeth's negligence to public notice.

In their 2003 submission to the Home Office Advisory Council on the Misuse of Drugs, Haslam and Behan suggested that there was an estimated UK long–term user population of benzodiazepines of between 1.2 and 1.9 million. With these long-term users there are two ancillary groups, those damaged in the womb and ex-addicts who have suffered permanent damage. Benzodiazepines are more addictive than heroin or cocaine, and the damage caused by addiction to them includes irreversible neurochemical brain damage, which leads quickly to a state of confusion where the addict is unable to assess his or her own health or actions.

Haslam and Behan quote referenced sources for their assertion that between 1990 and 1996 benzodiazepines caused more deaths than all class-A drugs put together (1,810 deaths).[30] Despite the fact that diazepines also cause suicidal ideation, no figures are available for the numbers of people who have taken their own lives while using them.

In an attempt, even now, to avoid responsibility for the terrible damage that benzodiazepines have wrought, the manufacturers and general physicians are reluctant to diagnose diazepine addiction, and,

---

30 Behan M, Haslam B. The benzodiazepines. Submission to the Home Office Advisory Council on the Misuse of Drugs, 26 July 2003. Citing Home Office figures on benzodiazepine deaths, 1990-96.

instead, dream up diagnoses of new, obscure, unidentifiable illnesses. As is the case with adverse reactions to HRT, patients can spend years on a time- and money-wasting journey through different diagnostic tests. As with HRT, the end of this diagnostic nightmare can often be with a psychiatrist, who may introduce other drug regimes to the patient or section him or her.

While Wyeth has done nothing for those addicted and damaged by the use of its diazepines, it has embedded itself in various areas of mental health care, through which involvement it might push its third-generation seratonin noradrenaline reuptake inhibitor (SNRI) antidepressant, Effexor. In North America, Wyeth has paraded Effexor on road shows, taking the billion–dollar–selling drug to the heart of its target audiences. In 2002, Wyeth staged a depression road show titled 'Depression in College – Real World, Real Life, Real Issues.' The 'lecture tour' visited 10 college cities, selling Effexor ($2.7 billion in 2003). To market this drug, Wyeth helped to invent two new types of depression, GAD (generalised anxiety disorder) and SAD (social anxiety disorder.)

Wyeth provides the award of bursaries such as the Wales Mental Health Primary Care Awards. And, as with the NHS, Wyeth is funding training programmes. In 1995, Wyeth began sponsoring Neurolink, an 'independent' board of experts in mental health, which offers patient-centred resources and training for health care professionals caring for people with depressive illness or anxiety disorders.

In March 2004, Wyeth was in trouble with the FDA over Effexor, accused of making false advertising claims and failing to warn consumers of specific adverse reactions.[31]

Getting the Needle

Vaccines are the biggest of big business for the pharmaceutical multinationals. The goal of vaccine research in the developed world is to create one super–vaccine, which will contain DNA from a large number of viruses, parasites and bacteria. The vaccine, which would be

---

31 US FDA says Wyeth made false claims about Effexor. March 26, 2004. Reuters.

time–released,[32] would be given to newborn babies. In North America and Britain, researchers are working on the development of 150 viral and bacterial vaccines.[33]

Vaccines are also the most contentious prophylactic medicines marketed. Nowhere is the argument more robust about whether public health is dependent upon hygiene or upon the intervention of the physician. On the fringes of this central conflict, over the past decade another important argument has developed about whether or not the long-term effects of vaccines could weaken the health of individuals or perhaps even make them prone to specific diseases later in life.

Both Wyeth and its partner company, Lederle, got involved in vaccine manufacture from the time it first became a commercial certainty. Wyeth produced whole-cell pertussis (whooping cough) vaccine from the 1950s. From the beginning of the production of this vaccine, it was known that it had very high adverse reactions, often resulting in central nervous system damage.[34] The linkage to adverse reactions was so strong[35] and so obvious that Sweden banned whole-cell pertussis vaccine in the 1970s. Despite an acellular vaccine being adopted in Japan, Sweden and a number of other countries, the US Government continued to partner Wyeth's whole-cell version.

In both Britain and North America, regulatory bodies concurred that there was no evidence of serious damage resulting from the vaccine. In 1979, in Tennessee, four infants died of SIDS within 24 hours, apparently from the administration of one batch of DPT (diphtheria–pertus-

32 With a time-released vaccine there could be no provable link between vaccine and adverse reaction, a definite step forward for the vaccine companies.

33 A global movement engineered by the pharmaceutical companies is behind this plan. It has been pushed by various organisations at various international meetings. The Children's Vaccine Initiative (CVI), for instance, was launched in 1990 at the cynically designated World Summit for Children in New York City. The Initiative presented global strategies for the development and utilisation of vaccines by the world's children. The CVI is funded by the world's largest vaccine manufacturers, the World Bank, the WHO, and the Rockefeller Foundation.

34 The information in this paragraph comes from Geier and Geier, *The True Story of Pertussis Vaccination: A sordid legacy*. This superb piece of medical sociology can be found in the *Journal of the History of Medicine*: Vol. 57, July 2002. P. 249 – 284, Oxford University Press.

35 Geier & Geier cite one estimate of a 93% adverse reaction to the vaccine.

sis–tetanus.) There were 96,105 doses from this batch given out before the batch was withdrawn. In order to avoid noticeable adverse reactions related to single batches of the vaccine, Wyeth began a policy of sending only small batches to widely-dispersed geographical areas. If there were serious adverse reactions from one batch, the statistics would render them insignificant.[36]

When, in the early 1980s, the first cases were brought against the manufacturers of DPT, defence attorneys found it almost impossible to find expert witnesses willing to give evidence. The first expert to testify against the vaccine manufacturers was Californian paediatrician Dr Kevin Geraghty. Geraghty and his family were so severely harassed by vaccine manufacturers that he had to file a civil suit against them. By 1985, however, 219 lawsuits had been filed against DPT manufacturers.

Unfortunately, these actions led in 1986 in the USA to the National Vaccine Injuries Act, and the National Vaccine Compensation Act, which resulted in the so-called 'no fault' awards. As with a similar Act in Britain, which had come into force in 1979, its sole purpose was to stop individuals or groups from taking civil liability actions against manufacturers.

Throughout the Seventies, Eighties and Nineties, Wyeth was the monopoly supplier of oral polio vaccine to the North American Government. In the early Nineties, the company was making $230 million from the supply of this vaccine. When, in 1995, the Centers for Disease Control and Prevention (CDC) Advisory Committee on Immunization Practice (ACIP) recommended a move to a safer, injectable vaccine produced by another company, Wyeth launched a massive lobbying campaign to hold on to its polio vaccine business.

In 2003, however, Wyeth got its fingers singed when it tried to scam a wary public into taking the FluMist nasally-administered vaccine to guard against a prophesied influenza epidemic, which Wyeth and the government presented to the population as a dead certainty. The vaccine was produced by MedImmune and marketed by Wyeth. Following an agreement with Wal-Mart, the world's biggest retailer, FluMist was due

---

36 Geier and Geier, p. 271: 'This small lot plan meant that no one region of the country would have enough adverse reactions to a single lot of whole-cell pertussis vaccine to alert the clinicians in the region to the fact that they were using a highly reactogenic lot.'

to be sold in Wal-Mart stores at almost $70 a shot. The budget for per-suading people to use FluMist was reckoned at $25 million over a two-and-a half-month period in autumn.

As Dr Sherri Tenpenny argues in her article, 'Risks of FluMist Vaccine',[37] the live virus vaccine actually gave people flu, while the pack-et instructions stated that all recipients were to 'avoid close contact with immuno-compromised individuals for at least 21 days'. Dr Tenpenny suggests that untold millions of North Americans are immune–compro-mised. When neither the take-up for FluMist nor the hyped epidemic materialised, Wyeth dumped MedImmune and its battle to free the world of flu.

Another Partnership with Government

In 1994, Wyeth had managed to set a precedent when it formed the first commercial partnership with the British Government over the marketing and post-licensing surveillance of their vaccines. The Public Health Laboratory Service devised a surveillance system for monitoring side effects of vaccines, which was tested in conjunction with the countrywide prescription of Wyeth's measles booster vaccine.[38]

As Lynne McTaggart pointed out in *What Doctors Don't Tell You*, 'By working with the PHLS, Wyeth ensured not only that its studies had the most positive spin possible, but also that the product would be given a blessing to be test-marketed on a mass basis through this new surveil-lance system.' In fact, as with the elusive flu, the much-hyped measles epidemic did not arrive; however, several hundred families began actions against Wyeth over brain damage, paralysis and death of their children.

From the time of this first co-operation, Wyeth Pharmaceuticals and the ABPI argued for a joining of venture and purpose in the production of vaccines. Working in partnership with government on production and post–licensing surveillance of drugs, gives the pharmaceutical company

---

37 Which appeared in the online vaccine conference at redflagsdaily.com and was cited in full by Dr Mercola on www.mercola.com/fcgi/pf/2003/oct/4.

38 McTaggart L. *What Doctors Don't Tell You: The truth about the dangers of modern med-icine.* London: Thorsons; 1996.

a massive advantage. First, the company has an assured market; and, second, it is guaranteed consistent government loyalty over the safety of the drug. Like the drug companies themselves, it is unlikely that the government, having invested millions of pounds in a project, will act with transparency when it comes to adverse reactions.

In the year 2000, the British Government became the first in the world to launch a mass immunisation programme against meningitis C. And, once again, under the leadership of Liam Donaldson, the NHS climbed into bed with Wyeth. The PHLS approached Wyeth and other companies to step up research into a meningitis C vaccine. When Wyeth came up with its product, the government's PHSL took over its testing, with many of the larger trials being conducted by the PHLS.[39]

After discussions with the pharmaceutical industry, the government decided to inoculate the nation's 14 million schoolchildren of 15–17 years of age, as well as babies under a year. The programme cost the NHS around £10 million. The Department of Health brought forward the launch date for the campaign by a year, acting on the basis of 'a few initial studies into Wyeth's new vaccine'.[40]

Conflicting Interests

Some of the members of the CSM who reviewed the meningitis C vaccine for licence disclosed links with Wyeth.[41] In August and September of 2000, Martin Bright and Tracy McVeigh of the *Observer* wrote two articles, which concluded that four of the medical experts advising the government on the safety of the meningitis C vaccine had links with Wyeth

---

39 Ibid.

40 Ibid.

41 Professor Janet Darbyshire is a member of the Government's Committee on Safety of Medicines. Darbyshire was, at that time, professor of epidemiology at London University and director of the Medical Research Council. Dr David Goldblatt of the Institute of Child Health has served on an expert advisory panel for Wyeth and received research grants from Wyeth and North American Vaccines, which produces a third meningitis C drug. Professor Keith Cartwright of the University of Bristol also received funding from pharmaceutical companies.

and Chiron.[42] The articles were written with the aid of some parents, who told the *Observer* that they had been denied access to information about adverse reactions.

In rebuttal of the *Observer* article, Donaldson said that information on adverse reactions and deaths is supplied only on request. A statement later sent out by the Medicines Control Agency said that there had been 16,527 reported adverse reactions from 7,742 patients, and 12 deaths. The statement stressed that none of the deaths reported by GPs had been found to be connected to the vaccine.

The other committee involved in production and licensing of vaccines is the Joint Committee on Vaccination and Immunisation. This committee begins the process of discussing, selecting and recommending particular vaccines as part of vaccine policy at the Department of Health. This committee advises the government on which vaccines will be needed and when. In 2002 (the last time that details of members' interests were released), many members on this 23-strong committee had interests of different kinds with a wide range of pharmaceutical companies. These included Professor Keith Cartwright, who had stated interests in Wyeth-Lederle and Chiron, and Professor David Goldblatt, who declared interests with Wyeth.

The matter of conflicts of interests in relation to Wyeth's vaccines had also come to light in North America, and had been skillfully written up by Michael Horwin, in his *Critical Review of Prevnar*.[43] The FDA approved Prevnar, manufactured by Wyeth-Lederle, in February 2000. The vaccine is designed to prevent pneumococcal infection, which can lead to meningitis, blood poisoning and pneumonia. In North America, all children are supposed to have four mandatory doses of the vaccine by the age of 15 months. Horwin raises a number of questions about the need for Prevnar and its efficacy. One of the central points in his paper, however, is that six of the most 'outspoken' physicians who have supported Prevnar in different stages of its production and marketing have received money from Wyeth.

---

42 Parents who were a party to the article claimed that they had rung the MCA asking about adverse reactions and had been told that they could not have the information.

43 Prevnar, A Critical Review of a New Childhood Vaccine. Michael Horwin MA, September 19, 2000.

According to Horwin, Dr Steven Black and Dr Henry Shinefield, both of whom work for Kaiser Permanente, carried out trials paid for by Wyeth-Lederle, which greatly enhanced the perceived efficacy and safety of the drug. Despite working for Kaiser, both doctors have a history of ties to Wyeth, and the 1997 Annual Report of American Home Products pictures them both dressed in white lab coats. After its licensing, both doctors attended international conferences funded by Wyeth to support and to advertise Prevnar.

Horwin's next pair of doctors, Stephen I. Pelton and Kathryn Edwards, both answer questions from concerned parents and give out good-news information about Prevnar on a website paid for in its entirety by Wyeth. Horwin points out that both these doctors never have a critical word to say about Prevnar and always reassure parents in answering their questions. A question from a concerned parent who has written in asking if there was any link between Prevnar and diabetes, for instance, is answered in the negative. Pelton does not disclose alarming information given to the FDA by Dr J. Bart Classen, who speculated that Prevnar 'may be seven times as toxic as the haemophilus vaccine, possibly causing an estimated 400 to 700 children to develop insulin-dependent diabetes per 100,000 children immunised'. These cases of diabetes, Classen said, 'may not occur until three to 10 years following immunisation'.

Horwin introduces us to Dr Jerome Klein, a member of the National Vaccine Advisory Committee, the body that recommends vaccines to the government in North America, made up of 17 members appointed on rotating four-year terms, by the director of the National Vaccine Program.

Dr Klein is also the chief 'editor' of Pneumo.com, the pro-Prevnar website supported by an unrestricted grant from Wyeth-Lederle Vaccines. As an example of how far it is possible to drift from science when there are conflicting interests, Horwin quotes from Leary v. Secretary of the Department of Health and Human Services in 1994,[44] a case in which Dr. Klein had given evidence.

On August 22, 1984, a healthy nine-month-old baby named Sean Leary was administered his third DPT vaccine. Sean immediately began

---

44 Leary v. Secretary of the Department of Health and Human Services, in 1994 WL 43395 (Fed.Cl.)

vomiting. The next day, he stopped eating. He stayed alert but was no longer active. That night he cried out every 15 to 30 minutes. The paediatrician immediately noted the 'obvious circulation collapse'. There at the paediatrician's office, 'Sean's eyes rolled back in his head and he stopped breathing.' He was rushed to an emergency room. Resuscitative efforts failed and Sean was pronounced dead at 1.44pm. Dr Jerome Klein testified that the relationship between vaccination and Sean's death was 'merely coincidental'.

RotaShield

The rotavirus causes acute gastroenteritis, which leads to diarrhoea and low-grade fever. Three strains of the virus, A, B and C, have been identified. The virus is spread mainly by person-to-person contact among children who have contaminated hands, and especially in larger closed communities such as hospital paediatric wards. Group A is the leading cause of severe diarrhoea among infants and children. Group C rotavirus has been associated with rare and sporadic cases of diarrhoea in children in a number of countries. The incubation period for the virus is 1-3 days, and although the symptoms can include vomiting and diarrhoea, recovery is usually complete. Childhood mortality from rotavirus complications is relatively low, resulting, in North America, for example, in 20 to 100 deaths per year (500 children died in total over a six-year period from diarrhoea diseases in the United States; 20 per cent of these deaths were caused by rotavirus infection).[45]

One of the doctors whom Horwin cites in his paper is Margaret B. Rennels. Rennels was involved in one of the studies that proved the safety and efficacy of Prevnar, which Horwin disputes, and she also carried out studies of the Wyeth rotavirus vaccine, RotaShield: 'She participated in virtually all phases of the testing of recently licensed rotavirus vaccine and was the lead author on the report of the pivotal US Efficacy Study.'[46] RotaShield was developed by Wyeth under intense competition from

---

45 All the information in this paragraph is taken from the majority Staff Report Committee on Government Reform.

46 Cited by Horwin; University of Maryland School of Medicine Faculty web site.

Merck. It was approved by the FDA in August 1998, was a monkey-based, live, oral vaccine, and had an overall relative efficacy of 49 per cent to 83 per cent for the four strains of the virus.

The US Rhesus Rotavirus Vaccine Study Group, of which Rennels was part, was subsidised by Wyeth. In 1998, Rennels wrote a refutation of any link between RotaShield and intussusception, a condition in which the intestines of children become so seriously restricted that parts have to be surgically removed. Her paper, which appeared in the *Pediatric Infectious Diseases Journal*, was entitled 'Lack of an apparent association between intussusception and wild or vaccine rotavirus infection.'[47] Horwin points out that Wyeth has donated a total of over $2.5 million to the University of Maryland School of Medicine where Dr Rennels works, and where she is now demonstrating the safety of Prevnar.

Just a year after RotaShield was licensed, in July 1999, it was withdrawn from the market after the Centers for Disease Control received mounting reports of intussusception or severe bowel obstruction in RotaShield vaccine cases from the Vaccine Adverse Events Reporting System (VAERS). In that year, there were more than 100 cases of intussusception; 57 of these were in children who had been vaccinated. Twenty-nine of these children required surgery and one five-month-old infant died of the condition.[48] A study of the link between intussusception and RotaShield showed that onset of the illness was increased by 60 per cent among children who received the vaccine.

In August 1999, the Committee on Government Reform of the US House of Representatives initiated an investigation into Federal Vaccine Policy. The investigation principally focused on Wyeth's RotaShield (UCLA). A part of their investigation, however, looked at conflicts of interest, and in 2000 the committee published a report: *Conflict Interests in Vaccine Policy Making*.

The Vaccines and Related Biological Products Advisory Committee (VRBPAC) advises the FDA on the licensing of new vaccines, and the

---

47 Cited by Horwin. Rennels MB, et al. Lack of an apparent association between intussusception and wild or vaccine rotavirus infection. *Pediatr Infect Dis J,* 1998 Oct; 17(10): 924-5.

48 These figures do not take into account cases which were diagnosed and treated but not reported specifically as intussusception or cases of mortality from other or unknown causes.

ACIP, whose members are appointed by the CDC, advises the CDC on guidelines to be issued to doctors and authorities for the appropriate use of vaccines.

The VRBPAC, which meets some six times a year, has 15 voting members, including the chair, selected by the commissioner of the FDA and serving overlapping four-year terms.

In the case of its 2000 report on RotaShield, the Committee on Government Reform found that, although cases of intussusception had been seen during trials of the vaccine, and although reports had been brought to the attention of the VRBPAC and the ACIP, both of these committees and the manufacturers, Wyeth, had decided that the levels of the disease found in trials were statistically insignificant. At the VRB-PAC approval meeting for RotaShield in 1998, further questions were raised about adverse reactions to the vaccine. These concerns included not only intussusception but failure to thrive and febrile reactions. Despite this, the Committee's vote for approval was unanimous. It would later emerge that some members, while voting for the go-ahead for RotaShield, had expressed the need for further investigations during the approval meeting.

The Committee found that all five of the standing members of the VRBPAC had conflicts of interests and three of these had taken part in the deliberations about RotaShield.[49] Two of them had financial ties to Wyeth.

Dr Kathryn Edwards had received a contract from Wyeth-Lederle for $255,023 per year between 1996 and 1998 for the study of their pneumococcal vaccines. She had also had thousands of dollars in numerous grants and contracts with NIAID, which was an affected company. She was, however, permitted by the FDA to vote on RotaShield because her work focused on other vaccines.

At the time of the approval meeting, Dr Mary Estes's employer, Baylor College, was receiving considerable funding for the development of rotavirus vaccines, including a $75,000 grant from Wyeth-Lederle's parent company, American Home Products. Dr Estes was also a principal investigator, using a grant from Merck for the development of rotavirus vaccine.

---

49 Two members of the Committee with conflicts had not been involved in the deliberations.

The Advisory Committee on Immunization Practices (ACIP) provides advice and guidance on vaccine policy to the Department of Health and Human Services (DHHS), the equivalent of the British Department of Health. It also compiles and reviews an official list of vaccines for administration to children. The Committee has 12 voting members, seven non–voting ex-officio members from federal agencies, and 16 non–voting liaison representatives from professional societies and organisations responsible for the development and execution of immunisation programmes for children and adults.

The chairman of the ACIP, Dr John Modlin, was not only a Merck shareholder but had sat on the Merck Immunization Advisory Board from 1996. Dr Paul Offit shares the patent on the rotavirus vaccine developed by Merck and had received substantial funds from Merck for his research. Dr Fernando Guerra had funding from a number of vaccine manufacturers and was a principal investigator for SmithKline-Beecham. Dr Marie Griffin declared consultancy fees and a salary from Merck as a chair of a Merck committee. Griffin's husband is a consultant for American Cyanamid, which at the time was a sister subsidiary with Wyeth-Lederle of American Home Products. Dr Chinh Le worked for Kaiser Permanente, which was carrying out vaccine studies for Merck, Wyeth-Lederle and SmithKline-Beecham. Dr Richard Clover declared grants from Merck and SmithKline-Beecham.

When it came to look at the liaison representatives, who came from different esteemed North American academies, societies and associations, the Committee on Government Reform recorded a massive number of funding links. The American Academy of Family Pediatrics had ties to no fewer than 26 vaccine manufacturers, including Wyeth.

The final report made 17 recommendations, which were preceded by three statements that summed up the Committee's overall view. The most general of these statements was as follows:

> Congress sought to eliminate 'the danger of allowing special interest groups to exercise undue influence upon the Government through dominance of advisory committees which deal with matters in which they have vested interests.' [50] However, the extensive use of working

---

50 FAC Standards ACT, supra note 10, at 6, reprinted FACA Source Book, supra note 2, at 276, citing Hearings on H.R. 4383 before the Legal and Monetary Affairs Subcommittee, (*cont.*)

groups in which conflict of interest procedures do not appear to be implemented, and the automatic waivers given to every advisory committee member, along with the absence of consumer representation, appears to thwart this goal.

Unsanitary Conditions

'Certain companies have repeated and ongoing problems with quality control,' wrote Barbara Seaman in *The Greatest Experiment Ever Performed on Women*,[51] 'Wyeth is one of them.'

Seaman recounts the case of the Today-brand contraceptive sponge, a non-hormonal barrier product manufactured by an affiliate of Wyeth. In 1994 the sponges suddenly went out of stock. Seaman reveals that an FDA inspection of the company plant had disclosed bacterial contamination of the water used to make the sponges. The FDA had found that the company had poor sanitation of their equipment. Faced with the high cost of bringing their plant up to scratch, the company stopped producing the sponge.

There had, says Seaman, been extensive problems with other AHP products, including metal contamination, yeast and mould on raw materials, and foreign matter in an arthritis pain formula preparation, failed uniformity codes and inaccurate package date codes.

The FDA had also cited serious violations at three different Wyeth-Ayerst plants in 1995. Five years later, in 2000, Wyeth agreed to pay a $30 million fine for its repeated violations of technical and contamination regulations which affected, among other things, the production of flu vaccine.

---

50 (*cont.*) of the House Committee on Government Operations, 92 Cong., 2nd Session, at 13-55 (1971), reprinted in 1972 U.S. Code Cong. & Admin. News 3434-76.

51 Seaman, Barbara. Op. cit.

Norplant

Norplant was developed in conjunction with the non-profit Population Council, and was introduced in the US in 1990 as a five-year, slow-release contraceptive, which delivers progestogen via small rods implanted in a woman's arm. After tracking down women in different parts of the world who had taken part in trials, US activists found that the majority of them had serious complaints about the implant, such as unpredictable and lengthy menstrual periods. Following complaints from these women, most physicians had refused to remove the implants, while those who had tried to remove them had often done serious damage to the woman hosting them. Seaman states that 'in one out of every five or six users, the rods migrated or broke, and the surgery got dicey'. The National Women's Health Network, and even the FDA's Dr Philip Corfman, asked the manufacturers to provide special training in rod-removal techniques.

Wyeth refused to accommodate any of the criticisms, and accused consumers of being 'too picky'. Norplant had a 12-year lifespan in the US, but for the last two years of this time, women who had the implant had to use another back-up contraceptive as well.

In 2002, European farmers threatened to sue Wyeth's Irish affiliate, Elan, after animal feed shipped from Ireland for cows and pigs turned out to be contaminated with Provera, a hormone product meant to induce growth. In Europe, hormone supplements are outlawed for animals.

Premarin

By the year 2000, recall of faulty Premarin conjugated oestrogen tablets, which did not dissolve in the way they were supposed to, covered around 382 million doses, equivalent to about 17 per cent of tablets sold in 1999. This recall was in effect in the US for almost four years, from 1999 to 2003.

Chapter Seven

A Vanishing History and Disposable Science

III Distribution: The Upper Reaches

Here's to confusion. And universal darkness covers all.

Ross Macdonald[1]

If an automobile does not have a motor, no amount of advertising can make it appear to have one. On the other hand, with a little luck, proper timing and a good promotion programme, a bag of asafoetida with a unique chemical side chain can be made to look like a wonder drug.

Dr Console[2]

Wyeth's attempts to influence drug-and-vaccine-associated health care have been aided by a remarkable campaign run by the company since the year 2000 to enter the British Parliament. In the year 2001, the charity *Women's* Health Concern (author's italics), chaired by Dr John

---

1 MacDonald R. *The Ivory Grin*. Glasgow: Fontana, 1973. Although Ross MacDonald has one of the characters in the book speak this line, he intimates that it is drawn from some more classical text, of which I am unaware.

2 Dr Console, former chief medical director E.R. Squibb & Sons. Quoted in Sjostrom H, Nilsson R. *Thalidomide and the Power of the Drug Companies*. Harmondsworth, Middlesex: Penguin Books; 1972.

Stevenson, accepted Don Barrett on to its committee. Up until the previous year, Barrett had been the corporate affairs executive of Wyeth Pharmaceuticals in the United Kingdom; he had spent almost his whole adult life selling drugs. Upon his invitation to the committee, *Women's Health Concern* issued this statement:

> The Committee invited Mr Don Barrett to join the committee. It was felt that his industry experience and contacts and long association with the WHC would make him a useful member. He was also made an honorary life member of the friends of WHC.[3]

Barrett is not a doctor, but he had clearly played a prominent role in advancing support to the WHC from Wyeth.[4]

In fact, Barrett is a corporate loyalist and his work for Wyeth did not finish on his retirement. When he was accepted on to the WHC committee, he was also a long-standing member of the British Menopausal Society – a lynchpin of Wyeth's operations to sell HRT in Britain and throughout the world, discussed in the next chapter – and had recently become a leading member of the Baby Lifeline charity. Barrett is also a director of Networking for Industry (NFI), a company that describes itself, with the North American term, as 'not for profit'. NFI is a lobby company, which has, on behalf of Wyeth Pharmaceuticals and seemingly with the full knowledge of New Labour, gone into partnership with Parliament.

Networking for Industry's sister company, also 'not for profit', is Partnership Sourcing Ltd. (PSL), which works out of the same Southwark offices. The main distinction between PSL and NFI is that PSL was set up in 1990 as a major initiative in partnership by the Department of Trade and Industry (Dti) and the Confederation of British Industry (CBI). Apparently, after some time in the business and ideological wilderness, PSL's time has come, and this independent, self–financing, 'not for profit' company is at the very centre of matchmaking between New Labour and private industry.

---

3 Annual Report for 2001 with the Charity Commission.

4 Barrett joined the pharmaceutical industry as a medical representative in 1959 and stayed with Wyeth Pharmaceuticals during his career, where he was also sales manager, director of marketing services and finally the company's UK main board director for corporate affairs. He claims to have been involved in the women's health field since the late Sixties.

PSL did early work for the Dti on partnering in the construction industry, and New Labour's modernising plans from this industry grew out of a joint government-industry report, chaired by Sir Michael Latham. PSL now works with all branches of industry, including the Ministry of Defence, in arranging partnership concords between buyers and sellers.[5] The company might be described as an independent think tank, which brings together industry and government for the purpose of organising partnership contracts.

However, in the business of selling drugs to the government, and of participating in health policy outside its formal committees, Networking for Industry (NFI) has taken over.

NFI is quite a different organisation from PSL because, although it leans heavily towards NHS modernisers, Wyeth Pharmaceuticals has considerable influence on its board.[6] The company claims to be 'dedicated to stimulating positive change in the UK by generating dialogue and understanding between key stakeholders on important issues'. NFI is, however, a lobby group that, in the field of health, has become deeply involved in Parliamentary affairs.

Networking for Industry is at the centre of four other lobby and 'communications' organisations, which it has set up: the Associate Party Sustainable Waste Group (APSWG), the All-Party Design and Innovation Group (APGDI), the Associate Parliamentary Manufacturing Industry

---

5 The PSL Board is made up of: Sir Michael Latham, chairman of the Construction Industry Board (1995 - 1996), author of the joint Government and industry review of construction published in 1994. In April 2004, Latham was appointed by Construction Minister Nigel Griffiths to carry out the review of the Construction Act promised by chancellor Gordon Brown. Richard Arnott of the Dti. Lord Berkeley, Civil engineer, Sir Alexander Gibb and Partners 1961-67; chairman, George Wimpey plc 1967-87; Public affairs manager, Euro Tunnel 1987-95; chairman, Piggyback Consortium 1995-98, Rail Freight Group from 1997. Andy Scott, the CBI's director of international competitiveness. Barry Sheerman, New Labour MP for Huddersfield since 1983, chairman of the Commons Education Select Committee and also a leading figure in Networking for Industry. Labour peer Lord Evans of Watford, non-executive chief executive officer, Union Income Benefit Holdings plc from 2001. The Steering Group of PSL has around 35 members who represent either government departments, national agencies, or large corporations which include: Scottish Water, Willmott Dixon, BAE Systems, Siemens, British Energy, Orange, the CBI, the Dti, and some University academic departments. The representatives are mainly involved in procurement. Fourteen organisations that work at partnership are PSL's complementary partners – organisations which work professionally in contractual or conflict resolution situations,   (cont.)

Group (APMIG), and the Associate Parliamentary Group on Health (APGH). The two groups that deal with industry links and technology design innovation, APMIG and APGDI, are integrated in the Dti network of partnering organisations. The APGH and APWG deal with two of the most lucrative and contentious post–industrial service areas: health and waste disposal.

There are two types of inter–party groups in the House of Commons: *All Party Parliamentary Groups*, which consist entirely of members of either House, and *Associate Parliamentary Groups*, which can have on them or associated with them 'strangers', those from outside either the House of Commons or the House of Lords. In 1984 and 1985, parliamentary regulations brought into practice an approved list and a register of All Party Groups. These regulatory measures gave Parliament assurances that groups that said they were 'all party' were recognised by Parliament, and at the same time gathered basic data about them and the outside bodies with which they were associated.

A good example of an associate parliamentary group, picked at random, would be the Associate Parliamentary Engineering Group. This, as its website says, 'is a well established group with a representative membership of over 110 MPs and peers, 44 non-parliamentary individuals and over 100 engineering companies, consultancies, universities and other corporate bodies'. Each Associate Parliamentary Group has a secretariat, which organises its affairs, issues statements and plans conferences or publishes position papers. The secretariat for the Associate Parliamentary Engineering Group is provided by the Royal Academy of Engineering.

As long as the constitution of the promoting body is good, and the body is as inclusive as possible, neither Parliament nor the people need have fear of a drift towards sectarianism or vested interests.[7] As one

---

5 (*cont.*) such as ACAS. These large groups are organised and serviced by the PSL executive and office team.

6 While PSL is an open and transparent organisation, which both the Dti and the CBI are happy to promote, after its successful work over the past decade, its sibling organisation Networking For Industry, is far more secretive. Nowhere on the Internet does the company give details of its board of directors.

7 In some small Associate Parliamentary Groups, such as the Associate Parliamentary Group on Political Art – yes there is one – a certain degree of vested interest is clearly a prerequisite for membership.

should expect with a Royal Academy, we are well on the way to a minimum of conflicting interests and no obvious routes to illicit pressure being brought on MPs or ultimately the government.

Taking the Associate Parliamentary Engineering Group as a model, one would expect the Associate Parliamentary Group on Health to be a large group representing health interests across the board, that is, everything from the Royal College of Physicians to the National Society of Homeopaths.

The APGH was set up by Networking for Industry and is administered by NFI from its Southwark offices. While the Associate Parliamentary Group on Health itself has all the appearance of being well grounded and exempt from conflict interests, the group has linked to it a panel of high-powered advisers. These advisers, drawn from experts with the narrowest specialised interests, are dominated by Labour modernisers and by Wyeth-Lederle interests. The secretariat for the APGH operates from the offices of NFI, and its senior officer is a serving Wyeth Pharmaceuticals executive, who works with two assistants paid out of money granted to the NFI by Wyeth and other pharmaceutical companies.

The APGH has registered a number of 'associate members' or industry backers, including, Wyeth, GlaxoSmithKline, AstraZeneca, BUPA, Abbott Laboratories, BT, Pfizer and PRI MED,[8] each of which – except Wyeth, which declares a contribution of £15,000 –[9] contribute £5,000 annually to the group's organisation. The big pharmaceutical companies, all member companies of the Association of the British Pharmaceutical Industry (ABPI), and BUPA, the largest medical insurance company in England, are all close to New Labour. BUPA, which, in theory, would have to deal with adverse effects of drugs, is headed by one of New

---

8 It is not necessarily the case that any of these companies are Wyeth competitors in this matter. Abbott Laboratories has links with Wyeth, Pfizer is also a member of the Rockefeller Empire, and BT, for instance, is contractually linked to Wyeth, for which it carries out the communications and website work. BT has been a partner in the funding of other organisations fronting for Wyeth, in particular, the Amarant Trust.

9 Wyeth's declared contribution of £15,000 is relatively meaningless. The APGH website advertises that it is backed by an unrestricted grant from Wyeth and in fact is probably webmastered by a Wyeth partner organisation.

Labour's principal donors. All of the pharmaceutical companies hope to sell products to the NHS. It is, however, Wyeth that is almost singularly involved in the provision of staff and finances and the extensive website facilities provided for Members of Parliament.

The APGH provides Wyeth Pharmaceuticals and, indirectly, the ABPI, with a direct influence on matters of health inside Parliament. Since 2002, the APGH has made available an extensive diary, advice on health issues and agenda for MPs who are members of its password-secure website. The secretariat, the advice group and the website have in fact done everything to support MPs on health matters that a good civil service would do if it had not been dismantled. The only difference is that, whereas the civil service used to be governed by strict rules to keep vested interests at bay, *this* civil service is run by Wyeth Pharmaceuticals. It has an agenda of breakfasts and mealtime meetings, seminars and talks, in buildings adjacent to the Commons, which introduce ministers, NHS and DH staff to drug company executives and private health service providers.

The setting up and funding of groups within Parliament by commercial lobby companies has become relatively commonplace since New Labour came to power. And perhaps few eyebrows would be raised at the disclosure that the ABPI is controlling a Parliamentary Group on Health. However, in the shadow of this group, Wyeth and the ABPI have selected another group of advisers, who are not Members of Parliament but who, through the APGH, have direct access to government offices. The advisers include two Wyeth executives.

The NFI website makes a point of informing us that 'the officers' of the Associate Parliamentary Group on Health are answerable to the Parliamentary Commissioner for Standards and Privileges, which of course they would be because they are Members of Parliament. In a clever piece of wording, the website then runs information about the group's advisers, intimating that they, too, are answerable to the Parliamentary Commissioner:

The Officers of the APGH are responsible to the Parliamentary Commissioner for Standards for the activities and conduct of the Group, and together with the Advisory Panel provide the motivation and leadership that makes the initiative a success.

Most incredible, among these advisers is Duncan Eaton, chief executive of the NHS Purchasing and Supply Agency.[10] Eaton has spent his career in the NHS and held senior positions in a number of health authorities. The other advisers are: Professor Kenneth Calman, a previous Government Chief Medical Officer; David Colin-Thome, the national clinical director for primary care at the Department of Health; Julie Dent, the Chief Executive of South West London Health Authority; Lord Toby Harris of Haringey, and Dame Deirdre Hine.

Sir Kenneth Calman was Chief Medical Officer to the government from 1991 to 1998. Calman's residency as CMO was beset with controversies, which included the BSE crisis, the biased CMO Report on myalgic encephalomyelitis/chronic fatigue syndrome,[11] and the beginning of the row over MMR, as well as the government support for banning vitamin B6. Calman has served on the executive board of the World Health Organisation and the European Environment and Health Committee. He was recently chosen by Lord Sainsbury to take part in the Chemistry Leadership Council (CLC), a body formed in 2003 by the Dti and described as 'an industry-led task force', which intends to develop a profitable future chemical industry.[12] One of the many matters on the agenda of the Council is 'self–regulation'; however, unlike the more obviously profit-generating roles of the Council, the CLC website says that, for the moment, 'Self Regulation is on the back-burner.'

The two Wyeth executives who act as advisers are Bernard Dunkley and Kevin James. Dunkley is also a director of Networking For Industry and was named as special adviser to the APHG.[13] With 37 years' experi-

---

10 Eaton has worked in the NHS for over 30 years. He is former director of operations with North West Thames Regional Health Authority, chief executive of South Bedfordshire Health Authority, and chief executive of Bedfordshire Health Authority, past president of the Chartered Institute of Purchasing and Supply and of the Healthcare Supplies Association.

11 Walker, Martin J. *Skewed: Psychiatric hegemony and the manufacture of mental illness in Multiple Chemical Sensitivity, Gulf War Syndrome, Myalgic Encephalomyelitis and Chronic Fatigue Syndrome*. London: Slingshot Publications; 2003. *Brave New World of Zero Risk* <www.zero-risk.org>.

12 Calman was given a place on the Futures strand of the CLC, which throws together for instance, environmentalists such as Jonathan Porritt with the chairman of BP, with the idea of resolving a green future for chemicals.

13 Former national field sales manager for Lederle Laboratories.

ence in drugs marketing, he is presently a serving *Government Affairs Director* for Lederle and Wyeth Laboratories UK, the part of Wyeth that develops vaccines.

Kevin James[14] is executive managing director for Wyeth UK. Perhaps more importantly, he is a member of the ABPI board of management. This, and the fact that in 2004 he took over chairmanship of the American Pharmaceutical (companies in England) Group (APG),[15] make him one of the highest-ranking drug salesmen in Britain. The previous chairman of the APG was Vincent Lawton (1999–2004), a committee member of both the Pharmaceutical Industry Competitive Task Force (PICTF) and the Ministerial (Pharmaceutical) Industry Strategy Group.

The last report of the APG, *Headroom for Innovation in Primary Care*, assessed the allocation of additional resources in primary care, while arguing for the faster uptake of new medicines by the NHS. On behalf of the ABPI, James has also argued before parliamentary committees for a closer partnership between the government and pharmaceutical companies in trials of new drugs and the conduct of post–licensing surveillance.

The actual Associated Parliamentary Group on Health, whose members put themselves forward to be selected by their parties in the Commons or Lords, and which is meant to be the main debating forum on health in the Houses of Parliament, consists of: Baroness Cumberlege, Baroness Masham of Ilton, David Amess MP, David Drew MP, Sandra Gidley MP, Patrick Hall MP, Dr Howard Stoate MP, and Dr Richard Taylor MP.

There can be no doubt that some of these members have no idea that they are a part of a manoeuvre by a lobby group. Some other members

---

14 He joined the Pharmaceutical Industry with Lederle Laboratories in 1975. His career has encompassed numerous sales and marketing positions in the UK. He was appointed pharmaceutical director for Wyeth at the time of the take-over of American Cyanamid and subsequently appointed managing director for the UK and ROI in February 2002.

15 American Pharmaceutical Group comprises 13 US-based pharmaceutical companies, which apparently account for 35% of sales for the UK industry. Chris Mockler, a senior policy adviser to GPC, acts as secretary to the APG, in the Long Acre offices of GPC International. GPC is a Canadian-based worldwide government and public relations consulting firm with a network of offices in 16 countries and 500 consultancy groups.

are in positions where they may be pressured by lobbying organisations, while others appear themselves to be familiar with the terrain of lobbying and pharmaceutical marketing.

David Amess MP is a current member of the Parliamentary Health Committee, a body appointed by the Commons to examine expenditure, administration and policy of the Department of Health and its associated bodies.[16]

At least one member of the APGH has links with drug companies. Dr Howard Stoate is now chair of the All Party Group on Men's Health (APGMH), of which David Amess and Sandra Gidley are also members. Stoate set up the APGMH on behalf of the Men's Health Forum (MHF), a registered charity. Despite being a charity, the Men's Health Forum is clearly an instrument of pharmaceutical marketing, supported by, among others, Merck Sharp & Dohme, Pfizer and Roche.

Undoubtedly, the two heavyweights from the Health Group and its advisers APGH are: Baroness Cumberlege, who is both a group member and an adviser,[17] and Lord Hunt of Kings Heath. Despite coming from different sides of the House, these two peers have a lot in common. They were both Ministers of Health, Cumberlege during the Premiership of John Major from 1992 to 1997, and Hunt from 1999 until 2003. They are both NHS modernisers, and they both have had dealings with pharmaceutical marketing in different forms. But perhaps most perversely, Lord Hunt is a director of Baroness Cumberlege's NHS integrated health consultancy company, Cumberlege Connections.

Lord Hunt, while Minister of Health, was the instigator of the Pharmaceutical Industry Competitive Task Force Report,[18] which later developed into the Ministerial Industry Strategy Group, set up to carry on a continuous dialogue between Ministers and pharmaceutical company executives. He also has links with the Sainsbury family and their trusts,

---

16 Just as I was finishing this book, the House of Commons Health Committee announced an Inquiry into the influence of the pharmaceutical industry. One of the members of the committee is David Amess and another is Dr Richard Taylor, both of whom are members of the APGH.

17 Perhaps she has a poor memory and has to advise herself.

18 During this time, he was also a member of the G10 Committee, an EU Commission Committee which mapped out the future for the European drugs industry competitiveness.

being a senior policy adviser to the Sainsbury Centre for Mental Health.[19] Lord Hunt is actually only a few years out of the tight policy group which steers New Labour through its relationships with the modernised NHS and the pharmaceutical companies. Only three years away from his statement, 'The UK has a thriving and successful pharmaceutical industry and we want to keep it that way.' From January 2004 until May 2005, he took up a £58,000 a year appointment to chair the new Patient Safety Agency, a post for which his meetings with pharmaceutical company executives made him eminently suited.

When Baroness Cumberlege was elevated to the Lords, she began the long haul through PR and health consultancy companies, which ended in 1993 with Cumberlege Connections, a consultative company that organises conferences and training courses to equip people to deal with government and what is left of the NHS.

On her way to Cumberlege Connections, the Baroness passed through some less well-known organisations. From 1997 to 2001 she was an executive director of MJM Healthcare Solutions, which, with its sister organisation Mental Health Strategies, is part of Niche Healthcare Consulting. Both MJM and MHS develop strategies, review provisions and provide special advice on resourcing healthcare solutions. In 2001, she joined the board of Huntsworth plc. The company, which describes itself as 'a specialised communications group with public relations at its core', is comprised of a number of market service agencies such as Counsel, ehpr, Greyling public relations and pbc. Major clients of Huntsworth plc are AstraZeneca, Pfizer, Chiron Evans vaccines,[20] Merck, Shire, Aventis, Novartis, Roche and Abbott Laboratories. In 2001, Cumberlege left Huntsworth to team up with Anthony McKeever[21] as co-

---

19 During the period that Hunt was the Minister of Health and one of the advisers to the APGH, another of the advisers, the previous Chief Medical Officer Sir Kenneth Calman, instigated a Chief Medical Officer's Committee on ME/CFS. One of the Sainsbury's Trusts, was allowed to buy a place on the committee, to make sure that the psychiatric view of ME was even better represented.

20 Chiron was one of the companies producing the meningitis vaccine agreed by the Committee on the Safety of Medicine, despite conflicting interests in both Wyeth and Chiron being declared by some of the Committee members.

21 A former Conservative government adviser and NHS Chief Executive. Quo Health describes itself as offering 'a practical yet visionary, idealistic yet pragmatic, combination of expertise from the world of business and the world of NHS senior management.'

director of Quo Health Management Consultancy. In January 2003, Quo Health was one of eight private companies added to the Franchising Register of Expertise, enabling them to submit management bids to rescue failing NHS hospitals.

It is easy to see why, with the overall objective of protecting markets and selling drugs, Wyeth and its team of advisers might want to influence, for example, matters to do with vaccines, HRT, and natural health and supplements, and why Wyeth and the ABPI might wish to talk regularly and 'covertly' to the PM about such matters. The advisory group to the APGH gives Wyeth executives almost direct access to Tony Blair, as if it were a Member of Parliament.[22,23]

Despite the presence of Kevin James in a high-powered position on the board of the ABPI, and despite Wyeth's close relationship with the government, the company was not involved in the Ministerial Pharmaceutical Company Task Force or the strategy meetings that followed.

There can be no doubt that the Advisory Group to the APGH leans towards New Labour's plans for modernisation. Equally, a number of the Advisory Committee members, people such as Calman, Thombe and Hunt, are government intimates as well as modernisers. Presumably, they have discussed matters with New Labour's senior ministers. Tony Blair and others in government know that Wyeth Pharmaceuticals and

---

22 Professor Andrew Wakefield, who has suggested a link between MMR and autism, has been all but run out of the country following a dirty tricks campaign by the medical establishment. The well respected doctor, alternative practitioner and world expert on childhood allergy and asthma, Dr Mansfield was arraigned on disciplinary charges before the GMC, following accusations that he had advocated separate single inoculations as an alternative to the autism associated MMR vaccine. The DoH mounted a massive campaign, costing thousands of pounds, against Dr David Pugh who offered parents single vaccines at exceptionally successful clinics in Elstree and Sheffield on the basis that there was some doubt about MMR contributing to autism. In December 2004 Dr Pugh was sentenced to nine months in prison after pleading guilty to 4 charges in the Crown Court, relating to faked children's blood test results.

23 The restrictions on vitamins and food supplements, beginning with the attempts to ban the sale of Vitamin B6, used incidentally by women suffering PMT or going through the menopause and, therefore, part of Wyeth's target market, has always been supported by the government and the Department of Health. The campaign against B6, which was waged in Britain and North America, was heavily backed by New Labour Ministers who used bogus studies to shore up their arguments that its sales should be restricted.

the ABPI are embedded within Parliament. Or were they invited there, anyway, by the PM's Policy Unit as an opaque way of continuing the policy discourse with Big Pharma?

The reason why Wyeth was chosen to head a mission to go where no pharmaceutical company had gone before, on behalf of the ABPI, can probably, in part, be traced back to the historical involvement of the Rockefeller drugs empire in the development of English medicine. In 1925, for example, Rockefeller donated millions of pounds to develop the medical research facilities of University College London, the Middlesex Hospital and University College Hospital. This funding was continued by the Wellcome Trust, which was until the mid-1990s in receipt of all the tax-exempt profits of the British part of the Anglo-North American drugs company Burroughs Wellcome. Since the early Nineties, Wyeth has curried favour with successive governments through such agencies as the Public Health Laboratory Services.[24]

Where does this manipulation of the democratic process leave patients? If the usual market devices utilised in the awarding of tenders and franchises have been ignored, if the normal academic and learned discourses are bypassed, if the ABPI has the Prime Minister's ear, how can we trust, or even assess the quality of or the need for the pharmaceutical services being offered and sold to the NHS?

In contemporary society, the desires, needs, feelings and voice of the individual are swamped, not necessarily within the community, where community exists, but in the much broader area of interaction between citizens and producing corporations of all kinds.

While there might be a vague tolerance given by most producers to complaints and the servicing of guarantees, the citizen is unlikely to get anywhere trying to make his or her voice heard against the 'sales gales' of most multinational producers and suppliers of services. Nowhere is this truer than in relation to medicine and pharmaceuticals. Trying to get a pharmaceutical company to listen to affected patients is a little less pos-

---

24 Now the Public Health Authority.

sible than a population with their hands and feet tied bringing down a despotic regime.

Maggie Tuttle had no idea what she was taking on when she tried to draw attention to the adverse reactions to HRT. The journey from personal experience to global change is possible only by those whose lives and ideas are synchronised with the prevailing economic system. Those who want to give voice to criticism and expect change are today always disappointed. Maggie was, of course, still living in the world of Prisoners' Wives and Families, at a time when there existed a tenuous relationship between the governors and the governed.

For Maggie, the extraordinary opposition faced by the Menopausal Helpline (MHL) came as a complete surprise. She was not to know that the pharmaceutical companies respond through their agents to everything that might appear critical of their product, to protect the product image as if it were royalty and they the praetorian guard.

Not long after she set up the MHL, Maggie, together with another four individuals, was summoned to Hull by Professor David Purdie, chairman of the British Menopause Society, at that time, head of the Centre for Metabolic Bone Disease at Hull Royal Infirmary and a long-time advocate of HRT. It was explained that while visiting him they could talk about her views and he could show her round his unit.

> Basically, he called me all the way up there to tell me that I was wrong and that I was denying other women access to the drug. I don't know how he got all the money from the NHS to fund his research on HRT and osteoporosis. While these doctors, like Whitehead and Purdie, always said that their patients did not suffer any side effects, I knew this to be wrong. I began looking out for patients of these doctors when they contacted the Menopausal Helpline. I always believed that the truth was with the women and not with the doctors.

At this time, Purdie's department was funded by Wyeth Pharmaceuticals and he had clearly been asked to try to win Maggie round.

At a later date, a *The Times* journalist unadvisedly put the contact details of the Menopausal Helpline at the end of a long article about Dr Purdie and his work. Maggie knew nothing about this and was surprised when she picked up the phone to find the good doctor unhealthily irate on the other end of the line.

Inevitably, not having an academic background, and being some-times roughly spoken, Maggie was judged unfair by some of the learned people with whom she argued. Professor Malcolm Whitehead, a pulpi-teer for HRT and consultant obstetrician at King's College Hospital, London, addressing a conference of black women with the Minister for Health, and exhorting them to try HRT, walked out of the room when Maggie subjected him to one of her tirades. Maggie sees clearly through these civilised obfuscations:

> When you see and hear women suffering and you get some idiot who you know is wrong arguing with you, I can't keep quiet. I wasn't brought up as an educated person. I'm not like a politician. I just say it as it is.

A large pharmaceutical company such as Wyeth, especially one manipu-lating a very focused market such as that for HRT, is in a constant state of alert, on a permanent war footing against any criticism of its products. It is continually building links with patient and consumer groups. Individuals and organisations are cultivated not simply to continue expanding the market, but also as a hedge against hard times. When legal actions are pending, when the wrong trial results are published, when patents are expiring and competition increases, these individuals and organisations are called upon to rally to the flag.

The late 1990s was a time of emerging crisis for the pharmaceutical industry, as the results began to appear of a series of studies that linked hormone replacement therapy to a variety of conditions. Between 2000 and 2004 (as described in the Introduction), two major studies and three smaller ones came to fruition or were halted. These studies demonstrated clearly that women who took HRT stood a greater chance of contracting breast cancer, heart disease and deep-vein thrombosis.[25]

In early 2003, US pharmacists were still filling in 45 million pre-scriptions for Premarin, and 22 million for Prempro, the same drug with a progestogen 'chaser'.[26] More than 100 million women worldwide, including 1.5 million in Britain, had taken HRT in 2001. Global sales amounted to $3.8 billion.

---

25 July 2002, Women's Health Initiative study. *New England Journal of Medicine,* 2003; 349:523-34. *The Lancet* 2003; 362:419-27.

26 Cowley G, Springen K. The end of the age of estrogen? *Newsweek,* 22 July 2002; 139 (4): 3841.

In the light of the new studies, despite prompt strategies, which the drug companies hoped would reassure consumers, Wyeth pharmaceutical stock fell from its highest at $58.48 in May 2002 to its lowest at $28.25 in July 2003,[27] as a reported 20 per cent of HRT prescriptions fell away.

Let a Thousand Strategies Blossom

Those who have greatest authority in contradicting negative medical research, in reassuring patients and in continuing market trends for medicines, are doctors and particularly consultants. While in most areas of medicine, the figure of the white-coated physician has been scratched from advertising, in relation to HRT this figure is ever present. Wyeth and other HRT manufacturers have attentively groomed a whole stable of them, which the British media are still wont to approach in a forelock-tugging manner to settle disputes about women's health.

With the gathering storm of study results at the end of the Nineties, all the HRT company men and a few women were brought out for public view. One of the essential defensive strategies for industries of all kinds is to quickly inter the body of critical history. It would, however, be a brave company that admitted that it had been making money from poisoning people, and, particularly in the business of harming people with pharmaceuticals, there is no reverse gear.

The effect of the cumulative new study results on Wyeth was predictable: from the company and their company-loyal acolytes in the medical and the 'communications' industry, we got more of the same. Diana Zuckerman suggested that the large number of articles critical of HRT in medical journals had little impact because 'without a PR machine behind them they received limited media attention'.[28] While this is true, we have to bear in mind, as well, that the company was, as all companies do, aggressively fighting back to obscure and bury any criticism.

---

27 Clark J. A hot flush for Big Pharma: how HRT studies have got drug firms rallying the troops. *Br Med J,* 2003; 327:400.

28 Zuckerman D. Hype in health reporting: "checkbook science" buys distortion of medical news. Extra! September/October 2002. www.fair.org/ *Fairness & Accuracy in Reporting.*

As well as being pressurised by the published results of one important study in 1997, the drug companies probably knew the forthcoming results of studies to be published at the turn of the century. Consequently, 1998 and 1999 became major years in public relations for these companies. From the beginning of 1998, everything was thrown into reassuring women and doctors that HRT did not really do any harm to anyone.

In the 12-month period ending in March 1999, drug companies in North America spent $1.53 billion on media advertisements aimed directly at consumers. Wyeth spent $31 million advertising Premarin on television alone. These figures do not include supportive articles about research papers or feature articles such as the one in the *Daily Telegraph* discussed below.[29] The overall pharmaceutical company budget for direct-to-consumer ads rose from $791 million in 1996 to $2.5 billion in 2000. The figures for overall marketing spending are astronomical. During 2000, more than $13.2 billion was spent on pharmaceutical marketing in the US alone.[30]

On all fronts, HRT was under serious assault, and if HRT was under attack, pharmaceutical companies were also under attack. Although the main thrust of the fight-back was organised by Wyeth and then some of the other companies that produced HRT, the whole industry geared up to defend itself. Wyeth's first recourse was to question study results, then to argue a positive position on HRT, if not as a defence against Alzheimer's, heart disease, cancer, and thrombosis, at least as the treatment for osteoporosis, and, of course, for its original purpose of combating any debilitating symptoms of the menopause. The only one of these symptoms that everyone agreed upon was 'hot flushes'. In the five years between 1999 and 2004, there was a clear danger that the market for HRT was about to diminish to a hot flash.

General arguments ran through Wyeth's fight-back. These were used immediately, to hold the fort before the heavy artillery could be rolled out. Wyeth rarely used the straightforward argument that research methodology was flawed. Knowing that it might have to justify a proper

29 *Daily Telegraph* of May 14 1998. Glowing Tribute to HRT 'magic'.
30 Burton B, Rowell A. Disease mongering. <www.prwatch.org>.

scrutiny of the research, and knowing that all the results had been peer reviewed, it restrained criticism of study results to superficial throwaway arguments.

One of the most focused lines of attack was to try and make clearer 'real risk'. PR companies and front organisations constantly repeated the argument, 'We have to get back to speaking in plain language, in actual numbers and not percentages.' To Wyeth it seemed sensible to change the message of the studies to 'X women in a 1,000', rather than leave it as an X per cent increased risk of breast cancer. While 'X women in every thousand' might sound like acceptable collateral damage, a percentage increase risk figure sometimes sounded like a holocaust.

The drug companies had learnt to deal with damaging statistics by 1997. That year, a paper published in *The Lancet* once again showed a high percentage increase in cases of breast cancer among women on HRT, and the pharmas made sure that, in their own propaganda at least, the percentage was converted to real numbers. In a half-page propaganda article published in the *Daily Telegraph* for the drug companies in May 1998,[31] percentages were played down, thus: 'among women of 50 taking HRT for ten years there would be six extra breast cancer cases (51 per 1,000).' Of course, to any right-thinking person, the fact that a pharmaceutical product could produce 51 cases of breast cancer in every one thousand users seems like a searing indictment of the manufacturer, but to the pharmaceutical companies and their loyal doctors, it could be shrugged off as a fair risk.

Other criticisms of studies were that they were not big enough, not long enough, or had used the wrong people or the wrong products. In 1998, the *Journal of the American Medical Association* reported the results of the HERS study involving 2,763 post-menopausal women with a mean age of 66.7 years, with a history of coronary disease.[32] The study showed conclusively that HRT gave no overall benefit to people with heart conditions. While both groups, HRT users and non HRT users, had

---

31 *Daily Telegraph* of May 14 1998. Glowing Tribute to HRT 'magic'.

32 Hulley S, Grady D, Bush T, Furberg C, Herrington D, Riggs B, Vittinghoff E; for the Heart and Estrogen/Progestin Replacement Study Research Group (HERS). Randomized trial of estrogen plus progestin for secondary prevention of coronary heart disease in post-menopausal women. *JAMA* 1998; 280:605-13.

the same incident outcome, in the first year of HRT use there was a higher but non-significant incident of heart attack. After five years of HRT, users began to have a slightly lower rate of coronary incident than those who did not take it.

Mr David Sturdee, consultant in obstetrics and gynaecology at Solihull hospital and a stalwart supporter of HRT, said that it was disappointing that the study follow-up had been only four years. Mr Sturdee mused that, had the follow-up been longer, researchers *might* have seen a trend towards *fewer* coronary incidents among those who remained alive in the study and who used HRT.[33]

An added problem for some drug companies, during the period of critical results between 1998 and 2004, was that they had new sex hormone products ready to launch on an unsuspecting public. These companies did not want their new products strangled at birth. In the climate, it seemed best to advertise new hormone products as if they had been designed just to meet new criteria raised by the critical studies. Of course, some of these drugs had been in development for over ten years.

In 1998, Eli Lilly gained a licence for the first of a new line of Selective Oestrogen Receptor Modulators (Serms), Raloxifene. This drug, according to the media, was 'a refined version of HRT' and 'a cousin of tamoxifen', which appeared, according to Eli Lilly and various HRT supporters, 'to combine the benefits of tamoxifen and HRT with none of their disadvantages'. The drug was claimed to have an oestrogen effect on some tissues but not on others.[34]

Maggie Tuttle's friend in the North, Professor David Purdie, suggested that the drug could be used by women in the long term after the menopause. The purpose of its prescription, he said, was to protect long-term health, to guard, for instance, against osteoporosis, an illness that the report claimed cost the NHS £1 billion a year. Professor Purdie had, in fact, been one of the investigators in the clinical trials for Raloxifene. All the same claims were made for this drug as were made previously for HRT. The drug was and still is sold as a prophylactic medicine, which, it

---

33 Unexpected HRT finding in women with coronary heart disease. *Pharm J*, 1998; 261:300.

34 Jeremy Laurence, 15 September 1998, the *Independent*, 'Doctors Hail New Drug for Women.'

is said, protects women against osteoporosis, cuts the risks of breast cancer and protects against heart disease. It was developed and marketed as a drug to be given *to all women* after the menopause.

In the middle of the fighting between the pro and anti trenches, in October 1998, speaking to reporters from the *Sunday Telegraph*, Malcolm Whitehead, that great contemporary visionary of HRT so keen to urge it on black women, seemed to lose the plot. According to journalists Victoria Macdonald and Simon Ferguson, who headed their article 'HRT problems are women's fault, says top doctor', Whitehead gave the injudicious opinion that:

> Fifty per cent of women who demand HRT from their doctors have heard about it in a conversation over the garden fence, from the television or relatives. Women do not think like men. Men do not rely on friends, next-door neighbours or relatives for medical advice or information; they go looking for the written word.

Coming from a man who makes a not-insubstantial income from treating women, one of the authors of the pulp paperback *The Amarant Book of Hormone Replacement Therapy*, and the person who has probably made more off-the-cuff remarks about HRT than anyone in Britain, this is an amazing statement. It is, though, the statement of a contemporary doctor: it implies that when ignorant people go to a doctor, the doctor usually gives them what they ask for. While this is, in fact, what the drug companies have tried to foster, it rarely works in practice, and most usually doctors remain in control of prescribing. It is doctors who prescribe with ignorance, not patients who ignorantly propose their own remedies.

According to Mr Whitehead, if you don't give women, on demand, the medicines they want and of which they have heard 'over the garden fence', 'they will go and loudly complain that you are an unsympathetic doctor'. These observations of Whitehead's signalled another very important general argument, which HRT-supporting physicians began to parrot increasingly during this period. Suddenly, it was women who had the right to decide their own medication, and consultants across the country were relinquishing their professional views and supporting a women's right to choose!

As the studies were publicised, Wyeth and other companies put into operation long-laid plans and called in their markers. Drug company sleepers came out of the woodwork and began banging the drum. The drug companies organised international consensus conferences. They made sure there was adequate funding for them, and they used their stalwarts to chair them. The two-day Consensus Conference on Hormone Replacement Therapy, for example, held in Edinburgh in October 2003 at the Royal College of Physicians and chaired by Professor David Purdie, was supported by the Society for Endocrinology and sponsored by Wyeth, Eli Lilly, Organon and Nova Nordisk.

Wyeth's media and PR companies also marshalled all the usual 'star' suspects to come forward and make clear statements in favour of women continuing to take HRT. Most of these statements were in contempt of science, logic and common sense. But, what the hell? If the PR companies could field for the media women who had taken HRT and even developed breast cancer but still argued that they thought it was a great product, it was hard to argue with their audacity.

In May 1998, Judy Finnigan came out as an HRT acolyte, sharing her very personal story with millions of viewers on the daytime TV *Richard and Judy* show, which she hosts with her husband, Richard Madeley. There were frequent pictures in all the newspapers of the major HRT disciples. Joan Collins, Kate O'Mara, Stephanie Beecham, Isla Blair (who?) and Fay Weldon, Jill Gascoine, Dr Miriam Stoppard and, of course, Teresa Gorman, all flashed their ageing, but apparently smooth skins, before the camera.

The *Daily Telegraph* article of May 1998, mentioned on page 315, served the drug companies' agenda absolutely.[35] Under the heading 'NEWS' on page 16, and accompanied by six-inch-high pictures of four long-term users of HRT, it unashamedly advertised HRT in all its different forms, with advice about how women could get it prescribed, and gave information on the conditions for which it was prescribed – as well as information about some for which it was not – together with an advert for the Amarant Trust.

There are a number of things to say about such ad-articles. Perhaps most importantly, it is against the law in England to advertise prescription drugs directly to consumers, and HRT is a prescription drug. Even if

---

35 *Daily Telegraph* of May 14 1998: Glowing Tribute to HRT 'magic'.

the law is not enforced and there is a tacit understanding that pharmaceutical companies can break it with impunity, any newspaper should make it an absolute requirement that such articles state clearly whether or not celebrities received money for endorsing products, and if so, how much.

It would be inappropriate to comment on the attitudes of the women involved unless one knew whether or not they were paid. But nothing exemplifies more clearly the insular, selfish and egocentric attitudes of celebrities in modern society, than these women who endorse HRT on the basis that it has been good for *them*, regardless of the dead and damaged.

Whatever the drug companies had planned, and despite their erecting their Siegfried Line late in the Nineties, when the study results came between 2002 and 2004, their message smashed over them like a tidal wave. Company-loyal physicians, paid media pundits and even the drug companies themselves were left clinging to the wreckage, waiting for the storm to pass.

Following the halted Women's Health Initiative study,[36] Wyeth made maximum use of its trusty consultants, who urged women not to abandon hormone replacement therapy. One of the arguments was that the study had used an HRT preparation different from the one prescribed to women in Britain.

The HRT used in the study was Wyeth's Prempro, manufactured by Wyeth and marketed as Premarin in North America. A similar combination of conjugated equine oestrogen and progestogen, Premique is, however, marketed by Wyeth in Britain and was being prescribed for around 330,000 British women at the time of the study. Malcolm Whitehead, although more reservedly, toed a similar line to that of the drugs company front helpline organisation, HRT Aware. 'This particular combination is not available here or in Europe, but similar ones are, and if you are having long-term treatment you should go to your doctor and talk about the risks and whether you should continue.'

---

36 Writing Group for the Women's Health Initiative Investigators. Risks and benefits of estrogen plus progestin in healthy postmenopausal women: principal results from the Women's Health Initiative randomized controlled trial. *JAMA,* 2002;288:321-33.

In 1986, Whitehead had joined up with Teresa Gorman MP, to set up the Amarant Trust.[37] Amarant was the bridgehead for Wyeth in marketing its HRT in Britain. In 1989, Gorman and Whitehead together produced *The Amarant Book of HRT*.[38] Following the critical trial results throughout 2000 to 2004, Gorman, and Whitehead, like British Communist Party members after the Hungarian uprising, continued to maintain a dogged and irrational loyalty to the HRT party line.

Teresa Gorman expressed the same rationalisations as Whitehead:

This is a study of a particular type of HRT administration – it wasn't all kinds of HRT. A five-year study is not a long study. It's absolute nonsense to scare women off this kind of treatment. My message to women is don't stop taking the tablets. There's massive evidence that the quality of life for women is much, much greater when they are accessing this treatment. It's something with a proven track record and that's what matters to me and that's what should matter to other women.[39]

Gorman says that she has taken HRT for 40 years [40] and speaks from the sincerely-held belief as to what the therapy has done for her. In a *Daily Telegraph* [41] interview in February 2004, she made good use of a copy line, which she had thought up herself or been given, and which was used to head the short interview: 'Why should women have to crumble and grumble into old age?' Gorman also put forward the pernicious view, which has been consistently touted by Wyeth and other advocates of HRT, that the menopause is actually the 'beginning of the end of women's lives'. She ended by suggesting that it would be monstrous if women were deprived of HRT.

In the *Telegraph* Gorman makes no mention of any scientific evidence about increased risk of cancer from HRT. In fact, she slips without faltering into the chemical industry line that 'breast cancer runs in families. It's genetically determined.' Of course she gives no references for per-

---

37 See next chapter.

38 See next chapter.

39 *Daily Telegraph*, 17 February 2004.

40 Some interviewers suggest twenty years.

41 *Daily Telegraph*, ibid.

centages before launching into a rebuke of the medical scientists who conducted studies of this kind: 'It's disgraceful *of the cancer people* to blame it on HRT, very irresponsible. They shouldn't put out scare stories.' [42]

While trying to minimise the importance of the findings, Whitehead, however, was more honest in telling *The Times* that even this 'relatively small risk' meant, over time, a large number of women getting breast cancer:

> Malcolm Whitehead, director of the Amarant Trust, which provides help and advice to menopausal women, said the extra risk of breast cancer was probably the same as that caused by being overweight, not having had children, or drinking too much alcohol. But the number of women who could get breast cancer because of HRT could be substantial over time, he said. 'If you had 30 million women taking treatments that's a lot of breast cancers.' [43]

Despite Whitehead's acknowledgement, in this quote, of the possible scale of HRT's carcinogenic effects, to hear him talk, it is all too easy to think that HRT is not a doctor-prescribed pharmaceutical product, but a natural self-chosen, life-style therapy.

Whitehead seems to sincerely believe that, if HRT is prescribed with correct information, it will be of undoubted benefit to everyone who uses it. In order to get round the ignorance of both men and women on this subject, he claimed in one interview to want to distribute dependable information at supermarket level. 'We have got to do things at the Sainsbury's checkout,' he said in an online BBC news interview,[44] which discussed a 'Mapping the Menopause' survey carried out by National Opinion Polls (NOP). This poll revealed that only 18 per cent of British women were taking HRT.[45] Although the news item told us that it was an NOP survey, it did not tell us who had funded it.

---

42 The *Daily Telegraph,* February 17, 2004. 'Time to replace HRT, says cancer expert'.

43 *The Times,* 10 July 2002. 'HRT is linked to breast cancer'.

44 Women match men in HRT ignorance. 5 July 1999. http://news.bbc.co.uk/1/hi/health/386819.stm.

45 One has got to be fairly sceptical about any such figures because there is a massive turnover of takers once individuals discover the adverse reactions. A figure of 18 per cent might, in reality, represent a large quota of women who never got through their first prescription.

Whitehead's public statements about HRT seem to conceal a not-quite-hidden message about sales. Writing in the *New Statesman*, he said that he had been approached by a number of female politicians asking about the use of testosterone implants, which they considered would make them more assertive and powerful. While, on the one hand, this is a silly and slightly amusing medical anecdote, which casts a new light on the intellectual credibility of Blair Babes – or were they Tories who made the enquiry? – it is also a straight advertisement for a new market, which Wyeth, for example, would love to open, providing hormone supplementation across the board and not just to pre- and post-menopausal women.

Whitehead is quick to reject any suggestion that HRT can lead to adverse reactions. In 1998, when women from the MHL started a civil action, the press approached him for a response. In an interview with BBC online news, he made light of all the cited side effects.[46] He said: 'I see women, perhaps two a month, who come to me complaining of hair loss who have never taken HRT. Indeed, they are asking me to give them HRT to try to make their hair better.' He added: 'I do not know of any evidence that oestrogens impair the ability to walk (a reference to dizziness produced by oestrogen overdose), otherwise girls going through puberty would suddenly start falling sideways.'

These comments are reprehensibly 'amusing' and provide a relatively good impression of the gravity with which consultant physicians countenance the complaints of women adversely affected by HRT. What is surprising, and what gives rise to serious questions about Whitehead's conflicting interests, is that the information sheets that accompany HRT make reference to these very side effects.

While it is to be expected that consultants would defend treatments in which they deal and which provide the basis for their life's work, it is more difficult to divine the motives of Teresa Gorman. In the 1990s, while Gorman was a Member of Parliament, she worked for Business Planning and Research International (BPRI);[47] she was, she says, a member of its 'political opinion panel'. Which, in lay language, means that she might,

---

46 September 14, 1998. Published at 20:49 GMT 21:49 UK.

47 Declared in list of members interests.

with others, have been consulted and paid for opinions about the political climate or situation, with regard to certain products.

If a product went through a particularly critical period, Gorman might be asked by BPRI what she thought the approach of government or regulatory agencies might be. On a number of occasions, Gorman asked questions in the House about the Amarant clinics, their advocacy of HRT and their availability to menopausal women. In North America this is recognised for what it is and called lobbying. In Britain, it does not have a separate name and is accepted as an integral part of being an MP.

In all probability, Teresa Gorman knew nothing about the wider connections and interests of BPRI, or the full story about why the company might be approaching MPs to give their opinions or intelligence on HRT or products.

BPRI is the name of the British division of the WPP Group, probably the biggest Advertising, PR and Public Affairs organisation in the world. WPP has under its wing Hill and Knowlton, The Ogilvy Group and Alexander Communications. Hill and Knowlton is one of the biggest PR companies for the pharmaceutical industry.

Other companies in the WPP Group, which deal almost exclusively with pharmaceutical companies, and which have a presence in London, are Healthworld and Shire Health London. Healthworld is itself a small group of companies, all of which work on behalf of pharmaceutical companies. Shire Health Group also has other agencies affiliated with it, including 4D Communications, a 'medical education agency' established in 1996.

Both Healthworld and Shire Health represent Wyeth and its associated companies. Healthworld represents Wyeth Pharmaceuticals, together with Bayer, Bristol Myers Squibb, GlaxoSmithKline, Novartis, Pfizer, Roche and Schering. Shire Health represents Wyeth-Ayerst along with 21 other pharmaceutical companies.[48]

Healthworld Communications incorporates the Global Business Group, which, as well as representing various pharmaceutical compa-

---

48   These include: Abbott Laboratories, AstraZeneca, Bristol-Myers Squibb, Glaxo-SmithKline, Janssen-Cilag, Johnson & Johnson, Merck Sharp & Dohme, Novartis, Novo Nordisk, Pfizer, Roche and Schering-Plough.

nies, runs two operations called Medical Education Europe (MEE) and Medical Education America (MEA). MEA 'provides a broad range of services from early stage strategic planning to developing and implementing comprehensive medical education and communications throughout the life cycle of the brand'. The service provided by Global Business Group through MEE includes 'opinion leader development and advisory board meetings'.

Healthworld has implemented thousands of 'physician peer-to-peer influence groups', and has wide-ranging experience in advocacy development and speaker training programmes.

In July 2002, Malcolm Whitehead and John C. Stevenson[49] jointly authored an editorial in the *BMJ*,[50] which reflected on the findings of the WHI trial.[51] They concluded, as they would, that the risk in taking HRT was not that great, and that women already taking it should continue to do so. This simple message, however, was becoming more sophisticated. Unable to uphold the idea that everything had always been all right in the past, company-loyal consultants took to preaching a kind of individualist medicine. Now and in the future, HRT in the UK should be prescribed, Stevenson and Whitehead wrote, only on an individual basis to suit individual women. This was assuredly a good 'line', which, although it promised something wonderful that HRT could not deliver, separated the 'consultants to the stars' from the inner-city physician forced to continue his or her tawdry, inexact and often damaging prescriptions to ordinary women.

In December 2003, the UK Committee on the Safety of Medicines made a pronouncement that women over 50 should not take HRT and should look for alternative treatments to prevent osteoporosis, because of

---

49 Dr John Stevenson, Reader in Endocrinology and Metabolic Medicine, Faculty of Medicine, Imperial College, London.

50 The declaration of conflicting interests at the end of the editorial is ambiguous and to a degree disingenuous. It states that both authors 'have attended meetings on lectures on HRT, sometimes with the support of various pharmaceutical companies'. It fails to make clear that they are both raving advocates of HRT and have consistently been involved in projects over the past decade that have received large amounts in funding from HRT manufacturers.

51 Stevenson JC, Whitehead MI. Hormone replacement therapy. *Br Med J*, 2002;325:113-4.

the possibility of breast cancer with long-term use. Professor David Purdie resigned from the European Advisory Committee on Hormone Replacement after this pronouncement.[52]

Professor Purdie, a canny Scot, had clearly been briefed from the same source as Malcolm Whitehead. His response to the abandoning of the WHI study and other statistical studies, in a *Guardian* article in 2004, shows him to be at the forefront of post-modern medical thinking.[53] He told Tania Branigan, who was trying her liberal best to tease out a balanced view on HRT: 'Women are individuals, not statistics, and the day we treat patients as numbers is the death of medicine as I understand it.' Funny, isn't it, how even the most committed allopaths can suddenly go all New Age on you?

In October 2004, the Executive Committee of the International Menopause Society issued a revised statement.[54] The writing group of three included Mr D.W. Sturdee – David Sturdee, that is, another *generalísimo* of HRT promotion, introduced above. The Society showed itself to be completely unmoved by recent research results. Before going on to state all the usual safeguards and advice to doctors about regular testing etc., the first two major guidelines proposed:

> The Executive Committee recommends the continuation of presently accepted global practice, including the use of oestrogen + progestin, or oestrogen alone in the case of women who have undergone hysterectomy, for the relief of menopausal and urinogenital symptoms, avoidance of bone wasting and fractures and atrophy of connective tissue and epithelia. *Possible clinical benefits in the prevention of cardiovascular disease and nervous system protection seem likely but have yet to be confirmed.* (author's italics).

> There are no new reasons to place mandatory limitations on the length of treatment, including arbitrary cessation of HRT in women who started replacement during the menopausal transition and remain symptom free while on hormones … such cessation may even be harmful.

---

52 Professor Purdie, with Margaret Rees, is the author of *Management of the Menopause*. The Handbook of the British Menopause Society. Marlow, Bucks: British Menopause Society; 2002. ISBN 0-9536228-1-9.

53 Life Change, Tania Branigan. Feb 17 2004, the *Guardian*.

54 Guidelines for hormone treatment of women in the menopausal transition and beyond. Position Statement by the Executive Committee of the International Menopause Society, Revised October 15 2004.

Whatever the drug-producing companies might say to placate licensing authorities, whatever fellow clinicians were beginning to say, whatever women's fears, and even despite the continuing scientific studies that were now raining down, the new position of those physicians locked into the marketing of HRT was, no new position – business as usual.

The problem with a new position that made concessions to limiting the prescription of HRT was that it was bound to fly in the face of both primary and secondary uses of the drug. Up until the post-2000 studies, company-loyal physicians had been able to say that HRT was a lifetime treatment after menopause for osteoporosis. The question of short-term use of HRT, which the studies raised, seriously flawed the prescribing patterns not only for osteoporosis, which gets worse very quickly if HRT is stopped, but for all menopausal problems, for as soon as women stop taking the treatment, they are again susceptible to the vicissitudes of fluctuating oestrogen levels.[55]

One strand of Wyeth's general damage limitation strategy was to muddy the water and to suggest that everyone was confused by the study results. In reality, of course, the study results of both the big US and UK studies could have been grasped by a five-year-old. This was shown to be the case when an FDA spokesperson, echoing study results, commented, 'Prempro does significantly more harm than good when taken for long periods.' [56]

The 'confusion' strategy was a good one. Like dripping water it would, if repeated enough, wear away the immutable quality of the research results. In February 2004, while the argument was still ongoing about the falling away of women patients on HRT, anyone who fed the words 'confused' and 'HRT' into Google would have come up with two pages of articles about HRT and the confusion that now apparently surrounded it.

People were 'confused by' HRT, 'confused over' HRT, they were 'still confused', 'confused about' around six times, 'confused at' HRT and

---

55 It has always been said by 'the experts' that women who want to use HRT as a prophylactic have to do so for long periods of time, and that stopping the treatment can actually reverse any gains made over short periods.

56 *The End of the Age of Estrogen*, op.cit.

'confused with' HRT. Not only were patients 'confused', but 'experts were also confused', even 'HRT was confused' … It was mainly 'women' who 'were confused' and some were even 'confused and afraid'. Almost everyone could, however, be forgiven for 'being confused'. On two web pages there were around 25 instances of the use of the word 'confused', in relation to the crystal-clear data produced by the scientific studies.

Chapter Eight

A Vanishing History and Disposable Science

IV Distribution: The Lower Depths

I can recognise a fact
Ross Macdonald[1]

In some quarters breast cancer is seen as just another fault in a female machine which cannot quite tune in to sophisticated twentieth century life.

Dr Cathy Read[2]

The numbers of physicians, women's health advisers and organisations that Wyeth was able to mobilise once the HRT hit the fan was truly impressive. The torrent of emotionally-committed support for this wonder elixir was testimony to years of in-placing and embedding work with activists, physicians, drug company agents, politicians, news producers and charities.

---

1 MacDonald R. *The Ivory Grin.* Glasgow: Fontana; 1973.

2 Read C. *Preventing Breast Cancer: The politics of an epidemic.* New York: HarperCollins; 1995.

The response of the involved drug companies to the immediate crisis between 2000 and 2004, was, however, only a small part of their overall strategy, which they had been implementing for the past decade. At the heart of this strategy was the medicalisation of the menopause. The industry, with its agent physicians was intent on turning the menopause into a health watershed in the lives of women.

With the menopause, the pharmaceutical companies suggested, women's health declines, and from this period onwards all women became prey to a series of illnesses, which it was best to begin treating. In fact, although there are obviously a range of illnesses associated with growing older, there are only discomforts associated specifically with the menopause in healthy women, many of whom sail through it without distress.

Persuade women that this was not the case, and you could generate one of the most lucrative global markets in pharmaceuticals. There is no other life event that affects whole populations in the way in which the pharmas suggest that the menopause affects women. In representing the menopause as the first of a whole collection of illnesses that were bound to affect women in the last third of their lives, they were opening a cash flow worth trillions of pounds. If, that is, women would fall for the story that they would be permanently ill, unattractive and sexually redundant from their mid-forties onwards, and that HRT could save them from all this.

The previous chapter described how the opinions of consultants loyal to pharmaceutical companies have shaped the cultural acceptance of HRT and have argued within the medical profession against the findings of studies. The corporate message, however, doesn't get out effectively into the public domain until it has been filtered along the many arterial courses that pass through voluntary organisations and charities.

In Britain, Wyeth has, like other pharmaceutical companies, extensive involvement in a number of charities that promote its products and advertise them to their customers and members, who are often patients. In the field of menopause, which Wyeth in particular has misrepresented as an illness demanding medication, the company has financial connections to the British Menopause Society (and menopause societies globally), the Amarant (Menopause) Trust, Women's Health Concern, and the industry-funded front organisation HRT Aware. It plays a part in the National Society for Osteoporosis, and helps to fund research through a number of universities in this area.[3]

Unlike the traditional PR company, the new organisations that deal with pharmaceutical meltdown are like complex intelligence organisations, spreading insidiously into different aspects of industry and everyday life. On a practical level, these groups deal with products throughout their whole life-cycle. On a conceptual level, the companies do not simply market products, but build markets by involving putative consumers in publicising those products.

These organisations are usually fire brigades *par excellence*, able to race their engine round the tightest corner and to travel in nano- seconds over vast distances. The science associated with pharmaceutical products is of no interest to them; they are interested only in manipulating patients' understanding of themselves and the drugs, shaping public belief and resurrecting sales.

> At any stage of your product's life cycle, we can help you <u>manage the clinical evidence and physician opinion to align with your product strategic plan</u>. We are the leaders in translating deep understanding into clear messages that <u>generate acceptance and advocacy</u>.[4]

Translated roughly into English, the first underlined portion of this message says: we will make sure that, whatever the publicised clinical evidence, we will promote acceptance of your product. 'Your product strategic plan' simply means 'Make a PROFIT.' Whatever the clinical evidence is, whatever the study results say, Healthworld, in this case, will ensure that all the public hears is what the producing company is saying.

At the end of a phone, fax or e-mail, these PR or communications companies can, at the drop of a hat, bring into public display a small army of scientists, doctors, ex-patients and journalists, who will say whatever

---

3 A long-term partner of the Meningitis Trust, Wyeth Vaccines recently donated £10,000 towards the Trust's information materials and support services. It also co-sponsored the Trust's Early Years Information Guide – an informative publication aimed at childcare professionals such as nursery nurses, playgroup managers and crèche assistants. (From the website of the Meningitis Trust.)

4 Susan Byrne, executive vice president & managing director, Medical Education Europe, part of Healthworld Communications Group, which services Wyeth Pharmaceuticals.

the drug manufacturer needs them to say. Television personalities, who deal in unreality all their professional lives, are good subjects – doctors less so, because they are often too flat and earnest. They are, thus, usually reserved to put across their message in more academic arenas.

It was through its PR advertising and communications companies, and through donations, that Wyeth began in the early Eighties to gain its foothold within organisations that spoke on behalf of women with menopausal problems, and played a part in setting up new organisations. By 1998, it and other HRT-producers had influence within, or had played some part in setting up, in varying degrees, the Amarant Trust, HRT Aware, Women's Health Concern and the British Menopause Society, together with a series of fly-by-night organisations which came and went as PR phantoms.

Wyeth gained its influence within organisations by time-honoured methods of infiltration and persuasion, by funding individuals, practices and groups, by fielding its agents to sit on boards, by funding conferences and seminars and by influencing politicians and civil servants.

Throughout the late Eighties and the early Nineties, the drug companies began to take over the medical charities by, first, changing their genre and imposing on them the name of *medical research* charities.[5] They embarked on this course for a number of reasons. For a start, they did not like the proliferation of lay groups. Whether they were collections of young people who were affected by asthma, or of the relatives of elderly people who had banded together over Alzheimer's disease, such campaigning groups would, if not subverted, become loose cannons.

Second, the pharmaceutical companies wanted control over and access to the membership of campaigning groups in order to use them in trials. The third reason is more difficult to explain: the pharmaceutical companies wanted only *their* kind of research to be carried out into illnesses for which they wanted to market cures. The last thing they wanted was for lay groups to discuss alternative and complementary medicine with those who suffered from illness; they needed to be in control of the paradigm, and patients always make up the greatest part of the paradigm.

---

5 For an account of this process in the early Nineties, see Walker, M.J., *Dirty Medicine: Science, big business and the assault on natural health care*, op. cit.

The fourth reason, the simplest, is that they wanted to sell drugs, and patients who present themselves at campaign-group meetings are both ready guinea pigs and ultimately good buyers. The fifth reason is, however, by far the most important: by controlling the medical charities, by putting in place doctors who are pharmaceutical-company-loyal, they can depend upon these organisations to defend their products. In emergencies, all kinds of voluntary patient groups come to the aid of Big Pharma.

Their critical faculty was, after all, one of the most important aspects of campaigning patient groups for any number of illnesses. It was these groups that, from the late Sixties onward, investigated doctors, that exposed iatrogenic crimes and that looked to alternatives. Between 1970 and the present, all of this critical acuity was swept away.

The Amarant Trust

In England, Teresa Gorman, whose wisdom we had a taste of in the preceding chapter, remains one of the most energetic advocates of hormone replacement therapy. Gorman was, from 1987 until 2001, the Conservative MP for Billericay in Essex.[6] As I write, she is 74 years old,[7] and her devotion to HRT is undiminished. A right-wing libertarian, she has a long history with the Institute of Economic Affairs and, at the time she retired from the House of Commons, she was Director of the Freedom Association.[8] On her retirement from the Commons, she suggested that she might like to travel to North America and set up businesses there.

---

6 Conservative MP Teresa Gorman was born in London in 1931. She was affiliated to the Institute of Economic Affairs, the Adam Smith Institute and the Centre for Political Studies. Mrs Gorman stood as Conservative Parliamentary candidate at Lambeth and Streatham. From 1982 to 1986 she was a member of Westminster City Council under Dame Shirley Porter, serving as a Whip and on several committees including Housing (Vice-Chairman), Social Services, General Purpose and Grants. From 1983 until 1988, she was a member of the Conservatives Women's National Council. In 1987 she was elected MP for Billericay, Essex, and the often-outspoken MP also gave her backing to incinerators in the county, despite strong public opinion against their introduction.

7 Teresa added ten years onto her age so that she could qualify to be selected as an MP in 1997.

8 The organisation began as the National Association for Freedom and was the apparently grass roots organisation which drummed the right-wing popular vote for Thatcher *(cont.)*

In 1986, a year before she became an MP, Teresa Gorman established The Amarant Trust with Malcolm Whitehead, whom you will remember, also, from Chapter Seven, for his witty and insightful remarks about women. In a way that is not altogether clear, the Amarant Trust was actually set up 'in association' with King's College Hospital. The department of women´s health at the hospital receives funding from, among others, Wyeth Pharmaceuticals.

The intention of the Trust was to set up clinics to provide HRT and to promote research into human ageing. Although the Trust was accepted for registration as a charity – odd in itself, given that it intended to advertise and to administer prescription drugs – it floundered until June 1989, when the *Amarant Book of Hormone Replacement Therapy* was published.

Between 1996 and 1998, much of the work of the charity was done by the staff of Teresa Gorman's company, Biological and Nursing Teaching Aids (BANTA), which she had set up after studying business techniques in North America. During 1989, the charity's funds went from a deficit of £13,000 for the previous year, to a surplus of £30,000. In the same year, the Amarant Trust received a declared donation of £5,550 from Wyeth, the major producer of HRT.

Teresa Gorman says in the Amarant book that she came to HRT after suffering 'devastating' effects of menopause in the early Eighties. She attended Dr Whitehead's clinic at King's College Hospital and became a committed supporter of HRT. When Gorman became an MP, she took every opportunity to promote the string of HRT-prescribing clinics across the country. Dr Whitehead went on, during Teresa Gorman's term as an MP, to become an adviser to the Department of Health on HRT.

The Trust, which provided a number of private clinics and on-line and telephone advice to women, advocated the prescription of HRT from the beginning. Gorman suggested that the chain of non-profit-making centres would offer a 'listening ear' to anyone who wanted advice about starting HRT.[9]

---

8 (*cont.*) as leader of the Conservative Party in the mid-Seventies. The organisation, while claiming to fight for the interests of small businesses, is, of course, backed by multinational corporations.

9 *Southend Echo*, 17 August 1998.

Also from the beginning, the Amarant Trust received its approval from the Charity Commission, and this was not withdrawn, even when it was partly funded by Wyeth. In a strange – some might say amazing – juxtaposition, the Amarant Trust has also been given money by the government. In 1990-1991 it received £13,400; in 1992-93, £9,000;[10] in 1995, 1996, 1997, 1998 and 1999, £10,000.[11] Why would the British Government want to help to finance a drug-company initiative, giving taxpayers' money to a company that had already sold its drugs to the NHS?

The Amarant Menopause Trust itself is advised by a small number of doctors who prescribe HRT. Despite the Trust being a charity, it is not possible to access sections of its website without a password, which has to be requested by e-mail – this is a strangely difficult, sometimes impossible task. It makes no declarations, on the open part of its website, about funding or the vested interests of its personnel. In fact, the Amarant Trust has, from the outset, been funded by HRT-producing pharmaceutical companies. The Trust is never short of people to speak on behalf of HRT, including its directors and consultants.

At the time this book was written, Sue Stoessl was the director of the Trust. Previously head of marketing at Channel 4, she has acted as a marketing consultant to TVAM, Yorkshire TV, Associated Newspapers, News International and the British Film Institute. Stoessl holds shares in Granada: Compass, part of the Compass Group, providing food and related services to clients including business and industry, healthcare, education, travel, sports and leisure. In 2003, the company had £8.3 billion of sales globally. In 2002, Stoessl was appointed to the Radioactive Waste Management Advisory Committee, a quango.

Dr. Val Godfree, BSc MRCOG MFFP, is the deputy director of the Trust. A gynaecologist, she is often approached for comment by the media when there is any conflict over HRT. Malcolm Whitehead is director of the Menopause Clinic at King's College Hospital, a senior lecturer in the Department of Women's Health at Guy's, King's College and St Thomas' (GKT) teaching hospitals and an NHS consultant who has his

---

10 Grants to voluntary organisations under S64 of the Health Services and Public Health Act 1968 – General Scheme. 1990-1991 and 1992-93.

11 From Charity Commission records of the Amarant Trust.

own Harley Street practice in HRT. Dr Whitehead also works from a private clinic at The Portland Hospital in Great Portland Street.

Whitehead and Godfree are involved in occasional, small-scale research, which never questions the basic assumptions about HRT. In 1998 they authored a paper which compared skin irritation with two transdermal oestradiol patches.[12] The study 'suggested that the cream does not boost the level of a woman's progesterone to an extent that would be considered protective'. In 1998, Whitehead gave a radio interview in which he talked about another cream preparation, which dispensed HRT.

Whitehead was introduced by the host, Norman Swan, as a man who had 'spent 20 years principally looking at disease within the womb lining – eight years at the Imperial Cancer Research Fund Laboratories here in London just studying the endometrium'. Whitehead was at pains to point out that the 'natural' cream that he and Godfree had looked at was not actually made from a vegetable or herbs or that kind of natural substance. Particularly, Dr Whitehead was careful to differentiate the 'natural' progesterone cream at which they had looked from the increasingly popular wild yam cream.

Malcolm Whitehead: We have done nothing with wild yam cream at all. The study that we did was looking at a cream called Progest, which is natural progesterone cream, which is manufactured by a company ...

Having committed himself to the word 'natural', Whitehead found himself fighting for an explanation. He might have spent years studying the endometrium, but when it came to explaining 'natural progesterone', he suddenly became scientifically challenged:

Norman Swan: And where does this natural progesterone come from in this cream, how is it made?

Malcolm Whitehead: I don't have information to that. I mean, it's called 'natural' progesterone, I presume, because the end product is identical to the progesterone produced either by the adrenal or by the ovary in the

---

12 Ross D, Rees M, Godfree V, Cooper A, Hart D, Kingsland C. Randomised crossover comparison of skin irritation with two transdermal oestradiol patches. *Br Med J,* 1997; 315:288.

body, but there must be some sort of laboratory-based synthetic process involved. So it's not purely natural, if you're going to be, I think, strictly correct.

Er, yes, doctor. Hmm, no, not strictly, er, 'purely natural', I think, at all.

A History of Misinformation

During the Cold War, the British Foreign Office worked with the Special Intelligence Services, through a department set up solely for propaganda purposes, called the Information Research Department (IRD). The IRD covertly published a large number of books through reputable publishing houses. These books, written by people who had been approached by the security services or by civil servants themselves, gave apparently liberal perspectives on various international situations, foreign crises and, of course, communism.

The IRD prepared various articles for newspapers and it joined with the CIA in the issue of thousands of journals and magazines, which went on news stands in most of Europe's larger cities. The CIA itself had an office covering the second floor of a building in Oxford Street, where various journals and newsletters were churned out. The fact that the British Government was doing exactly what it was accusing the communist states of doing doesn't seem to have occurred to Whitehall as something at all lamentable.

No other corporate organisation has taken on the mantle of the intelligence services, both in relation to covert publishing and infiltration of activist or grass roots groups, with as much alacrity as pharmaceutical companies.

In both Britain and North America, books have played a considerable role in the marketing of HRT.[13] In 1973, Sondra Gorney, a New York public relations woman, wrote *After Forty* with Claire Cox.[14] Gorney also

---

13 Among the excellent chapters in Barbara Seaman's latest book, there is a chapter on Dr Robert Benjamin Greenblatt, a major advocate of hormone supplementation. Seaman goes into his attitudes and working life in detail.

14 Gorney S, Cox C. *After Forty*. New York: Dial Press; 1973.

set up The Information Centre on the Mature Woman, a front for HRT advertising.

In Britain, Wendy Cooper's book *No Change: A Biological Revolution for Women* was published in 1975. The book undoubtedly played a significant part in pushing up the sales figures for HRT between 1972, when the prescriptions for HRT were 500,000, and 1976, when they reached 1,300,000.[15]

In the years of 1998 and 1999, as Wyeth was preparing to face the results of critical studies, Cooper, by then aged 78, was still being hauled out to promote HRT. In 1998 she was working on the ninth update of her book[16] – and had been on HRT for 25 years.

Besides writing their own books, both Sondra Gorney and Wendy Cooper promoted *Feminine Forever*, the book written by Robert Wilson in 1966. This book, which prised open a massive new market for Wyeth-Ayerst's oestrogen therapy Premarin, crudely set about undermining the security of middle-aged women and eliciting the help of their male partners in getting them hooked on Premarin. It played on women's guilt about the family, fears of the possible onset of illness in old age, and insecurity over being left by their partners as they 'came down with' the menopause.

Wilson's message was about something which no modern woman could live without, something that could save women from the lingering hell of constant and painful decay and rescue their partners from living with mad harridans who would inevitably deny them sexual relations. This book about women, written by a man, sent millions of women flocking to their doctors, urged on by their male partners, to sign up for HRT.

Wilson did not confine his cynical and misogynist views to the book; he wrote articles, he went on lecture tours, he appeared on television and the radio, while writing more academic papers for journals. In an article published in 1972, he gave a summary description of what women – and their men – might look forward to after menopause if they took HRT:

15 Coney S. *The Menopause Industry: How the medical establishment exploits women.* Alameda, CA: Hunter House; 1994.

16 *Sunday Telegraph*, 20 September 1998.

'Breasts and genital organs will not shrivel. Such women will be more pleasant to live with and not become dull and unattractive.'

Wyeth-Ayerst used the publication of *Feminine Forever* to aggressively market Premarin, playing on the same insecurities and misogyny. One ad that appeared in the early 1970s read: 'Almost any tranquilliser might calm her down, but oestrogen is what she really needs.' [17]

No one in North American society, however, commented on the fact that HRT could well be a metaphor for the culture produced by capitalism. Like no other pharmaceutical ever manufactured, HRT held out the grail of post-industrial capitalism. We were all going to live a life of leisure in a world constructed of mechanical aids, the physical luxuries of sensuality and sex would be available for all the everlasting years of our life, and the crudely physical would be eschewed, replaced by an ethereal romance. For rich women, HRT represented, or so they thought, a birthright; for the poor and the working-class woman it represented a shortcut to beauty everlasting, despite economic, domestic and environmental oppressions.

Nine years after the book's publication, in 1975, the first studies that warned of endometrial cancer in women taking unopposed oestrogen therapy (ie., oestrogen alone, not combined with progestogen) were published in the *New England Journal of Medicine*. According to the studies, five years' use of oestrogen replacement therapy increased the chances of endometrial cancer by six times; in the longer term the chances went up to fifteen times.

Faced with the indisputable evidence, Wilson's peers and the FDA called Wilson's research into oestrogen replacement therapy 'flawed and invalid'. The FDA made Wilson himself persona non grata by defining him as an 'unacceptable investigator'. Wyeth quickly came up with a conjugated oestrogen – containing progesterone – which it began marketing as a safe HRT. Implicit in this is the admission that the company had been selling an unsafe product – one which Wilson's writings had so shamelessly endorsed. No action was taken against the publishers of

---

17 Oats C. Premarin®: straight from the horse's what? <ww.wintdusa.com.>. (A good article with a great title).

Feminine Forever for making false claims, however, and the book continued to circulate.[18]

In 2002, after the WHI study had shown that HRT heightened the risk of breast cancer, Ronald Wilson, Robert's son, disclosed his father's financial relationship with Wyeth. Not only had Wyeth-Ayerst paid Wilson to write the book, but it had also funded his lecture tours, his plush offices in New York, the research institute that he had set up, and all his research. Despite these revelations, *still* no action was taken against either Wyeth-Ayerst or the publishers of *Feminine Forever* for quackery or for making false claims.

The Wilson Research Foundation had actually been funded by a whole clutch of drugs companies, including Searle, Ayerst and Upjohn. He promoted different oestrogen therapies, regardless of whether or not he believed in using them in his own clinical practice.[19]

While both the FDA in North America and the MCA in England have been keen to tackle claim-making literature that accompanies alternative therapies, nothing was done about the publication of Wilson's book. Consequently, the covert production of books that advertise and sell prescription medicines, the use of brand names in novels and the making of films specifically around brand-name products is a strategic ploy, which the pharmaceutical companies have continued to develop.[20]

The Amarant Book of Hormone Replacement Therapy

The first British issue of *The Amarant Book of Hormone Replacement Therapy* did not have the names of the authors on the cover, and the first data pages of the book do everything to obscure the nature of authorship.

---

18 A second-hand copy of the book today can cost up to $50.

19 Cited in *Women and the Crisis in Sex Hormones* from an article by Mintz M. The Pill: an alarming report. Greenwich, CT: Fawcett; 1969.

20 The production of books, films and videos, some meant for professionals, some sold to television, and some meant to accompany medication to patients, all of which can find their way into the hands of consumers, is now common practice. In *Secrets of the Drugs Industry*, Bryan Hubbard cites the production and distribution of a book that accompanied the *(cont.)*

While Teresa Gorman and Malcolm Whitehead are named on the title page, and while there is a full-page paragraph biography of them both, the book's acknowledgements state, 'The authors are greatly indebted to Audrey Slaughter, journalist and author, who worked so hard to compile the main structure of this book.' Teresa Gorman signed the introduction. The copyright to the book is held by the Amarant Trust, so neither party need claim personal responsibility for it.

When I first saw a copy of *The Amarant Book of Hormone Replacement Therapy*, I reached for the dictionary to look up the definition of 'book'. The Oxford English Dictionary generously allows a book to consist simply of written pages between covers. Frustratingly, on this basis, I cannot honestly suggest that *The Amarant Book of Hormone Replacement Therapy* is not a book. However, as well as being a book, it is something that other books are not – directed at specific health concerned consumers.

Such advertising has been illegal in England for many years, especially since the 1968 Medicines Act and the later 1994 consolidation of European legislation on the advertising of prescription medicines. Regrettably, despite their constant vigilance over health food products, the advertisement and sale of alternative therapies and remedies and associated literature, neither the Medicines Control Agency (now the MHRA), nor any other regulatory body has bothered to prosecute the book's publishers or authors. Perhaps there is still time. After all, the very existence of the book implicates its authors and publishers in a crime.

The book was first published in 1989 in Britain by Pan, and in the United States by Transatlantic Publications Inc.[21] The whole of the front cover of the first Pan edition of *The Amarant Book of Hormone*

---

20 (*cont.*) trials of Rapamune, a Wyeth immunosuppressant. Hubbard B. *Secrets of the Drugs Industry*. London: What Doctors Don't Tell You; 2002. See Walker M.J. *Dirty Medicine* for details about the production of videos and educational material about AZT, op. cit.

21 Transatlantic publishers do not have a website and I found out nothing about them from Internet research except that they have a sister company, Coronet Publications Inc., at the same address in California. Coronet distributes academic books from a small number of University academic departments and the London-based Institute of Economic Affairs. The IEA is a free market organisation for which Teresa Gorman has often written. The IEA promotes free-market policies in health, and for pharmaceutical companies.

Replacement Therapy is taken up with an unattributed quote: 'HRT is the greatest treasure of a middle-aged woman´s life. I've reached fifty but feel twenty.' Beneath is the apparent title of the book, *The Amarant Book of Hormone Replacement Therapy*. It is difficult to think of a slogan or phrase that did not more completely break the law under the Medicines Act than this one.

The back cover of the book breaks the law perhaps even more blatantly than the front, when it uses the word 'safe' without any qualification, telling prospective buyers, 'Until recently it's been controversial, but now the majority of medical opinion has accepted that HRT is not only highly effective, it is also *safe*.' The blurb further states unequivocally that HRT 'protects against heart attack, strokes, brittle bones and fractures as well as improving memory and concentration'.

Although the Amarant book on HRT does not deal with the numerous studies that had, even at the time of its publication, reported the carcinogenic qualities of HRT, it does have good news for any women who might have contracted endometrial cancer after using the treatment. The cancers caused by oestrogen are, the book maintains, 'less invasive, and therefore less dangerous, than those which develop naturally', a proposition often repeated in defence of oestrogen.[22]

Ever since I began writing this book, I have been conscious of the fact that it is women who are being exploited by the HRT experts and the drug companies. Occasionally, this has made me feel despondent, almost as if I was faced each day with having to reflect on my situation as a man before I write anything. *The Amarant Book of Hormone Replacement Therapy*, however, gives me the opportunity to wade into the fray as a man. The most disgusting three pages in the book, which make up Chapter 12, are an exhortation addressed to a man, presumably by another man, asking, 'What are you going to do about your partner?'

This exhortation takes the male reader (were there any?) on an emotional rollercoaster ride, as it explores the apparently traditional male approach to 'his partner' as she goes through the menopause. The interlocutor in these pages is something else. While the writer was clearly no Shakespeare, his alter ego might have been crudely modelled on Iago,

22 Coney S, op. cit.

pouring poison into the ear of the husband/reader, who finds himself cast as Othello. For some reason best known to the drug company employee who crafted this pernicious text, the insistent interior mono-logue never once urges the simple expedient of talking to his partner.

> Can't be anything medically wrong with her. You made her see the doctor not long ago and he said there was nothing really the matter. Perhaps she needs a holiday ...

> Perhaps there's someone else? She certainly seems to toss and turn a lot at night, perhaps she has a guilty conscience. Wakes you up sometimes too. Doesn't she realise that you *need* your sleep?

Personally, I feel that this guy has problems that will not simply be solved by medicating his partner. However, this is the solution put forward by the book. With HRT, it says:

> Not only will she return to 'normal' very shortly, but the treatment will also protect against bone loss. Once she is taking oestrogen regularly there is a reduced likelihood of your wife risking the fractures that bedevil many women after their fifties, some of them proving fatal. Nor will she be quite so liable to heart attacks and strokes. When the benefits are so great, and the drawbacks so small [*these drawbacks are not actually mentioned in the book*] there seems little point in hesitating, does there? And it may save your marriage.

Is it possible to put this book down to a reasonable, if crude, attempt by a doctor and an MP to proselytise on behalf of something which they believe constitutes a real health benefit for women? It might be, if it were not for the publishers. Two years before the publication of the book, Pan had been bought up by Macmillan, then one of the world's largest pub-lishers.[23] Perhaps unknown to the majority of the public, Macmillan has, since the 19th century, assumed a quite determined responsibility for the ethics and regulation of writing on science; it was, at that time, the pub-lisher of the world's leading science journal, *Nature*.

---

23 More recently, Macmillan was taken over by another of the world's biggest publishing companies, a German combine.

HRT Aware

HRT Aware is, as stated above, a drug company front organisation, set up by Wyeth and other companies[24] to advocate and proselytise the benefits of HRT. In 1998, HRT Aware, linked to The Amarant Trust, went to opinion-poll company MORI and had it carry out a very restricted survey of women taking HRT. As was to become the pattern, HRT Aware got a figurehead women to lend her name to their eulogy for hormone replacement – in this case, Judy Finnigan.[25]

If we look at some of the articles that grew out of this industry-funded survey, we can see the part played by the press in advertising HRT directly to the public. *The Londonderry Sentinel*, for example, on August 26 of that year, carried a single-column article headed *HRT makes you feel good!* It began with a quote from Judy Finnigan, who had recently 'made public' her use of HRT: 'I feel so alive and happier than I've felt in years.' Then, without giving any detailed information about the survey, the article went on to say, 'The benefits of hormone replacement therapy have recently been confirmed in a national survey on women's attitudes towards this particular treatment ... Nearly nine out of ten women who currently take HRT would recommend other women to take it ... The long list of benefits includes ...'

These social science absurdities are followed by a quote from a Dr Annie Evans: 'Since taking HRT after having a hysterectomy, I feel 150 per cent.' The article doesn't say whether or not Dr Evans recommends hysterectomies on the road to fulfilment.[26]

The article is simply an advertisement for HRT, and it makes no attempt at all to be balanced or even rational. Flagged up at the end of the article are three of the organisations that support the prescription of HRT,

---

24 Funded by Wyeth and five other pharmaceutical companies.

25 You might not have heard of her, but she's big in daytime television with her husband, Richard. They give off a very chatty, superficial warmth when they talk about their everyday lives. They are both very nice people.

26 Dr Annie Evans, who was prominent in the HRT Aware campaign presented *The A-Z of Rude Health*, a five-week series 'covering everything from Kinky Sex to Contraception and Flatulence to Prostitution'. Produced by Mark Ashton at HTV West in Bristol.

and that had the monopoly on pro-HRT advice: Women's Health Concern, the Amarant Trust HRT Helpline and the National Osteoporosis Society.

On September 3, the *Newtonards Chronicle* ran a three-column eighth-of-a-page article headed 'Feelgood factor is back – thanks to HRT'. This article also began with a quote from Judy, 'I feel so alive and happier than I've felt in years.' [27] And Dr Annie Evans was again credited with her asinine 150 per cent feel-better factor. Again, the article said nothing about adverse side effects or any connection with breast cancer, heart attack or thrombosis. It is clear, looking at the similarities in the articles, that most newspapers simply printed a press release sent out by an agency on Wyeth's behalf. For example:

> Such are the positive effects of HRT that, according to the survey, nearly nine out of 10 women who take HRT would recommend other women to take it.[28]

> Such are the positive effects of Hormonal Replacement Therapy, that according to the survey, nearly nine out of 10 women who currently take HRT would recommend other women to take it.[29]

As well as the small HRT Aware campaign, which got off the ground with its MORI poll in 1998, there were other, smaller, quite traditional PR initiatives. One involved an organisation called Fab After Fifty, which was championed by John Austin MP and TV presenter Gloria Hunniford. FAF ran from a Freepost address in St Leonards on Sea, probably in order to avoid paying someone the minimum wage. Spookily, Fab After Fifty used the same news information distribution system, PR Newswire, as Wyeth Pharmaceuticals did, but this was probably a coincidence.

In 1998, FAF apparently initiated a Women Health Achievers Award. It was the intention of the awards to target women aged 50 and over who 'had actively helped encourage other women's awareness of

---

27 You can imagine the outcry if a newspaper were to carry a similar story quoting a regular user of cannabis, which does not have the same high degree of adverse reactions provoked by HRT.

28 *Colne Valley Chronicle*, 4 September 1998 'Judy feels like a new woman', September 4 1998.

29 *Newtonards Chronicle*, 3 September 1998.'Feelgood factor is back – thanks to HRT'.

health risks that affect them as they get older. These health risks include cardiovascular (heart) disease, osteoporosis (thinning of the bones) and certain cancers.' At this time, Wyeth was selling the idea that HRT guarded against these illnesses.

This campaign, from the start, seemed dead in the water. Either the PR company employed by the drug producers was no good, or Wyeth and other companies told it to hang back. As a consequence, there was no mention of HRT, and it was almost impossible for anyone to pick up the idea of the campaign. It was, however, another drop of water on the forehead of the older women who might, with the relentless drip, drip, drip of propaganda, be worried about her health.

In the first half of 2002, HRT Aware was guided towards The RED Consultants, a discreet public relations company in central London. The RED Consultancy, founded in 1994, became a member of the Incepta Group plc,[30] 'a marketing communications group', in 2001. Incepta was formed after the merger of a number of separate PR and marketing agencies. RED offers strategic advice and implementation in the business-to-business, corporate and consumer public relations market. Founded in 1994 by Lesley Brend and David Fuller, RED employed approximately 85 professionals. RED's other clients included Ladbrokes and Batchelors Foods, Kelloggs, Lever Brothers, McDonald's, Novartis UK, Johnson & Johnson, Aventis Pharma and the BBC.

At the same time as Incepta acquired RED, it also bought up Broad Street, a small New York company. Founded in 1981, Broad Street specialises in 'high-end' corporate videos, major corporate conferences, interactive media and design and branding programmes for large corporate clients in the financial services, entertainment, technology and pharma-

---

30 Incepta Group, the international communications and marketing group has 58 offices and 1,600 clients worldwide, including, Hewlett-Packard, H.J. Heinz Company, Honeywell, HSBC. The biggest group affiliated to Incepta is Citigate, which runs a global PR operation, in Britain. In 2002 Incepta had revenues of $241m. Incepta is an affiliate of Bechtel Enterprises Holdings Inc., the development, financing, and ownership affiliate of the Bechtel organisation, which is one of the world's largest engineering, construction and project management companies. Bechtel has more than 20,000 projects in 140 countries. It was Bechtel which won the contract to reconstruct the Kuwait oil fields after the first Gulf War, and the Iraqi oil fields after the last war. Fifty-one-year-old Riley P. Bechtel, the Chairman and Chief Executive Officer of Bechtel Group Inc., is a director of J.P. Morgan Chase & Co. (Incepta Group plc Annual Review 2002).

ceutical industries. Its 'convergence communications' services help clients to integrate video and other rich media into their Internet and Intranet sites, bringing corporate communications into the digital age. Broad Street was already well integrated in the Rockefeller estate, having AOL Time Warner as one of its main clients.

The RED Consultancy was told that HRT Aware wanted to run a campaign through a new affiliate organisation, and came up with the Choices campaign. RED then designed a campaign for Choices, which took the drugs directly to their target audience, women over 45. One major aspect of the Choices campaign had to be that it linked HRT to an aspirational lifestyle. RED pushed Choices out at venues such as Bingo halls, which held Choices evenings, and on a media tour involving an ex-*EastEnders* soap star.

The RED Consultancy decided on three basic approaches, all as tacky as the other. Having come up with the Choices campaign, they would 'create' a piece of research that would 'show how today's generation of 50-year-old women are vastly different from their counterparts of 50 years ago', and link this to the 'improvements in quality of life with HRT'. The Red Consultancy commissioned the research from the Social Issues Research Centre (SIRC).

The SIRC published a glossy 12-page report after focus group interviews and a survey. The report purported to show that improvements in health and happiness in contemporary women were more marked in those taking HRT. The work is skimpy and intellectually minimalist. It might just pass muster for a local newspaper article, were it not for the fact that the last section, which puts many of the historical changes in women's lives entirely down to HRT, is laughably superficial and transparent. On the back of the *Jubilee Report*, the contact address for help and advice for women experiencing the menopause is that of the Amarant Trust.

Kate Fox, co-director of the SIRC, says in the report's introduction: 'I had heard people say that "life begins at 50", but as a scientist I needed evidence to believe such statements. Now I have some.' Thank God Fox didn't join the police force!

Like many contemporary social and medical research groups, the Social Issues Research Centre claims to be an independent, non-profit-making organisation, founded to conduct research on social and lifestyle issues. However, it is mainly funded from the profits of a sister organisation, MCM, and both organisations share a founding management staff.[31]

MCM Research is a problem-solving, risk-management research, positive communication and PR organisation, which works almost entirely for the food-and-drinks industry. MCM presents positive marketing campaigns for the sugar and alcohol industries, among other clients. It works for: Conoco, Grand Metropolitan Retail, Kingfisher Leisure, Marks and Spencer, Mars Confectionery, the Ministry of Defence and the Sugar Bureau. In the case of the work for HRT Aware, any pretence of independence was purely token, because the whole project was paid for by Wyeth and other pharmaceutical companies.

For the British project, The RED Consultancy lined up 'desirable media spokespeople', and their Choices Campaign booklet featured side bars with support from science journalist and broadcaster Judith Hann[32] and, again, women's health specialist Dr Annie Evans.

The campaign was judged a success by the PR industry when, in a later survey of the coverage of the campaign launch, '100 per cent of the articles mentioned HRT positively, 85 per cent referenced women on HRT reporting greater enhancement in all areas of life compared to those who are not'. Even later, RED won an award for its campaign. Awards such as this within the industry are essential to keep up the morale of the PR community.

Enemies of Knowledge

While HRT Aware, the RED Consultancy and the SIRC were presenting Wyeth's case for HRT in Britain, the company was presenting a North American campaign with the same themes. Wyeth linked its news stories

---

31 In May 1999 a House of Commons Select Committee on Science and Technology recommended in its report, *Scientific Advisory System: Genetically Modified Foods*, 'media coverage of scientific matters should be governed by a Code of Practice, which stipulates that scientific stories should be factually accurate. Breaches of the Code should be referred to the Press Complaints Commission. The SIRC, together with the Royal Institution of Great Britain, were appointed to develop this code.

32 Judith Hann also supported the HRT Alert campaign. For 20 years she was the presenter of the BBC's *Tomorrow's World*, then a presenter of the *Watchdog* programme,   (cont.)

about the advantages of HRT to the 60-year anniversary of the making of Premarin. Suddenly, all the advantages gained by women over the past century in the developed world were credited to mares' urine.

This drivel history is even less credible than the medical history that maintains that immunisation is the sole cause of disease eradication. Unfortunately, it is a powerful marketing ploy, it sells drugs directly to women at a time when they might feel insecure and dissatisfied and while they might have uncomfortable signs of the 'change of life'.

A press release on behalf of Wyeth emphasised, 'the massive improvement in women's lives brought on by HRT', and the company presented 12 'Remarkable Women',[33] who they claimed redefined life after 50 and inspired other women.[34] The press release claimed that Premarin was 'the world's most scientifically cited menopause therapy, with an unparalleled body of science and clinical research'.

Wyeth didn't only bring revisionist history to the North American public; it also brought drug-derived culture. The images of the 12 'honorees', along with 48 additional extraordinary women, were featured in a specially-commissioned 60-photograph exhibit by photographer Jayne Wexler, entitled, 'A Celebration of Women in Midlife and Beyond'.

Joseph Mahady, president of Wyeth Pharmaceuticals North America, commenting on the exhibition, said 'More than 11 million women take a Premarin *Family* (sic) Product on a daily basis, and this exhibit tries to take that statistic and make it a little bit more personal by understanding something about the lives of the women who are using a Premarin Family (sic) Product every day.' He added that the exhibition

---

32 (*cont.*) *Healthcheck*, on BBC1. Hann is a member of Speakers for Business and Celebrity Speakers Ltd. She runs a media training centre in Gloucestershire, The Media Advantage. She has written eight books on science, child care, cooking and healthy lifestyle. Her book, *How Science Works* (Hann J. *How science works*. Pleasantville, NY: Reader's Digest Association; 1991), has become an international bestseller! She makes company in-house videos and regularly chairs conferences for large companies such as British Airways, Cadbury, IBM and Metal Box, as well as government departments.

33 Wyeth claimed to have selected these women 'from among the thousands of stories received', after they asked 'women nationwide to share their personal stories about their accomplishments, how they are embracing their menopausal years and their experience with its products'.

34 Press release, May 8 2002, from PR Newswire-FirstCall.

was to travel to museums, galleries and medical meetings across the country. When the tour was completed, Mahady said, the photographs would be donated to a national museum that honours women.

In 2002, a few weeks before the results of the WHI study were made public, the Society For Women's Health Research, a New York society, whose the stated goal is to 'improve the health of women through research', held a celebrity Gala entirely financed by Wyeth. After the Gala and a few weeks before the results were made public, the company donated $250,000 to the society. Following the announcement of the WHI findings, Phyllis Greenberger, the SWHR chief executive, and her staff, went on television and radio, taking the side of Wyeth, downplaying the negative findings of the study and urging women not to stop taking HRT. The Society did not disclose its links with Wyeth and other drug companies.[35]

The British Menopause Society

The British Menopause Society is just one of a global network of societies that all advocate HRT to a great swath of the world's female population. All of the societies and their activities are funded by a variety of pharmaceutical companies. None of the societies discusses, in any serious way, either alternative remedies or a natural, non-medicated path through menopause.

All the societies, despite any debate about the details, are heavily committed to selling HRT to the menopausal population. The consultants who speak for the societies propose that women try HRT as a first option. More disturbingly than any of this, the clutch of male consultants who direct the policy of the societies, all defend HRT and consistently write against studies that appear to suggest that the drug regime might damage women.

The most prominent consultants based as council members within the British Menopause Society, whose writings are used for many other

---

35 Mundy A. Hot flash, cold cash. *Washington Monthly*, 1 February 2003.

foreign societies are: David H. Barlow, Timothy Hillard, David W. Purdie, Anthony Seeley, John Stevenson, Professor John Studd[36] and David W. Sturdee.

As soon as the 2003 study results became available, the British Menopause Society quickly set up meetings with other societies, with the intention of making a series of statements that would stabilise the consensus view of HRT. Like Commintern meetings during a Cold War crisis, these joint initiatives were funded by Wyeth and the other HRT producers, and the principle organiser of them was Professor David Purdie, whose work has been funded by Wyeth and Organon, and whom we met trying to win over Maggie Tuttle in Chapter Seven.

The organisation of the British and other national menopause societies bears all the hallmarks of a massive pharma operation. The writings of consultants in favour of HRT are used on different national websites where there are clearly not enough motivated medics to write material in the native language. As soon as it became apparent in 2003 that there would be public criticism of HRT as a consequence of the WHI study and the Million Women study, the British Menopause Society issued what it called a 'consensus statement', which went up on many other national society websites.

The British Society also moved quickly to call conferences, in order to issue consensus statements. In fact, these conferences, including one with the Irish Menopause Society and another with the South African Menopause Society, were simply ways for the drug companies to rally the troops, to strengthen morale and to fight back against scientific information that was likely to undermine sales.

In 2002, Sharyl Attkinson, a North American journalist, outed two of the most widely-quoted menopause experts, Dr Lila Nachtigall, and Dr Wulf Utian, director of the American Menopause Society, who both took funding from Wyeth-Ayerst.

---

36 Professor John Studd is a consultant Gynaecologist in London and a Professor of Gynaecology at Imperial College. He started the first menopause clinic in the country in Birmingham in 1969. The hormone treatment for menopause was so controversial at the time that the clinic was closed down for three months by the BMA. He now runs PMS/Menopause clinics at the Chelsea and Westminster Hospital, the Lister Hospital (cont.)

In Australia, the head of the Australian Menopause Society found herself in deep water after it became known that she had accepted funding from Organon. The Society itself was criticised for issuing a booklet on menopause that was entirely funded by Wyeth. The booklet played down cancer risks.[37]

Women's Health Concern

Woman's Health Concern was founded in 1972 by the late Joan Jenkins, a nurse and champion of HRT. The organisation began with an open-access clinic in London, and went on to establish a counselling and advice service, as well as a telephone helpline. WHC holds an annual medical symposium for professionals, which is now funded by Wyeth. The organisation registered as a charity in 1978.

To help it in its work of promoting HRT, the Department of Health awarded grants to WHC in 1998, 1999 and 2000. This last grant was of £15,000. In 2001, *Women's* Health Concern invited Mr Don Barrett, ex-director of corporate affairs at Wyeth pharmaceuticals, to sit on their board.[38]

In 1992, Dr John C. Stevenson had been appointed to the board. Stevenson is a gynaecologist, reader in human metabolism and consultant physician at the Royal Brompton Hospital, London. At the time of

---

36 (*cont.*) and the Wellington Hospital. He is founder and vice-president of the National Osteoporosis Society and has been a council member of the Royal College of Obstetricians and Gynaecologists for 12 years and a past president of the section of Obstetrics and Gynaecology at the Royal Society of Medicine.

Hormone replacement therapy has become so enshrouded in a myth of beneficence that it has been referred to more than once as 'the most important preventive medicine of the century'. John Studd, who has done a great deal to promote the drug, is so confident of its benefits that he dismisses the need for any extra monitoring: 'As *all* of the effects of long-term HRT seem to be protective, with the questionable exception of breast cancer, it is illogical to recommend that these women need any extra monitoring,' he announced in 1992. (Summarised from McTaggart L. *What Doctors Don't Tell You: The truth about the dangers of modern medicine.* London: Thorsons; 1996).

37 Hughes G, Minchin L. Taking your medicine. *The Age*, 13 December 2003..

38 Also see previous chapter. Just to give a flavour of Barrett's work for Wyeth: in 2002, during an exposé and the resultant row by the *Observer* about Wyeth's funding to (*cont.*)

writing, he is chairman of WHC, and an executive committee member of the European Menopause Society and the British Menopause Society. Dr Stevenson is an advocate of HRT, and the WHC collectively stands solidly behind its prescription. When the results of the Million Women study were announced in 2003, WHC took the opportunity to publish a position statement on HRT and breast cancer – except it wasn't really a position statement, it was a cross between a defence of HRT and a rant.

Is it justified, ask the writers, that negative publicity should be created by the results of the study? Well, obviously it isn't justified, nor is it fair: the study reported only a small increase in the risk of developing breast cancer, and the follow-up of the study is too short. So nothing to worry about there, and anyway, as Dr Stevenson goes on to point out, the women who got breast cancer were probably developing it before the study began (what the significance of this is, is not explained). Dr Stevenson, however, has got some heavy manners to hand out to the authors of the study.

> I find it astonishing that the authors confuse ethinyloestradiol (a synthetic oestrogen used in the contraceptive pill) with oestradiol (a natural oestrogen used in HRT [by this he means the one farmed from pregnant mares' urine and then 'naturally' made into pills]) in one of their tables. But *much more* worrying is that neither the editors of the *Lancet* nor their 'expert' reviewers noticed such a glaring error. *Even worse* [*how much worse could it get?*] is the accompanying editorial written by Dutch GPs, which reads like a party political broadcast rather than a scientific critique. This recommends that women taking combined HRT for an extended period of time should discontinue 'as soon as possible'. It seems most surprising that a British study performed in (sic) British women by a British group should be interpreted in a British journal by doctors from a different country. (author's italics).

Phew! You really might get the impression from this piece of medical jingoism that the Women's Health Concern organisation didn't think much of the British Million Women study. And what about that Dr Stevenson? He really lays it on the line. Its true, he doesn't pussyfoot around when it comes to HRT, but, then, why should he? He knows that it's perfectly safe.

---

38 (*cont.*) research members of the Committee for the Safety of Medicine, Barrett, at that time corporate affairs executive, told the *Observer* that figures for funding given by Wyeth to universities for research were confidential.

In a recent BBC Internet phone-in, Dr Stevenson gave a good example of his persuasive bedside manner.

> Caller: I seem to lose concentration and my memory is sometimes poor. I'm 51 and still have my periods. Will this get better once I've gone through the menopause? I'm not keen to take HRT as I did not respond well to the Pill.

> Dr Stevenson: This is a very common symptom of the menopause, and it may get worse, not better, once your periods stop. It would be worth trying HRT to see if this helps. But you may not notice any improvement until you have been on it for many months.

Dr Stevenson is obviously a listening doctor – but did he hear the caller say that she wasn't keen on taking HRT, – or that she 'didn't respond well to the Pill'? Apparently not. Well that's that sorted. On to the next caller. In fact, two of the next callers suggested that they might have relatively unpleasant side effects from HRT, both of which are well recognised among affected patients, if not among prescribing doctors. One woman said that since taking HRT she was increasingly suffering from dry eyes. Could this be caused by HRT, she wanted to know? Contrary to contemporary research, Dr Stevenson suggested it was unlikely. The other caller wanted to know if her two-stone weight gain could have anything to do with her two years on HRT. Dr Stevenson was very understanding. He pointed out that, although many women did think that HRT caused weight gain, this was a mistake. He advised the caller, 'Reduce the size of the portions of your food to achieve weight loss.' Wow! The intellectual insight and erudition is positively blinding. But, then, what Dr Stevenson doesn't know about human metabolism is probably not worth knowing.

Dr Stevenson is always at pains to point out that Women's Health Concern is an independent organisation, which gives unbiased advice about HRT. However, within five years of being set up, it was taking money from the drugs and chemical companies. In 1986, it took money from Roche, Unilever and the Dunhill Medical Trust. In 1987/88, the massive US PR company, which, among others, represents pharmaceutical interests, donated almost £12,000, while Wyeth and Ciba Geigy also donated independently. By 1994, Women's Health Concern was in a position to commit £30,000 to the production and promotion of a book, *Menopause and HRT – The Facts*, which was distributed to all the libraries in Britain. By 1999, as well as its support from commercial concerns, it began to receive £15,000 grants from the Department of Health.

In August 2003, Dr Margaret Upsdell, a supporter of HRT, a GP and one of the senior trustees of Women's Health Concern, commissioned a survey from NOP. A group of 300 women were interviewed about their use of HRT. The survey concluded that *HRT could be the world's best sex aid for women reaching middle age*. Fifty per cent of the women questioned claimed that they had rediscovered their sex drive. And 60 per cent of those taking part, said that HRT had helped them to 'feel like a woman' – presumably they had felt like ... what before?

The higher reaches of menopause drug treatment propaganda are off in Pharmaland. Above the international base of the menopausal societies is The European Menopause and Andropause Society (EMAS), publishers of the European menopause journal *Maturitas* [39] and creators of World Menopause Day, which falls on October 18, in 2006 – make sure you bookmark it! [40]

EMAS also organises a major, world menopause conference. The publication of the journal and the work on the international conference is done by Mark Two Communications from an office in the Netherlands. Above EMAS in the pharmasphere is the European HRT Network Foundation, set up by 11 pharmaceutical companies with an interest in selling HRT.

Professor Manuel Neves-e-Castro, based in Portugal, is the co-ordinator of EMAS and the founder of the Portuguese Menopause Society, which began with a newsletter and now exists as a website. Neves-e-Castro was interviewed at the Year 2000 EMAS Conference in Copen-

---

39 Dr John Stevenson is an editor of *Maturitas*, and the editorial board includes John Studd and David Sturdee.

40 Nothing shows the cynicism associated with these PR gimmicks more clearly than the proforma shown in Appendix III. This press-rallying call was issued to be sent out by different national Menopausal Societies. There is, in reality, no popular base to these events, and they are just another way for the pharmaceutical companies to bring up the issue of HRT through the press to the public.

hagen. He explained that the object of EMAS was to bring together the experience of all the national European menopause societies, and he explained World Menopause Day in the following terms:

> It is running within the context of CAMS, which is the Counsel of Affiliated Menopause Societies. I have the pleasure to be the Project Leader for this particular initiative and the purpose I had in mind when I proposed it was just to have the opportunity once a year all over the world and wherever we have people involved in the delivery of care for menopausal women or menopause societies to talk about menopause. We are not going to teach anything during this day but we are going to try to sensitize politicians, health providers, women, families, you name it, that this problem exists, and it's the beginning of risk factors that can be prevented for the benefit of the individual's health and public health and to decrease costs of healthcare by preventative medicine.[41]

I find it very reassuring that there are groups of men out there organising to sensitise women to the menopause, don't you? The 4th Amsterdam Menopause Symposium, organised by EMAS, took place over three days in October 2004, with an attendance of over one thousand people, and focused on 'Tailor-Made Menopause Management'. The central theme was 'menopause management as adapted to the individual woman's needs'. Like the 3rd Amsterdam conference in 2001,[42] the 4th conference entailed reviews and debates with leading experts during the morning sessions, drug company-sponsored symposia at lunch time, and poster sessions and satellite symposia and workshops during the afternoons. The morning sessions were advertised as including assessment of individual risks and benefits of HRT.

One of the most important European journals that discusses risk and HRT is *Gynaecological Forum*, which now exists as a website journal. It is published by Medical Forum International (MFI), which describes itself as a Medical Publishing and Health Care Communications Agency, based in Zeist, Netherlands. MFI says it is 'dedicated to furthering internation-

---

41 Interview by OBGYN.net with Manuel Neves-e-Castro from Portugal, the co-ordinator of the EMAS.

42 As part of the 3rd Amsterdam Symposium, Novartis Pharma held its own one-day symposium. This included a session from Juan Mantelle, Noven Pharmaceuticals vice-president and chief technical officer, on 'Innovative Technology for Menopause', which addressed transdermal drug delivery.

al exchange of medical experience and opinion through our worldwide network of professionals and opinion leaders'. MFI's principle client is Novo Nordisk, for whom it publishes *Gynaecological Forum*. Medical Forum International also publishes *International Diabetes Monitor*, which is financed entirely by Novo Nordisk, which, as well as producing a range of hormone contraceptives and HRT preparations, also produces drugs for diabetes.

The editor-in-chief of the *Gynaecological Forum*, from the UK, is S. R. Killick, professor of reproductive medicine and surgery at the University of Hull. Professor Killick is also a director of East Riding Fertility Services Ltd. Among many other positions and memberships, he is a member of the Hull and East Riding Ethics Committee. Medical Forum International works hard for its editors and those associated with its journals, and the biographical material on Professor Killick is well laid out and beautifully designed on its website.

In Britain, we are clearly too nice to accuse people of sordid conflicts of interest. If the British Menopause Society's conferences are funded by Wyeth and other HRT-providers, this is no doubt done in a spirit of pure philanthropy. In Australia, however, questions have been asked of Professor Susan Davis, now president of the Australasian Menopause Society, after Proctor and Gamble paid for trials of testosterone patches for women with a new illness that they had dreamed up – Hypoactive Sexual Desire Disorder. Not only did P&G pay for a trial, but also for Dr Davis to present the results in San Antonio, Texas. Professor Davis has previously declared consultancies and honorariums from drug companies. She has spoken in favour of a product by Organon, which is said to increase sex drive in menopausal women.[43]

In 2002, the Australasian Menopause Society was criticised for issuing a booklet on menopause paid for by Wyeth. The booklet played down the risk of breast cancer.

---

43 'Taking Your Medicine', Gary Hughes and Liz Michin, an excellent article for *The Age*. http://www.theage.com.au

The Lunatic Fringes

Other individuals and organisations outside medicine also gathered, after the adverse study findings, to help Wyeth and to support HRT. A sure sign that any movement is an industry front, is support from Steven Milloy. In his time, Milloy has fronted for most toxins and environmental dangers.

In the early 1990s, Milloy worked with James Tozzi, one of the principal communications links between tobacco giant Phillip Morris and the EPA. Tozzi set up a non-profit think tank called the Institute of Regulatory Policy for Philip Morris. For this, according to the North American writers Rampton and Stauber,[44] his company was paid $880,000. On behalf of Philip Morris the IRP constructed three coalitions to support 'sound science' and tobacco research. Since then and the setting up of his Junk Science website, he has attacked any science that endeavours to criticise industry.[45]

In 1998, in what he called a 'special' report on his web page, Milloy came out in defence of the pharmaceutical companies over HRT. After singing the praises of hormone replacement, he rounded on the 'junk science mobsters' who were using circumstantial evidence to scare women into thinking that HRT can cause breast cancer. Why, asks Milloy, should critics try to stir up trouble over a therapy that has been used successfully for 55 years? Simple, Milloy answers himself, pharmaceutical companies are trying to take advantage of the breast cancer scare to sell their own brands of HRT. Milloy calls on David Sturdee, the former chairman of the British Menopause Society, saying, 'It will be very unfortunate if this investigation causes women to stop taking HRT.'

HealthWatch, the British arm of the US National Council Against Health Fraud, which has crusaded vehemently on the subject of double-blind placebo trials since its inception in 1987, found the WHI trials that looked at HRT to be seriously problematic.

---

44 Rampton S, Stauber J. How Big Tobacco helped create "the Junkman". http://www.prwatch.org/prissues/2000Q3/junkman.html and Rampton S, Stauber J. *Trust us we're experts: how industry manipulates science and gambles with your future.* New York: Tarcher/Putnam; 2001.

45 *Trust Us We're Experts.* Ibid.

In an article entitled 'Damned Lies, Statistics and HRT', in the HealthWatch newsletter circulated on the Internet, Michael Henk, an honorary consultant clinical oncologist at the Royal Marsden Hospital, London, made great play of the way in which statistical results of studies scare patients.

> On 10 July *The Times* carried the headline 'HRT is linked to breast cancer: US study is halted after health fears rise: patients suffer 41% increase in stroke: 22% increase in risk of heart disease'! Equally sensational headlines appeared in other newspapers. *Behind this propagation of alarm and despondency to millions of woman* was the publication in *JAMA* of preliminary results from a large US randomised controlled trial of hormone replacement therapy (HRT) in post-menopausal women. (author's italics).

Perhaps the article should have been entitled 'Damned Quackbusters, Statistics and HRT', for, although Henk is very erudite and intellectually streets ahead of the rank-and-file quackbuster associated with Health-Watch, his arguments are the same as those shaped by Wyeth and the other pharmaceutical companies to minimise the perceived damage of the WHI study.

Part of Henk's argument is the return-to-real-figures argument propagated by Wyeth-loyal physicians between 1998 and 2004. He suggests that the 5 per cent statistical significance barrier is too low, and that rigorous adherence to it is hampering the general truth about risk and, in this case, HRT.

> The use of the 5% probability level, "p<0.05", as the index of a 'statistically significant' result has become a ritual in clinical research. All it means is that the probability that the observed result of a trial would occur by chance if there were no real difference is no more than 5%. In other words, one in twenty 'significant' results are false positives. The 5% level was chosen arbitrarily by Sir Ronald Fisher many years ago, only because it was mathematically convenient, yet it has become the yardstick for publication of clinical trials. It is something of a quirk of mathematics that the smaller the absolute percentages the smaller the difference between them that will achieve statistical significance, hence the number of reportedly significant risks of HRT.

It is quite astonishing the way in which apparently rational people want to move the goalposts when they don't agree with the results. What is Henk suggesting? That we have different levels of significance for different studies?

At one point in the article, Henk suggests that the reason why the WHI trial was halted was simply that, with the litigious atmosphere in North America, the trial would have to be stopped for fear of the researchers being sued.

Henk is, it is worth reminding ourselves, an *oncologist*. Day in, day out, he must be confronted by the pain and abject misery caused not just by cancer but by modern cancer therapies. Malignant tumours, not hot flushes, are his specialty. What, then, does he say to himself, when he sits across a desk from a woman with breast cancer, who has been for years on HRT? 'Hmm, another statistically insignificant quirk of mathematics, we can blame Sir Ronald Fisher for this'?

All quackbusters *appear* to be steadfastly in favour of science and rationality, while standing four square against irrationality and mysticism in all its forms. However, the truth is that they are primarily in favour of industrial science and the pharmaceutical industry. While they spend an enormous amount of time attacking alternatives, arguing that they are accompanied by serious risks, they hardly ever report the iatrogenic effects of pharmaceuticals.

The Misinformation on the Street

Information and misinformation about HRT and about critical study results finally reach the public after being filtered through physicians, celebrities, societies, associations and the local newspaper. The misinformation that the pharmaceutical companies used in Britain to respond to both the launch of individual lawsuits in 1997, and the complainants' accession to legal aid in 1998, and that they used later in 2002 to combat the scientific findings of studies on HRT, comes as close to illiteracy as is possible in a developed society when served up by the gullible or complicit national and regional press.

The *Northern Echo* on September 15, 1998, in response to the first steps in litigation, reported that 'the majority of women who take HRT are perfectly happy'. Perhaps the journalist, Karen Smith, writing in Darlington in the Northeast of England, is here making a claim for HRT to be prescribed in place of Prozac. She goes on to say that 'hundreds of GPs across the North East have prescribed the drug for years and say they will continue to do so'; a reassuringly sensible approach by physicians from the North East! *Nul points* for patients.

Even more reassuring was the story of Britain's first surrogate grandmother, who had radically increased her dosage of HRT when she decided to be a host mother for her daughter's embryo. According to Karen Smith, only HRT could help Edith Jones to prepare for this medical milestone. The baby was born in 1996, and in 1998 Mrs Jones developed breast cancer and opted for having her right breast removed. She took a stoical, level-headed and completely English approach to the loss of her breast, implying that it was a fair exchange for a beautiful granddaughter. Pharmaceutical company representatives must have rubbed their hands in glee when she went on to say, 'HRT may have had something to do with the breast cancer, it may have been the sole cause of it, but we will never know and I'm not interested.'

For an expert quote, Karen Smith, approached consultant gynaecologist David Vasey, then working at Ipswich General Hospital. Funnily enough, he couldn't see anything wrong with HRT, and said that he would continue to prescribe it without any great concern. Quietly sidestepping the results of any studies, Vasey gave voice to the developing drug company line that women had freedom of choice: 'At the end of the day, I think it's purely a personal thing.' Ahh, the pleasures of perfect information! [46]

Another common approach to reporting about HRT in the late Nineties was to talk about weighing up the pros and cons, or 'balancing the dangers and benefits', as an avuncular Fred Kavalier (who, to judge by his portrait, bears a striking resemblance to Josef Stalin), put it in the

---

[46] What Karen Smith could not have known was that two years into the future, Dr Vasey would appear before the GMC. One of the charges brought by the GMC related to a trial that he had run with HRT. The GMC suggested that Dr Vasey had not clearly presented the results, and Dr Vasey admitted to this.

short-lived weekly *Sunday Business.'* [47] The problem with balancing the dangers and benefits is that some writers make it appear that both reactions happen to the same patient: in other words, HRT is worth tolerating because, although you might have some adverse reactions, it will also give you some benefits.

This *balanced* view of pharmaceutical action takes rational discourse off into Lala Land; the problem with HRT is specifically that, while for some people their prescription seems to work, others can find their lives destroyed. The only people who can 'balance' these two experiences are the managing directors of the drug companies. Anyway, is this actually the way to assess the quality of a pharmaceutical – perhaps physicians should carry around a set of scales with which to measure, on the one hand, 'bad bits', and on the other, 'good bits'.

At least Britain is fortunate in being the home of Dr Hilary Jones, the once-youthful media doctor with the looks of a television chef. In an issue of Rosemary Conley's diet and fitness magazine, under the heading 'In the surgery', Hilary puts everything in perspective. 'Hormone replacement therapy merely replaces what your ovaries have given up producing, namely the two female sex hormones oestrogen and progesterone ... doctors can always find a form to suit any individual.' This should be called The Wizard of Oz approach to medicine, after the scarecrow who says, 'My straw has come out!' When Dorothy asks, 'Doesn't it hurt you?' The scarecrow replies, 'No, I just keep picking it up and putting it back in again.'

---

47 *Sunday Business,* 18 October 1998.

PART FOUR

Chapter Nine

The Woman Who Slipped Through the Net

Most people lead lives of quiet desperation.
Adapted from Henry David Thoreau[1]

In 2006, Barbara is not yet 'better', nor has she returned to what she had grown to know as her normal self in the first 35 years of her life. She is, however, over the cusp of 11 years of serious illness caused by the first administration of HRT in 1989 to 'aid childbirth', and then later its prescription for an 'early menopause' in 1990. My second visit to interview Barbara occurred on a public holiday after Christmas, in January 2003. At this time, Barbara had been housebound for most of those 11 years.

There was work on the line from London to Stafford and a 'connecting bus service' for the last part of the journey. Having had experience of *connecting bus services* in the past, I decided to work out my own route by train, as far as I could, thinking that it would take me less time than the almost five-hour journey from London that I was offered.

I arrived at Barbara's, after a door-to-door journey of around six hours, feeling victimised by the privatised rail system, and wondering

---

1 Thoreau (1817-1862) actually said, 'Most men lead lives of quiet desperation.'

why they didn't do track repairs on working days and give working people paid holidays. The idea that the community leisure time is less important than paid work time sums up the way that capitalism operates in England. I felt alone, cold and quite separate from the rest of the world.

I had alighted from my last train, to find myself in a station car park, still supposedly to pick up a 'connecting bus service'. Standing there, however, I knew from the first that any 'connecting buses' existed only in the energetic mind of the last train's ticket collector. I wandered into the small town adjacent to the station. Its centre consisted of a concrete-and-brick arcade of about ten shops, and a broken concrete apron of a bus station with two abandoned reinforced-plastic shelters. The place was deserted apart from a young guy in a parka untidily eating a burger, and a couple of elderly women in similar thick blue coats who sat tight to each other as if warding off nonconformity.

The impact of post-industrial decline first affects Britain's housing estates, lending them an air of desertion, and in the Midlands, North and Northeast, this feeling stretches to envelope whole towns and their concrete centres. The older generations, despite frugality and infirmity, often struggle to dress for the shops, even on a bank holiday. The women powder their faces; the men wear good jackets and, carrying sticks, put on their best caps.

The sight of the younger generations comes as a blow to the senses. Nylon clothes, hoodies, untied trainers, invariably eating on the buses, in the streets. Playing constantly with mobile phones. Musical dregs leaching from their Walkmans.

When the bus eventually came, a woman with a child sat behind me. The young girl was trying out the mobile phone that her mother had just bought her for Christmas. She sat two seats away while her mother called her. They rejoined each other and the mother explained the functions on the phone, in the same way that a parent 20 years ago might have explained how to understand a difficult passage in a book or a maths problem.

The mother changed the subject. 'When we get home, we'll make some tea and settle down on the sofa and watch a film, OK?' The girl agreed.

Everyone is looking for a place of safety, which is not now to be found outside the home, in the barren landscape of post-industrialism, where community has collapsed. Any security, however meagre, is 'at home', 'indoors', in a world that now wards off visitors and rarely leaves doors open to a multitude of neighbours, as it used to.

Especially in this age of easy mobility, the urban environment creates anonymity as the town spins out into impenetrable suburbs. The Thorntree estate outside Stafford bestows upon its residents an even greater anonymity than is usually the case. Square, box-like white homes, spread for miles, sit ambivalently on short drives surrounded by narrow grass aprons, which reach the pavement unobstructed by fences or walls. There are few walkers and no casual strollers. Everyone is either purposefully visiting a house or moving quickly from one house to another.

The occupants of Barbara's house know more than most about anonymity and isolation. Even with the anchoring reassurance of her family – her husband, Pete, and the son who remains at home, 14-year-old Stuart – the community around her might just as well have vanished. People on the whole had stopped talking to her, believing that she had been involved in a marathon of malingering.

Stepping into the house after my long journey, I was immediately enveloped by a feeling of comfortable safety. Stuart sat gluing together a large grey plastic model of a tank on the kitchen table, and Pete, a lanky, slightly balding man, hovered with a mug of tea. Except for the large windows, the light and planned kitchen, I might have stepped back into a working-class household of the Fifties.

While I sat with Barbara in the small front room, Stuart and his father made plans to go to the pictures; they tossed up between this film and that, talked amiably to each other, before waving goodbye.

Like a great percentage of the respectable working class, Barbara can be described by all those words and phrases now little used in every day conversation; words that have described for years the moral heart of British working-class-society: 'law-abiding', 'public-service-orientated', 'neighbourly', and, in Barbara's case 'churchgoing'. Barbara is the kind of ideal citizen that developed post-war British society.

Despite the value of her life, its model integrity and its interlocking with and use to the rest of her extended family, Barbara's existence has been shattered by professional medicine in the form of hormone replacement therapy. It cost her 11 years of her life and its value to her, her family and the community. No one person or group of people has accepted responsibility or had responsibility thrust upon them for this theft.

Until his retirement, Barbara's father was an ambulance driver. He always spoke well of the nurses and auxiliary staff, but rarely commented on the doctors. Their family did not really need a doctor until her mother became ill at the age of 42, when Barbara was 14. It transpired that her mother had cancer and was to die quickly, after a mastectomy of her left breast.

During the weeks that Barbara's mother was having chemotherapy, she travelled to Wolverhampton every day. Barbara wonders, a slight anger breaking beneath the surface of her face, why she could not have stayed in the hospital – even, though Barbara does not voice this – why she could not have been treated at home. But in an age where medicine has moved out of the community and into the specialist centres that suit the order, discipline and lives of its technicians, the sick have to travel to their treatment. At home, Barbara's father did all the caring for her mother, changing her dressings and feeding her; he was, Barbara says, a very capable nurse.

But Barbara also has good memories of the doctor of her childhood, the family doctor. Almost a member of the family, he had a feeling for its members, he knew how they all were, because he came to the house and knew how they lived, what they ate, when people were working and when they were unemployed. He was interested in the whole situation, the whole person.

'When I went on to HRT, the first thing that occurred to me was that my mum had died of breast cancer, and from what little I knew about HRT, this increased the risks for me.' Barbara has told every doctor who has treated her with HRT about her mother, but none has ever thought it worth noting. The last consultant Barbara saw, told her that if her mother had been under 40 when she got breast cancer, it might have been a cause for concern in her own case. However, because she was 42, there was no need to worry. Barbara was not reassured by this bit of off-the-cuff scientific maths.

Her family was religious, and her Sunday visits to the Baptist Chapel stayed with her into her later life, when she became a part of one of the first Christian folk groups to sing in a church.

She was rarely ill as a child, although she had measles and slight psoriasis, which finally disappeared after she had her first child. It reoccurred with a vengeance when she started taking HRT. When it came back, is was in the form of thick, bleeding scabs all over her back and completely covering the top of her legs. It was so bad that there were periods when she was unable to sit down.

Barbara married Pete in 1977 when she was 22. Pete, five years her senior, came from another working-class family. He had a steady job with a large telecommunications company, which also employed his father. Miraculously, against modern trends, in 2003 Pete was still working for the same corporation, despite it having changed ownership.

After marrying, Barbara and Pete moved eight miles up the road. Barbara's dad still feels put out about this because, for him, it is now a day's trip to visit them. Even this short move broke up the close community which he had been used to all his life. Pete's parents had grown up in London, so he was a little more used to the idea of living in different places.

When she was a girl, Barbara had passed through the area in which she now lives, going into Stafford on a Saturday morning to shop. 'This area outside,' she points to the small French windows on to the garden, 'was open fields, and I remember coming up here to shop in the town and saying to my parents, "Oh, wouldn't it be nice to live here in this countryside?"' Pete and Barbara bought their house on that land, not long after being married. The sprawling estate was built in the late Sixties, and they moved into one of the houses a decade later. Pete's dad died about six months after he and Barbara got married, and his mum a couple of years after that.

When they moved, Barbara gave up her other activities and focused on working with the Girl Guide movement. Barbara's early married life could not have been happier, she says. She had a job, and a smashing husband, also with a steady job. She had everything that she wanted. Lots of friends lived around them. They would go to 'South End', a working men's club, at the weekends, to be entertained by live acts, then on to a friend's house. Barbara did a cookery course with a friend who lived nearby. Once a week they would buy a bottle of wine on the way home and, with their husbands, eat what they had cooked. And at weekends, before the children came along, they'd go to a club in Stafford and dance to live bands.

Barbara worked shifts in those days. Pete taught her to drive and bought her a car. Pete also enjoyed working for the Girl Guide Association; he would go with Barbara when they took the girls away. He would do all the logistical work, figuring out where they were going, organising the entertainment, the treasure trails, or whatever.

As in most extended families, in the main, their parents looked after their kids when they went out. At other times, Pete and Barbara would take their kids with them and put them upstairs to sleep in their friends' houses. Barbara is dismissive – as if it would have been irresponsible – of the idea of using a babysitter.

Her life, before HRT, could not have been better, she says. Of course, this is a slight retrospective simplification. Her health problems, which developed four years after the birth of her first child, and which led up to her being given HRT, exist in a kind of limbo, part of her period of being young and happy, but also an introduction to the ensuing years of pain and hopelessness.

As I listened to Barbara's account of her life, she repeated a number of times that her life was very 'normal', 'yes, very normal'. This mantra of the 'normality' of her life is a hedge against what was to happen to her. It is as if now, in hindsight, she is trying to denounce her illness for choosing to alight on her and not on someone whose lifestyle made them obviously more deserving.

Barbara and Pete always planned to have children; she wanted a big family. It took four years before Barbara conceived. In the days before she was due to have the baby, her GP was away on holiday, so she had no one familiar from whom to seek second opinions. She was, however, happy with the support that the doctors at the hospital gave her when they told her that baby had to be induced because of her rising blood pressure. As a measure of how good her GP was, Barbara says that on his way home from his holiday, on the day that she was due to give birth, he rang Pete from the airport as soon as he and his family landed, to ask after her and the baby.

Barbara is full of praise and admiration for her GP, who has now moved away. Despite having come to Britain from the other side of the world, he and his family were like neighbourhood friends. One of the marks of his ability, Barbara suggests, was the fact that, like her childhood family doctor, he knew everything about everybody. The closeness of this doctor to his patients, to their problems and health issues, which he considered the bedrock of his job, can be seen by Barbara's description of him knocking on their door on his way to afternoon surgery, coming in and switching on the television with the words, 'I've just come to see the cricket scores before I start work.'

One of Barbara's ways of describing how good a doctor he was, is encapsulated in the idea, sometimes expressed by working-class people about professionals: 'He had a lot of bluff and bluster and he would shout at you, but if you shouted back it was OK.' This willingness to take part in heated exchanges without ill feelings, a working-class trait, separates the scientific and cold medical professional from the ones who feel things about their patients. Interestingly, it is quite the opposite quality that a middle-class person looks for in a professional, particularly a doctor.

He was, Barbara says, a brilliant doctor, one who would drop in on his patients relatively regularly, simply because he hadn't seen them for a while. But again, like other people who have become seriously ill, Barbara seems to view her past through rose-tinted glasses. While she tells me how good a doctor he was, she suddenly realises that he was of little help relatively recently when she came close to being sectioned as a consequence of adverse reactions to HRT. With regard to HRT, she says, perhaps he had some of the same blind spots as other doctors.

Barbara did not have any problems with the birth of her first child, Ian. Nor did she have much pre-birth medical interference. She says this, principally, because the occasion of her second pregnancy has clouded out any critical view about the birth of Ian and the fact that he had to be induced because of her hypotension. Barbara tries to hide her disappointment at not being able to breastfeed because one of her nipples was inverted. This problem gave her a great deal of pain as her breasts filled with milk.

Eleven weeks after Ian's trouble-free birth, he was nearly lost in a crisis precipitated by his having been induced. Here, Barbara cites another example of how exceptional her GP was. In the middle of the crisis, with Ian very sick, Barbara and Pete called him at his home and then went straight round to his house with Ian. The GP's wife, a trained children's nurse, sat with Ian all day. Then, when they went to the hospital and it became clear that Ian might have to stay, the GP's wife offered to care for him in their home, rather than have him go into the hospital some distance away.

Barbara and Pete did not want too much time to pass between the births of their children. She conceived as soon as they began trying for a second child. From the beginning this pregnancy was quite different from her first, and it was now that her horror of the NHS began to set in. For the first five months, everything seemed fine. The baby appeared to be the normal size and to be growing. However, Barbara gradually began to think that she was not experiencing any movement. She was examined at the hospital and they found nothing wrong. Still, intuitively Barbara knew that something wasn't right.

That August, Barbara was supposed to be taking the Guides away. Pete was working in London. Just before they were about to set off, Barbara had a small but worrying discharge. Following the move of her trusted family doctor, she had been landed with what she now refers to as 'our new, useless GP', or 'that idiot of a doctor'.

She called the GP to the house, where he examined her. He then asked how many weeks pregnant she was, and she told him 22. As Barbara describes it now, the doctor then simply said, 'I think your baby's dead.' He went on to suggest that she provide a urine sample and bring it to the surgery, then, without another word, he left.

Not knowing where to turn, Barbara telephoned the midwife who had attended Ian's birth. The midwife was at home, in the middle of her dinner, but she arrived at the door within minutes. She examined Barbara and said she thought that the doctor was probably right. She was, however, appalled that he had walked away from Barbara following his examination and his devastating diagnosis. She immediately rang the hospital, made arrangements for Barbara to be admitted, then reported the doctor. She also stayed with Barbara and explained to her that the baby could have died earlier but not come away from the lining of the womb and been expelled.

The dead foetus, she said, needed to be 'evacuated' as soon as possible. This, however, did not happen, and so began the worst five days of Barbara's life. It took almost four days for the hospital to admit her, and it was another day before she could be operated on.

Although the doctors described a simple operation to remove the baby, it was finally argued that, because it had grown to such a size, Barbara should actually be induced, without anaesthetic, and give birth to the dead baby. She was told that this birth might be painful, and she was given the option of painkillers at any time she felt that she needed them. After she 'gave birth', a young nurse, who had been sullen throughout the whole procedure, disposed of the baby like so much debris, without a thought that Barbara might have wanted to see it.

Unfortunately, the afterbirth did not follow the baby, and Barbara had to endure another crisis. The doctors could not operate to remove it until the following day. They clamped her so thoroughly that, she says now, any movement was accompanied by clanking, and she was left for another 12 hours waiting for the operation.

The whole thing was a nightmare, with an argument between the ward sister and the sullen nurse as to whether or not Barbara could be allowed to have a mouthwash, which the nurse considered to be a 'drink', when Barbara was supposed to be 'nil by mouth' in preparation for the surgery.

It was only later that Barbara found out that a number of nurses had waited outside her room throughout the night, praying that she did not go to sleep. Had she, they believed, she could well have died. The hospital had failed to telephone Pete, who was by then at home looking after Ian, so he did not know that Barbara had been in crisis throughout the night.

After losing the baby, Barbara's life returned to normal and she recalls that she was more-or-less happy again. It was, she says, an episode with which she and Pete dealt as best they could. She knows that they were both affected by her experience in various ways, but they went back to work and back to making their lives.

Barbara's next pregnancy was also doomed to fail because of a 'blighted ovum'. This refers to a pregnancy in which the embryo did not develop, or failed earlier than six-and-a-half-weeks, due usually to some chromosomal abnormality. Ultrasound reveals only the gestational sac that would have surrounded the embryo. She had a D&C (dilation and curettage), by which the womb lining is scraped away. This experience, she maintains, had little psychological effect on her because it was recognised so quickly and she could not conceive of the little blob of misshapen material that had showed up on the scan as a baby.

Neither of these experiences stopped Barbara and Pete from trying for another baby, although Pete did worry when Barbara next got pregnant, because he didn't want her to go through another trauma. With this next pregnancy, aged 35, however, she was delivered of Stuart in an hour and a half, without significant problems, although, because of raised blood pressure, doctors insisted on inducing her again. They had also given Barbara hormone injections for some time before the birth, just so that, they said, the baby would continue to grow and there would be no chance of a repetition of the first miscarriage. Barbara can remember no discussion about the injections, which she had for the last five months of the pregnancy.

Almost eight months passed between Barbara giving birth to Stuart and her realisation that she was unwell. She was in Torquay with the Guides and she didn't leave the flat that she and Pete were in. She began to have panic attacks and palpitations, and was very lethargic.

When she got back to Stafford, she began seeing doctors, who all seemed to agree that she was suffering from post-natal depression, or 'baby blues' as they insisted on calling it. This kind of depression was completely outside Barbara's experience; nothing like it had ever happened to her, and she had no way of understanding it. She would lie on the floor with her head in a cushion, screaming 'Why is this happening to me?'

Knowing that there was something badly wrong, Barbara asked her GP in vain for psychiatric help. Eventually, she and Pete decided that they would have to go privately to a psychiatrist. They approached a hospital psychologist, who came to see her at the house. He recognised immediately that Barbara was seriously ill and, after counselling and a six-month course of antidepressants, she came out of the depression. Although it felt wonderful that the worst of the gloom had lifted, she was left with an underlying lethargy and still did not feel right.

BARBARA

The psychologist, who felt that he had done as much as he was able, told Barbara that he saw many women on the wards who could be 'cured of depression'. The underlying problem, however, which in his opinion was hormonal, did not correct itself. He suggested that Barbara go to her GP and then to a consultant to have her hormone levels checked.

If Barbara's life had been destabilised by the birth of her second son, or by the administration of oestrogen for five months prior to the birth, and if the depression following the birth had confused her, nothing had prepared her for the changes in her life and personality that HRT would bring. And this time, no one was going to recognise her illness for what it was. No one was going to suggest any way out. No one was going to tell her the truth.

Summing up the situation that was to disrupt the next chapter of her life, she now says simply, 'The many doctors I saw did not accept that medicine could harm people.' These doctors refused to give Barbara's illness a name or the authority of an aetiology. For the next nine years while taking HRT Barbara was to suffer from an 'unexplained illness'.

In 1990, Barbara went to see her gynaecologist. By then she had no energy, was severely depressed and had started to experience hot flushes and panic attacks. The gynaecologist suggested that she was going through an early menopause. She was then just 36. Tests that the gynaecologist ordered showed that Barbara had low levels of oestrogen. With next to no discussion, the doctor gave her a 100mg oestrogen implant, telling her she would 'soon by smiling'. As she would comment to me 13 years later, she had not smiled since.

Looking back on the start of her life-wrecking problems, with all that she has since found out, Barbara finds it hard to believe that the gynaecologist did not first try pills or patches but went straight for the irreversible implant. She is astonished that he paid no attention to Barbara's concerns that her mother had died of breast cancer or the fact that she had had episodes of high blood pressure.

After three implants, delivered at six-month intervals, they were stopped because it was discovered that Barbara's blood pressure was too high. She was then prescribed pills. Throughout this period of treatment, Barbara experienced no change for the better in her general health; rather, the symptoms that she had originally reported to the doctor were consistently worse. Concerned that she was being treated with no release from the symptoms, Barbara insisted on transferring to another hospital, where she was prescribed HRT pills and then patches.

Still her symptoms of anxiety, hot flushes, headaches and 'jelly legs' all got worse. She had frequent bleeding, when she passed clots and had a lot of pain on one side of her abdomen. Finally, her general health became so bad that she spent almost all of one month, apart from six days, laid up in bed. Following this month, she was referred back to her original hospital, where she 'consulted' with the doctor about a hysterectomy. Within 20 minutes, the consultant had decided that the best strategy to deal with Barbara's problems would be an urgent hysterectomy and oophorectomy (to remove her womb and ovaries), followed by yet another 100mg oestrogen implant.

Barbara was now so ill that she would, she says, have agreed to anything, and in November 1994 she had the operation, received the implant and went home within five days. Even her return home was not uneventful: she had an infection, probably picked up in the hospital, and was laid up in bed for two weeks. By Christmas, however, Barbara was feeling a little better.

At her next six-weekly check-up at the doctor's, she was given an analysis of her dissected ovaries. Fortunately, the doctor told her there was no sign of cancer, which came as a double surprise to Barbara, since no one had so far mentioned cancer. Her ovaries, however, had many cysts on them. These, she thought, could only have been caused by HRT, because when she had had a laparoscopy in 1991, her ovaries had been clear. The consultant told her that she would have to be on HRT until she was 65, and that she should see her GP about pills or patches, until she found something that would suit her.

Over the next year, Barbara began to feel more ill. She was referred back to the hospital to see if she should have another course of implants. In November 1995, she was implanted with a combined 100mg of oestrogen and 100mg of testosterone. Following these implants, she felt well enough to go back to work for the first time. She found, however, that she was fighting a constant battle against attacks of anxiety and panic. In May 1996, she was given another implant, because the doctor told her that her body needed more of both oestrogen and testosterone and they had decided to put in an implant every five months.

Following an implant in September 1997, Barbara came home with double vision, was unable to walk, and felt as if she were going to die. She could feel that her blood pressure had shot up. When she telephoned the doctor, he told her not to worry, she was evidently hyperventilating. He made no mention of the implant, and at another visit to his surgery he prescribed blood pressure tablets and tranquillisers. Barbara struggled with her symptoms, which became worse over the next two weeks.

When she was due for her next implant, in February 1998, she mentioned the problems she had had last time on returning home. Most probably, she was told, she had reacted to the local anaesthetic, and she was given the new implant. This time, on returning home, she had very frightening three-way-split vision. She was unable to stand, felt unbalanced, and again she could sense that her blood pressure had shot up. A friend took her to the doctors. Barbara told the doctor that she was sure it was the implant that caused her problems. He was equally insistent that her complaints had nothing to do with the implant.

Barbara then tried to see an NHS consultant gynaecologist, but was told that there was not an appointment available until September. In July 1998, Barbara annoyed her doctor by refusing her next implant. She was, in fact, becoming increasingly concerned, not just about the side effects, but about the fact that the doctors at the hospital carried out no monitoring. No blood tests were taken and her breasts were never examined.

At this time, Barbara was suffering everyday symptoms of severe anxiety, giddiness, migraine, nausea, weakness in her legs, and felt unable to leave the house. She had long ago stopped working, and rarely met anyone or spoke to her friends. Most of her acquaintances had 'given up' on her because she was continuously ill for no apparent reason. Friends began to think she was neurotic.

Finally, she and Pete decided to pay privately to see a consultant. She got an appointment *the day after making the phone call to her secretary,* with the self-same female consultant whom she would have seen if she had made an NHS appointment. As she remarks now, 'Funny what money can do.' From the blood tests that her consultant ordered, Barbara found that she had had oestrogen levels of 1,540. When she asked what they should have been, the consultant said 200 and told her that she had never seen anyone with such high oestrogen levels. It was obvious, she said, that Barbara was suffering from oestrogen overdose.

The consultant stopped all Barbara's HRT immediately, and told her that she would have difficulties until her oestrogen levels fell and returned to some kind of normality. Five years later, at the end of 2003, the most serious affects of the oestrogen overdose were beginning to recede.

The terrible biological consequences of her final implant in January 1998, and the unbelievably high levels of oestrogen in her body, continued to oppress Barbara. Like most people, she has difficulty in articulating the states of ill health produced by the drugs she had been given, but her accounting is more real and more graphic than any doctor's terse notes.

> Everything just seemed to fall in on itself. My body didn't seem to do what I wanted it to do. I was in touch with the situation in my mind, but my brain didn't seem to be telling my body what to do. I had this giddy sense in my head, which affected my balance. I couldn't walk properly. I couldn't sleep in the same bed as my husband, because the slightest movement and I thought I was floating off in space. I couldn't even let anyone sit next to me on the settee, because if they were to move, get up or sit down, the movement was terrible for me. It was as if my whole co-ordination and balance had packed up. On the nights that I could get into bed, I had to sit up. Most nights, however, I stayed on the settee. I felt as if there was pressure forcing down on my head, as if my head was full of cotton wool. I was also getting serious heart palpitations.

Although Barbara's ordeal was not over when she stopped taking HRT, at least it could be said that the medical profession made it easy for her to stop taking the drug. Her consultant stated quite plainly that she was suffering from an excess of oestrogen. She asked why she had not seen Barbara before, and when Barbara replied that she had *tried* to see the consultant, she suggested that Barbara must have 'slipped through the net'.

When Barbara asked what would have happened if she had had the last implant in July, the consultant told her candidly that it would be 'best not to go down that road'. And when Barbara insisted, she confessed that she doubted Barbara would have survived.

During this consultation, for the first time, Barbara began to lose her temper with the medical profession. Being told that she would have to wait any time between ten and 15 years for the oestrogen to work its way out of her body, she told the consultant that this was not good enough. There followed a question-and-answer session, in which Barbara demanded to know what the NHS would do for her after it had over-dosed her on oestrogen. The consultant insisted that there was nothing that could be done for her. The stand-off ended when the consultant told Barbara that she would be discharging her from her clinic, and followed this with an order for her to leave the office. She had, the consultant said, other patients to see.

Despite the fact that cause had been established, and obviously con-cerned that Barbara might well sue the hospital, the consultant did, how-ever, send her to an endocrinologist. The task of this other specialist appears to have been to find another, any other, cause of Barbara's 'mys-terious' ill health. Barbara found the endocrinologist to be the most arro-gant and off-handed doctor she had so far had to deal with. Against all science and logic, he insisted that the high levels of oestrogen in Barbara's body were not actually due to the implants. In fact, contrary to the con-sultant, he suggested that the levels were not unduly high, anyway. Later he wrote in her notes, 'The patient looked disappointed when I told her this.' Barbara asked me how I thought one looks 'disappointed'. I thought that it might take a master class in doctor-patient role-play to find this out.

From this point onwards, Barbara found it impossible to know who was telling her the truth. Almost immediately after her private consulta-tion, she had made a formal complaint to the hospital about her treat-ment.

First the 'problem-solving' endocrinologist diagnosed depression and a psychiatric condition, and sent Barbara to a psychiatrist. The psy-chiatrist, however, agreed with her that she was not depressed, and sug-gested that her recognisable anxiety was being created by the behaviour of the hospital towards her. Next, the consultant gynaecologist decided that there must have been an ovarian remnant left, and ordered another laparoscopy. This turned out to be a complete waste of time and only made Barbara more ill. The consultant next suggested a tumour on the adrenal gland, but the expensive CT scan for this showed it to be clear.

For the next three years, the endocrinologist turned Barbara's life into another kind of hell, arranging every test, analysis, scan and X-ray available to modern technology in a search for tumours and other non-existent problems.

For the first two years after she stopped having HRT, no one would give her any support and none of the physicians she dealt with at the hospital acknowledged that HRT might be responsible. Her GP gave her some support, but seemed relieved that the problem was now the responsibility of the hospital. While accepting that she was not clinically depressed, her GP prescribed Barbara antidepressants. Even one tablet, however, knocked her out when the medication interacted with the synthetic oestrogen residues in her body.

In March 2000, Barbara contacted the Menopausal Helpline, and for the first time found someone, in the person of Maggie Tuttle, who was willing to listen to her and to advise her. Following discussions with the Helpline and more reading, Barbara arranged an appointment with the endocrinologist who had subjected her to a barrage of tests. This time, however, she went armed with questions, together with proof of her own contentions. One of her main suspicions after speaking to Maggie was that the implants that she had been given had probably not gone from her body, and to see whether or not this was the case, she insisted on an ultrasound scan.

The doctor was staggered by his new 'fight back' patient; in Barbara's words, 'I floored him, he was lost for words.' Although he said that, after three years, the implants would all be gone from her body, the consultant, evidently still thinking about a suit against the hospital, arranged for ultra-sound soon after Barbara left the appointment. She was not at all surprised when the results of this scan showed that the implants were still there.

In December 2000, Barbara went to see a medical professor, who said that the implants could not now be removed, and that he could tell her authoritatively that she was suffering from oestrogen storage in her body. His counsel on how long it would take for her to 'get better' and for the oestrogen to be used up or expelled was, unfortunately, indeterminate.

From being a healthy wife and mother who rarely had a day's illness, Barbara says, she became a woman who could not leave the house, who was unable to do things with her husband or sons. A woman who was, and still is, in constant battle with her body. Because of her illness, Stuart, she says, has not known what it's like to have a mother.

When I asked her what effect her illness had on her everyday life over the first two years, she said simply, 'I didn't have an everyday life. It could take me nearly all day to wash up, because I couldn't stand for more than a few moments. I couldn't watch television or even read a book. The faintest sign of movement would create spinning inside my head. I could not concentrate.'

In 2002 Barbara summed up her health status since 1998, to me, in this way: 'Every day, I battle with light-headedness, giddiness, my whole body is in constant pain, severe leg pains and swellings, weakness and faintness, hot and cold spells, incontinence, virginal itching, weight gain, bloating and lethargy.'

Beneath Barbara's rather timid first appearance there is a strong, determined woman whose experience with HRT has forced her to do battle with medical professionals in a way in which only the strongest and most focused people are able. She pushes herself daily, because she refuses to let oestrogen and physicians beat her. She has, in her words, 'taken charge of my own body'; she now speaks the language of campaigning women. She says about the Helpline, 'With help from other women who are feeling like me – and there are many – we get each other through the bad times.'

While Barbara cannot help but consider that most of her long years of illness could have been avoided by efficient monitoring of her oestrogen levels, she is quite certain now that it is women themselves who have to take responsibility for their own health. 'We have to stand up to doctors and say no to things we are unsure about. After all, it is our body and no one knows it as we do. We have got to see doctors, already armed with the information on which we should base our decisions.'

Barbara says that she is now haunted by the question, 'How did I let doctors do this to me?' In 2003, her oestrogen levels were still around 500, two-and-a-half times normal.

The year before that, in 2002, on the advice of the community health team and her GP, Barbara decided to write to the NHS Trust, pointing out what had happened to her. She received, in reply, a letter apologising to her for what the Trust called 'inappropriate treatment', saying that it had changed its policy on the use of implants. Barbara was advised to find a lawyer and to sue the Trust. After a search, she and Pete found a local solicitor who was willing to take the case on and who, after taking a statement, applied for legal aid. Unfortunately, although partial legal aid was granted, Barbara and Pete would have had to make a personal contribution of £150 a month, for the duration of the case – anything between three and ten years.

One day, not long after being forced to drop the case for financial reasons, Barbara saw a television advertisement for a no-win no-fee medical negligence practice. She rang the company, which, after taking details from her over the phone, called back and told her that they thought she had a winnable case, which they would take. The practice obtained her medical records and arranged for her to see an 'independent consultant' in an adjoining county. Barbara was told by the practice that whether or not they would pursue the case to trial depended entirely on this expert's advice.

In his report, the 'independent expert', despite agreeing with almost everything put to him by Barbara's solicitor in their face-to-face interview, suggested that the hospital could not be held responsible for Barbara's illness. In his opinion, it predated her prescription of HRT, and he could find nothing to suggest that the hospital had been negligent. He was not alarmed about the high levels of oestrogen in Barbara's body, and said that, in his experience, there was nothing unusual about levels remaining high for a long period after implants had been removed.

He made the point throughout his advice, that Barbara's problems with depression predated the administration of HRT.

> Although it is my opinion the administration of hormone replacement therapy to a woman aged thirty-seven, suffering from post-natal depression, is inappropriate, we cannot claim that it gave rise to her present problems. These definitely predated the administration of the hormone replacement therapy.

The idea of the illness predating the prescription of the drug is a regular and automatic way out for drug companies and doctors. It is particularly disingenuous, relying on the fact that it is often hard to disassociate original illnesses from the adverse effects of drugs given to 'treat' those illnesses. In Barbara's case, the argument was doubly unsuitable because her doctors had told her frequently that her first bout of illness, whether or not it was brought on by the administration in pregnancy of oestrogen supplements, was post-natal depression. Other experts had told her consistently that, after taking HRT, she did not have depression but clearly suffered from a syndrome of physical illnesses.

Given that the hospital Trust had written to Barbara admitting that she had had inappropriate treatment, the opinion of the 'independent expert' seems, at best, sloppy. At worst, the opinion was not independent and was certainly not given with the intention of furthering any kind of justice for the claimant, who had been ill for around 12 years, during the first eight of which she had been implanted with HRT. At the very least, the question of Barbara's overdosing, during which time oestrogen levels in her body had not been monitored, clearly suggested a claim for some period of her treatment.

Following the receipt of the opinion, Barbara received a letter from her solicitors informing her that, as they had warned, without a favourable report from an expert, they would be unable to pursue the NHS Trust for compensation. Barbara's case stopped there and joined the ranks of the many unresolved civil actions initiated by ordinary people in Britain over the years. Barbara's no-win no-fee solicitors told her that there was the possibility of approaching another 'independent expert'. This however, would cost her a £1,000 – an amount that was beyond Barbara's means.

Barbara is quite sure why she began the case: 'I wasn't doing it for the money, but to get these damned doctors who can ruin women's lives.' This, of course, is also the reason why her case was lost so quickly. Barbara points to another thing that stands between many claimants and success in their cases. Trying to get justice in Britain for iatrogenic damage with all its concomitant worry can make the claimant even more ill.

Often, a dichotomy can be observed between the informal culture of doctors and their more formal protective stance. While many doctors are happy to admit in private that HRT has damaged or killed patients, when it comes to court cases or newspaper articles they 'cover up' for the profession. In 2006 Barbara saw a consultant, in the presence of a medical student. Introducing Barbara, the consultant said to the student, 'This is Barbara, she has been poisoned with HRT.'

After I left my second interview with Barbara, she argued herself into giving me a lift to the station. She brought Stuart along to give her reassurance and to make decisions for her. I felt, even before we got in the car, that this was a terrible imposition to put on a sick woman. But I could sense the fight that was going on inside her, she was doing what she had taught herself to do – to face up to things and to continually test herself.

As we drew to a stop behind another car at the lights on the busy ring road, she explained why even recently she had found it difficult to return to driving. 'It wasn't anything really obvious,' she said. On those days when I felt well enough to drive, I used to get nervous when I was stopped, waiting. It was like a shadow hovering over me; I worried, and quickly became hesitant and nervous. I stopped knowing what to do.' I could imagine this feeling, the kind of nervous debility you have when you have spent a few days without sleep. This debility, however, was just a lingering taint of the terrible times that Barbara had been through over the years.

In some ways, this feeling of nerviness was almost a sign of her return to normality, a feeling that more and more people have in post-industrial society, a constant edginess, which comes with isolation; lack of confidence and a sense of estrangement from the communal structures in society.

Barbara's health is improving as she leaves this isolation behind and gradually gets back into the swim. If Maggie Tuttle had not set up the Menopausal Helpline, she would have found it much more difficult to take these steps towards rehabilitation. The Helpline did exactly what it was set up to do. It gave Barbara back her strength. It armed Barbara in her war against the NHS, medicine and professional physicians. It shared collective experiences with her, and it gave her the confidence of a community of other women.

By the time of my third interview with Barbara, she was working. She and her family took over the stall on which her son Stuart had been working for his Saturday job in the local market. The stallholder had moved and, after a discussion, they decided to buy the stall on the grounds that it would be good to aid Barbara's recovery.

Barbara has undoubtedly been lucky with her husband and family. Though she tries, she finds it hard to understand or to explain how Pete has managed to cope with her illness. 'Pete,' she says, 'is a very personal person. Even though we talk about things, he doesn't discuss his feelings with you. I don't think he does with anyone.' But for the two years when she was almost bed-bound, Pete ran the household. 'He made sure that the kids were ready for school. He would make his sandwiches, go to work himself, leaving soup in a flask for me in the fridge. If he hadn't done that for me, I wouldn't have been able to get myself meals.' After work, Pete came home, did the washing-up if there was any, then prepared the evening meal for the family. On Saturday, for six years, he went out and did the weekly shopping.

As well as the domestic chores, Pete has also taken care of the children as they were going through school, buying their clothes and going to see teachers. Barbara's voice rises in a kind of unbelieving question: 'He's done everything and he hasn't complained once.' When I ask her if Pete got any support from anyone, she reminds me that, in the main, his relatives are dead and that he has few close friends. 'No one gave Pete any support.' It occurs to me that this quiet, pragmatic and stoical male 'character' is, in some ways, quite British.

As she is talking about her husband, it drifts back into Barbara's mind that no friends came to visit her while she was ill. 'You find out who your friends are. People got fed up with you being ill. "Oh, she's not still at home is she?" they say.'

Barbara finds her new work exhausting, but it has returned her 'to the land of the living'. She has support from the women who occupy the stalls around her, all of whom understand that she is recovering from an illness and give her space when she needs it. She has also lost weight by attending keep-fit classes. She is convinced that losing four stone has also brought down her oestrogen levels, and she wonders why her doctors did not inform her that there is a connection between fat and stored oestrogen.

When Barbara was in contact with the MHL, she was put in touch with other women in her area, and now they share their problems and discuss their difficulties. She has met one woman who has been on HRT for 12 years. In the market, a number of women have now approached her, asking for advice about their adverse reactions to HRT. Barbara is pleased with her new role as supporter and adviser to women who are having problems; it makes her feel that she has not simply got better herself and then deserted the field.

She is wary about giving women advice about stopping HRT, but she loans out her books and she passes on literature from the MHL. The most important message that she has to pass on is, however, that 'although the medical profession treats us all as if we were the same, we are all different and any treatment has to be tailored to the individual.'

Far from helping Barbara to grow old gracefully, and to feel attractive and confident in later life, HRT destroyed her independence and wiped out her confidence. The drug oppressed her, made her withdrawn, unable to socialise or pursue employment. In doing all this it confirmed, particularly, the male medical stereotype of the female patient. HRT and its adverse after-effects took over Barbara's life completely for 14 years, in a way not dissimilar to an addictive street drug, and it did her just as much harm – if not more. The drug, she says, 'came to affect every single aspect of my life'.

It has affected every relationship within her family. In the week before she took over the market stall, Barbara had to go into town to buy some stock. Not having been in town for 14 years, she asked Stuart to go with her. 'Walking in town, Stuart said, "Mum, do you realise that this is the first time you have walked through town with me?" I thought to myself, "How often has my son thought things like that, how often has my illness robbed my children of a life with me?"'

Chapter Ten

Coming Off, Getting On and Coping

The fundamental principle of true healing consists of a return to natural habits of living.

Jethro Kloss[1]

The truth is that really healthy women seldom experience menopausal difficulties. So the secret of a trouble-free menopause is to get yourself into really good shape well before it starts.

Kitty Campion[2]

Although it has proved easy for millions of women to obtain HRT, and some have even had it administered without their permission, a large number of women have found it impossible to get off it, and an even larger number have been unable to return to good health after coming off. Many women have found, to their cost, that synthetic oestrogen is addictive, in the sense that they begin to live 'normal' lives with a changed hormonal balance. Abstention from the drug can often provoke physical problems severely worse than any complaint for which it was originally

---

1 Kloss J. *Back to Eden.* Loma Linda, CA: Back to Eden Books Publishing Company; 1988.
2 Campion K. *A Woman's Herbal.* London: Century; 1988.

prescribed. Some women lose their battle to come off and are forced to return to a drug regime which increasingly threatens their lives, the longer it continues.

For those who do manage to come off, the long-term adverse reactions created by taking HRT or by coming off it, can themselves take the form of serious illnesses. The consumption of synthetic hormones can so thoroughly derail many biological functions that the body is never able to regain its balance. This chapter looks at the alternative ways in which the menopause might be dealt with, and poses positive arguments against ever taking hormonal supplements in the first place. It looks at the difficulties women have in coming off the drug, and at what they might expect even when they cease a course of treatment. The chapter is illustrated with five short case histories of women who have had to battle with serious long-term adverse reactions. Finally, the chapter looks at health revival programmes for those women who feel capable of overcoming the damage which HRT has done to them.

Ellen Williams

In the front room of Ellen Williams's Liverpool council house, her favourite dog lies before the fireplace and pushes its greying muzzle into the rug. To the dog's right, on two double sheets of newspaper, sits a large and very healthy-looking, dark grey rabbit, surrounded by a dwindling stock of carrots and lettuce. Ellen Williams and her husband do not have any children.

In 1986, following an infection, thirty-one-year-old Ellen had a hysterectomy and oophorectomy. Following the operation Ellen was given HRT tablets and began a 9-year HRT nightmare. After 12 months of tablets made her increasingly ill, she began 5 years of implants; around 20 in all. Despite stopping any form of HRT in 1997, Ellen has never recovered her health; her operation has been followed by 20 years of debilitating illness.

Ellen has long hair, which streams down both sides of her face like a 1970s folk singer's; she parts it and draws it from her face with her index finger as she talks. Rather than capitulate to the pain, the loss of life, eroded at the edges, many women claim something back from their illness; Ellen Williams is one of these.

Ellen is possessed of a steely resolve. When her consultant refused to believe that she had been bleeding while taking HRT, she decided not to wash before she was next examined. It was, she says, 'humiliating', but it had to be done. She sits very upright; the pain she is in is visible in her face, beneath the surface, and behind her eyes. At one point during the interview, I notice that her nose has begun to bleed. I tell her and, as she dabs at her nose, accustomed to not being believed, she says with relief, 'I'm glad this happened while you were here.'

In 2005, the year we meet, on a normal day, Ellen Williams wakes up with chronic pain; everything hurts, her muscles go into spasm. She expects to see blood in the water after she has gone to the toilet. Her breasts are sore and the flesh beneath her skin burns. Even now, a decade after coming off HRT, Ellen can expect to spend at least one day a week in bed. As her day progresses, she finds she gets stiffer and stiffer. She has constant headaches, but, she says, 'You can't give in to them.'

When Ellen was first given implants, the adverse reactions were immediate: she had a terrible burning sensation in her stomach and her groin. Her breasts became unbearably sore. Two years into HRT, Ellen began to bleed heavily. When her oestrogen levels were belatedly, and for the first time, checked, it was found to be 4,000. She was immediately taken off implants.

At this time, her doctor told her that, because her oestrogen levels were too high, she could expect to be not very well for another 12 months. There followed two years of changing therapies, a phantom pregnancy, endometriosis and constant worry about such debilitating problems as bleeding from the back passage and the vagina, and a constant consciousness of pain.

Ellen has, luckily, been partnered throughout her illness by a close friend, Jill, whom she met at an HRT conference. Jill too has endometriosis, and now serious adverse reactions to many of the drugs she has been prescribed during the illness. Jill and Ellen help to fight each other's cases; Jill acts as the Internet search engine, providing the information they need to inform themselves and to campaign. The two of them have been working together for over ten years. Jill has being struck off her local practice register and has lost her GP as a consequence of seeking a solution for her illness.

Ellen's self-treatment is heavily circumscribed by her lack of finances. On benefits, she is too hard pressed to afford much in the way of organic produce. 'I try to stay as mobile as possible, and I eat a lot of fresh vegetables and fruit. Since HRT, I have found that I am very allergic, so I have real difficulty, not just with medicines, which I don't take, but even with vitamins and herbal preparations. I drink grapefruit and lemon juice for my liver.'

The only thing that Ellen and her husband have been able to afford to help in her campaign, to prove her illness, besides a handful of key books, is a photocopier. While I finish the interview, Ellen's husband makes photocopies for me. Ellen hands me the fruits of Jill's labour, documents filed in large, clean, white envelopes. 'I do wonder what the future holds,' Ellen says in a voice overloaded with pragmatism. 'I tell myself that you just have to cope with it the best way you can and not let the depression take over.'

Having a pleasant dinner with friends recently, I got into an argument about tax, finance and education. My hosts had different political views from mine. They were implacably opposed to paying any more for education and kept asking me where the money would come from to keep paying for more and more young people to receive a tertiary education.

Of course, I was reluctant to answer this question, but prodded into a corner, I said a little angrily, 'Well, I wouldn't have got into this predicament in the first place.' I was about to go on to say I wouldn't have spent billions on the war in Iraq etc., but my host interrupted, laughing, and said, 'Oh no, "I wouldn't start from here." A very good argument.' His

ELLEN

expression stuck with me; it was the reply of a pragmatist to an idealist, and it brought me hard up against political realities, which I often refuse to consider.

However, I think I can say without the slightest hesitation when talking about health, orthodox medicine and pharmaceuticals that it is nearly always better to start from *there* rather than *here*, from 'some other place' rather than the contemporary reality of industrial healthcare. If we could briefly define that 'other place', it might make the specific suggestions of this chapter more easily understood.

My 'other' starting place is one where we accept into our bodies none – or the absolute minimum – of the chemical toxins prescribed for us. It is one where we enjoy nutritious and, as far as is possible, organic fruit and vegetables. I, personally, would like this place, eventually to be vegan – in such quantities and proportions and cooked in such ways that we have a properly balanced diet. By 'balanced', I don't mean two potatoes today and an orange tomorrow, but a diet that satisfies our bodies' need for a complex intake of vitamins and minerals.

This other place is one where we try to control our immediate environment as best we are able, so as to exclude environmental toxins. A place where we don't smoke cigarettes and we consume next to no alcohol; where we ensure that we get sufficient exercise every day, to keep our bodies in shape. It is a place where we have as little to do with pharmaceuticals and pharmaceutical procedures as possible and where we avoid hospitals like the plague.

My ideal place is one where, from an early age, we gain as much information as possible about our bodies and how they work; a place where we try to understand how to respect our bodies and treat them with the various healing arts. It is a place where we take what is best from our collective culture and history, and repudiate the violence and emptiness of commercial culture.

In this place, beauty is not just a thin Hollywood veneer, nor sexuality just alienating, animalistic, penetrative and male-initiated. In this place, women do not consider that a sensuous life ends at menopause, and everyone can still naturally enjoy their sexuality, touching and loving in an individual and sensuous manner, without body-altering drugs.

If we did start from this 'other place', there is little doubt that most women would have few, if any, menopausal problems. Anthropological and clinical research has shown that women who live in societies where physical exercise is common into old age, where there is good nutrition, a low intake of protein and a relatively low intake of dairy produce, with plenty of fresh vegetables and fruit, have few problems during menopause.

In many developing societies, the time of the passing of childbearing is signalled by few physical signs, and accompanied by a supporting philosophy that grants the elder a respected place.[3] In developed society, in order to push drugs, the medical profession and the pharmaceutical companies have medicalised the time of the menopause.

Contemporary developed society is a laboratory in which the habitat and inner lives of its subjects have become simply the victims of commercial interests. The social environment in which this experiment takes place pressures women to turn to their doctors and to drugs in order to see them through the change of life. The extended family, in which elderly people come into contact with younger ones, is, meanwhile, diminished and communities are fragmented. Life science engineers have turned the menopause into a time of loss and regret, to create markets for powerful, illness-inducing drugs. The female elderly in many developed societies have been taught that they have to expect only isolation and rejection to look forward to, accompanied by slowly declining health – unless, that is, they take synthetic hormones.

Linked to this suggestion that with age our health inevitably needs shoring up with chemical nostrums, is an ardent determination within the medical profession to refuse to deal in either preventive or environmental health, or to engage in robust discussion of healthy lifestyles. In fact, flying in the face of reason, it goes farther than this. Not only are pharmaceutical companies bent on flooding the market with quack cures, but they are also spending millions of dollars organising against vitamins, food supplements and natural health care.

While, on the one hand, major pharmaceutical companies manufacture and distribute life-threatening hormone replacement therapies, on

---

3 See Germaine Greer, *The Change: Women, aging and the menopause*. London: Hamish Hamilton; 1991.

---

the other they wage war against long-established self-help treatments for menopausal problems. In the past decade, there have been consistent campaigns against a number of vitamins and food supplements, including vitamins B1, B6 and B12, and magnesium. Each of these plays an important part in self-treatment for menopausal problems. This, of course, is only a small example of the global assault on the levels of all vitamins, food supplements and herbal preparations that women might want if they are to avoid chemical treatments.

The reason for these negations of health-care policies is fairly obvious. If doctors pursued preventive therapies, lifestyle advice and natural remedies, they would find themselves in serious conflict with the medical industrial complex, and, it has to be said, with some of their patients. Orthodox medicine sets women up for the menopause and creates a dependency, which leads them to accept drugs when they are not ill.

Maggie Tuttle

For the past nine years, Maggie Tuttle has had been immersed in illnesses created by HRT; her heart has bled for the women who have had these illnesses. Maggie wanted this book to contain information about every single adverse reaction created by HRT. In this sense, the book probably hasn't done its job. The problem, from my point of view as a writer, is that I have to place the adverse reactions in a social, political and personal context.

Perhaps the most important of these contexts is the personal one. Illness is a very personal matter, in its origins, its progress and its eventual conquest of, or defeat by, the individual whom it inhabits. Women damaged by HRT live for the rest of their lives beneath the shadow of its reckless action on their bodies, like the wounded in a forgotten war. Society, medicine and institutions move on, but the wounded are left to live with their personal damage.

290

Despite having closed down the Helpline, Maggie is in touch with a number of the women whom she met through it, and she still fiercely defends their cases. To her, all the essential questions of this book and any other project around HRT boil down to how it might be possible to make *her women* better. She is haunted by the constant reminder, not only of her own physical problems, but of those of all the women who wrote to or telephoned her.

For herself, Maggie long ago gave up seeking medical advice. After various operations and medicines, many adverse reactions and destroyed days, months and years, she now accepts that her initial faith in the medical profession was an obscure desire that had been fraudulently foisted upon her generation. She follows a routine of self-treatment in an attempt to minimise the most painful remaining effects of the HRT.

Ten years after weaning herself off HRT, Maggie still has muscles that lock in her shoulder and her neck. When she wakes in the mornings she has constant pain from spine to shoulder and then into her eyes. If she is unable to control the pain on waking, she has to take painkillers to stop it from setting into her day. If she does not take the drugs and the pain persists, on that morning her sight might also be affected. At her most badly affected, Maggie is overcome with terrible tiredness, similar to that experienced in myalgic encephalomyelitis (ME) or chronic fatigue syndrome (CFS). This tiredness often results in women who have been made ill by HRT being falsely diagnosed, not only with ME and CFS, but also with fibromyalgia and even multiple sclerosis.

Maggie's constant reading and Internet research has persuaded her that HRT has affected the nerve endings in her body. In her most optimistic moods, Maggie takes on the world, but at her more pessimistic and reflective, she says quietly, 'It's ten years down the road and I'm still suffering.'

During and after taking HRT, Maggie, like other women, suffered respiratory problems; she had to struggle for breath. This adverse reaction to the drug led her into hospital for an emergency operation on her throat. In this case, the doctors had decided that her airways were blocked. However, when they operated, they found no evidence of this. Since the operation, Maggie has found it difficult to blow her nose. Now, sometimes her mouth will go dry and she is unable to produce saliva; she again has trouble breathing.

Maggie understands that every woman is affected differently by HRT – even that some women, taking the drug for only short periods, can escape with their health almost intact. She is, however, quite sure where the blame and responsibility lies in those cases where women's lives have been destroyed. 'The Government is mainly responsible for the condition of the affected women, because it allows the pharmaceutical companies to manufacture and give out these drugs without sufficient control. And the regulatory agencies are full of people with conflicting interests. My answer to any pharmaceutical company executive who says that it is not possible to do long-term trials of a drug would be: "I think that *you* should take it. And I think that you should stop testing drugs on animals, because the results bear no relationship to the effect on humans". If you are going to put out a drug *en masse* before it has been thoroughly tested, not only have you to tell people this, but *you have to listen to them when they report adverse reactions*. Politicians have to listen to the people. That's why we vote in governments, I thought – to listen to the people.'

At the forefront of Maggie's work for women who contacted the Menopausal Helpline, was the continuous search for the supplements, herbs and treatments that could help women suffering from adverse reactions, restoring some of their previous health. She is sceptical of many of the alternative products on offer, which are said to either help with the menopause or to restore health to women who suffer post-menopausal conditions, mainly because they are not specifically geared to treating serious adverse effects of HRT. Maggie's way of dealing with the adverse effects of HRT are similar to those used for chemical sensitivity.

'I have been very keen on women taking vitamin B complex because HRT inhibits the absorption of B vitamins. I am also keen on Dong

Quai, which is popular in China, where women take it prior to the menopause and to help with PMT. Also, lecithin, which is very good for the memory, the function of which can be harmed by HRT, and milk thistle, which, used over long periods, help to clean the liver. I don't drink tap water, but I do drink lemon juice every day to try to detoxify my liver. And I recommend vitamin E to women who haven't got high blood pressure or heart problems.'

As well as trying to treat herself while running the MHL, Maggie also had to bear the added burden of fighting the pharmaceutical companies. She knew that her phone was tapped, particularly during the time of the Brighton conference, and she remains suspicious about the fact that a wheel came off her trusted car and the steering collapsed, in the week prior to the conference.

I suppose I think that the scientific contribution to health is far less than has been suggested. When I came to write this chapter and I looked at the literature, I found that nearly all the work on alternative health therapies for aspects of the menopause was done from a scientific viewpoint. It's not that I don't believe the results of scientific studies of alternative treatments; it is just that I have grown used to considering healing to be an art rather than a science.

The *art* of health care means that the individual has a much greater involvement in his or her own care; it means a more dynamic relationship between therapeutic subject and therapist; it means that health care is a viable and intimate aspect of community.

Health care of all kinds has to become more accessible, and if we want to learn about our bodies and our illnesses, it is important that we ditch ideas of 'magic bullets'. The journey to self-administered health care is not best served by immediately buying a remedy that in trial A stopped every other hot flush that occurred after 5.30 in the evening in 58 per cent of the respondents who were between 45 and 56 years of age, who favoured purple frocks and lived in a green-belt area just west of Birmingham.

With respect to alternative treatments for difficulties during the menopause, very few women, unless they have been taking care of their bodies for the 40 years prior to the event, are going to find a quick fix. The treatments that they try, and with which they might have varying degrees of success, are treatments at which they will arrive in discussion with a herbalist, a homeopath or a nutritionist – perhaps all three, and maybe more. In dealing with their feelings about their bodies, as against serious ailments or diseases, it is better to explore the possibilities than to opt for a 'cure'.

In many of the letters from women on which I drew in previous chapters, individuals say, 'I tried to come off HRT and started taking herbs', or 'I went to a homeopath'. It is an unfortunate fact that most alternative therapies do no offer a 'quick fix'. In fact, quite the opposite: most forms of worthwhile alternatives, will want, while dealing with contemporary problems, to sort out your lifestyle and nutrition, and, in the case of homeopathy, even to examine your family history of illness, before, or perhaps at the same time as, introducing you to a better way of health. On the whole, only orthodox medicine purports to offer elixirs, and when they are prescribed, you are never told about either the true cost of the side effects, or the long-term consequences of the apparent and specific cure.

This is why, in this discourse, I feel that it is only possible to start from 'there' rather than 'here'. So, although what I suggest from this point onwards is specifically aimed at women who begin to sense the signs of the menopause, many of the suggestions should be taken seriously by both men and women of any age.

Jan

I have prayed some days, that the Lord would take me away, rather than face another day of it. I thought HRT was a wonderful thing; now I realise it's a killer. If I had my time over again, I wouldn't touch it. It's ruined my life. The pain is everywhere.'

An attractive 73-year-old woman, Jan is still very conscious of her figure and her looks. While I interviewed her, she folded and unfolded a photocopied data sheet. This page and the scar that runs from her abdomen to her groin, are the most persistent reminders of what HRT has done to her.

Feeling tired in her late fifties, Jan was prescribed HRT by her GP. Her first two years on the treatment went perfectly. 'I felt fantastic, reborn, with boundless energy.' However, her new youth melted away as quickly as it had appeared, to be replaced by all the classic adverse reactions. One summer's morning, hurrying through the dining room to the kitchen from the garden to reach the phone, Jan found herself breathless. She had been prescribed the birth Pill when she was 50 to stop heavy bleeding. As well as stopping the bleeding, however, the hormone Pill had also provoked a classic allergic response of heavy itching, and after two years on it, when she also began to get very bad migraines, Jan had stopped taking it.

Had the itching and scalding started again as soon as she began HRT, Jan says now, she would have had an early warning of what was to come, but only after two years did that symptom return with a vengeance. Following her lack of breath, the symptoms began to pile up: burning started in her mouth and it became painful to speak or eat properly; she was forced to consume only liquids. And still her doctors couldn't find anything wrong with her.

Jan changed her prescription from a cream to a patch, which was given together with a course of pills. When she took the last pill on her course, she suddenly got terrible pains in her legs. The following morning, she started to bleed profusely. She bled for seven days, but her legs stopped being painful. She resumed using the patch and took the next course of pills; with the last of which, she again got serious leg pains. The next morning, she noticed that her ankles had swollen badly. This time, she experienced bleeding for eight days. The doctor put the swelling in her ankles down to arthritis.

Since that time, the burning sensation has covered every part of her body. 'It is mainly on the inside, although I have had terrible skin eruptions, also.' These have taken the form of great, big blotches, about the size of an egg. She has, further, had very bad rashes around her hairline – all this, more than a decade since she came off HRT completely.

Jan sleeps at night only because she takes painkillers and sleeping tablets. In the morning when she wakes, she is usually without pain, but as soon as she goes to the toilet, it all starts – all her problems. She has terrible stinging and burning, a hundred times worse than cystitis. This pain is with her all day. She has had trouble with breathing, an inflamed stomach, damaged ankles, rashes at different times all over her body. In the past year, she has lost a lot of her hair. She lost her nails, which came back only after a year. Her skin gets very dry in places. She has had dizzy spells. The doctor has told her that for the rest of her life she will have to put up with 'an unidentified infection'.

Jan's worst problems to date occurred in April 2004, when her doctor had diagnosed a swelling in her abdomen and other problems as 'a very large tumour' round her colon and kidneys. Her first operation was followed by another stay in hospital to remove various devices, and then a third, because her doctor thought that she might have had a blood clot, an embolism or a slight heart attack. Since they operated on the 'tumour', another consultant has suggested that it was no such thing, but diverticulitis.

'I suffer from all the side effects here on this data sheet,' Jan says as she unfolds again the pieces of lined paper. 'Not one of the doctors I saw has taken any notice of what I said about HRT. At one time, my consultant sent me to see a psychologist. She turned out to be immediately sympathetic, and when I told her my fears about HRT, she reassured me and recommended that I had more urological tests.'

Alternative Menopause

It is inevitably the case that individuals tend to see conditions in the way in which they have been culturally taught. In the case of the menopause, cultural teaching could lead you to conclude that you should take HRT.

It is, therefore, important that you don't include a whole series of conditions, such as osteoporosis, in your self-help on problems of menopause. Don't be tricked by the cultural fables of drug pushers: if you have hot flushes or depression, try to work on these problems, rather than seek a panacea for the menopause or 'illnesses of the elderly'.

As in almost every area relating to the menopause, the information you need is contained in Barbara Seaman's book, *Women and the Crisis in Sex Hormones*.[4] Anyone who wants to read in detail about alternative approaches to discomfort during menopause should read this book. I do, however, summarise below the therapeutic approaches suggested by Seaman and a couple of other writers.

At the heart of any treatment or therapy must be food and nutrition. To some extent, many of the rules about nutrition and health are immutable, while others can be shaped around the slowing of the production of oestrogen during menopause.

Barbara Seaman's general nutritional advice to women during the menopause, and for that matter throughout their lives, is to eat fewer sweets, starches, and fried or fatty foods, especially saturated fats, and to increase consumption of fibre, raw fruit and vegetables, whole grains and cereals, especially iron-rich beans, bran, dried fruit, green vegetables, nuts and cereals.

Advice about food and supplementation during or prior to the menopause tends to fall into two categories: foods and supplements that can provide the body with oestrogens or progesterone when your own output declines, and foods and supplements that might help to alleviate some of the actual symptoms of the menopause.

With respect to foods and supplementation, which provide the body with oestrogens, the objective is not to raise oestrogen levels to the levels that existed prior to the menopause, or to exceed these levels. Nor is the objective, as it so often appears to be with HRT, to live the rest of your life with a high oestrogen count. The idea is to smooth out the curve of the change and make it seamless.

---

4 Seaman B, Seaman G. *Women and the Crisis in Sex Hormones*. New York: Rawson Associates; 1977.

Many of the foods that are high in phyto-oestrogens can be made into cakes or breakfast dishes. Phyto-oestrogens, which are only 1/200th as strong as natural, bodily-produced oestrogens, are found in around 300 foods. Rich sources include whole grains, flax seed, rye, millet, chick-peas, soya beans, lentils and peas. Rhubarb has been found to contain oestrogen-like compounds, as have, anise, celery, fennel, ginseng, alfalfa, red clover and liquorice. A hormone-porridge is recommended by Kitty Campion in her book *A Woman's Herbal.* [5]

> Early in the evening fill a wide-necked thermos flask one third full with whole buckwheat, whole millet, whole wheat, whole oats or whole barley. Fill the rest of the flask with boiling water. Seal, shake and leave overnight. In the morning serve the grains with unsalted butter, honey, maple syrup, ginger or cinnamon and add pre-soaked dried fruit. Sprinkle in equal parts with sunflower seeds, sesame seeds and pumpkin seeds.

The following is a cake recipe sent by the Menopausal Helpline to anyone who contacted it:

4oz/100g each of soya flour, whole wheat flour, porridge oats, lin-seeds

2oz/50g of sunflower seeds, pumpkin seeds, sesame seeds, flaked almonds

2 pieces of stem ginger

8oz/200g raisins

3/4 litre soya milk

1tbsp malt extract

1/2 tsp nutmeg 1/2 tsp cinnamon

I/2 tsp ground ginger

Put dry ingredients into a large bowl and mix thoroughly, then add soya milk and malt extract. Mix well and leave to soak for about half an hour. If the mixture is too stiff, add more soya milk. Spoon into a

---

5 Campion K. *A Woman's Herbal.* London: Century; 1988.

loaf tin lined with oiled greaseproof paper. Bake in oven gas mark 5/190c for about 15 minutes or until cooked through (test with skewer). Turn out and leave to cool.[6]

Natural progesterone is more rare than oestrogen but can be found in wild yam.

Hot Flushes

The National Women's Health Network (NWHN) suggests that slow, deep breathing will help with hot flushes, and that exercise generally helps. Studies at Wayne State University showed that a combination of progressive muscle relaxation and deep, slow breathing reduced women's hot flushes by about 50 per cent.[7]

Certain foods are also suspected of provoking hot flushes. This fits with the idea expressed by a group of British doctors and therapists that hot flushes and some of the other signs of the menopause might actually be caused by food sensitivities. The NWHN suggests cutting down on caffeine, chocolate, spicy or hot foods and alcohol. John Robbins, author of *Reclaiming Our Health*, advises that regular exercise and a vegetarian diet cuts down on hot flushes – called hot 'flashes' in North America.

Herbs

Herbalists, on the whole, seem to agree about the plants that help with hot flushes and other problems of the menopause. For hot flushes, Kitty Campion recommends rosemary, spearmint, mugwort, St John's wort,

---

6 As you can see, this recipe is for a vegan cake. People who are not vegans might want to add organic free range eggs. People might also want to add apple juice as a sweetener and some first cold-pressed organic olive oil. The recipe is taken from a leaflet produced by Wellfoods Ltd., Unit 6, Mapplewell Business Park, Mapplewell, Barnsley, South Yorkshire, S75 6BP. http:\\www.bake-it.com.

7 Robbins J. *Reclaiming Our Health: Exploding the medical myth and embracing the source of true healing.* Tiburon, CA: H J Kramer; 1996.

vervain and false unicorn.[8] She also suggests taking three drops of essential oil of sage with honey and hot water just before bed.

Herbs that should be tried for menopausal problems generally include black cohosh (said to lessen sweating), chasteberry (Agnus castus), dong quai, Siberian ginseng, evening primrose oil, ginkgo biloba, kava-kava, liquorice and sage.

Herbs thought specifically to promote oestrogen production or that contain oestrogen-like substances are: false unicorn, liquorice, blessed thistle, raspberry leaf, wild yam, sage, lady's slipper, pasque-flower, elderflowers and lobelia.

According to Robbins, who cites a study by Tori Hudson *et al*, 'A pilot study using botanical medicines in the treatment of menopause symptoms',[9] the herbs liquorice root, burdock root, wild yam root, dong quai root and motherwort, taken in a single capsule against a placebo, reduced the severity of menopausal symptoms in 100 per cent of the participants. Only 6 per cent of the placebo-takers noted a reduction in symptoms.

In the transcript to what appears to have been an excellent day's symposium on 'Natural Approaches to the Menopause', organised by *Positive Health* in 1998, a large number of remedies for menopausal problems are laid out.[10] The herbalist who spoke at the symposium was Judy Griffin, the author of *Mother Nature's Herbal*, among other books. Griffin's recipe for hot flushes, night sweats, fatigue, depression and mental fogginess, combines black cohosh, dong quai, wild yam root, chasteberry and ginger or liquorice root.

---

8 Campion, op. cit.

9 Hudson T, Standish L, Bettenburg R. A pilot study using botanical medicines in the treatment of menopause symptoms. *Townsend Letter for Doctors and Patients,* 1994; 137:1372.

10 With its contribution from the late Dr John Lee, this document makes very interesting reading. Besides Dr Lee, other contributors to the Symposium included Dr Shirley Bond, Dr David Smallbone, Dr Judy Griffin, Beth MacEoin and Leslie Kenton. The symposium was introduced and chaired by the founder of *Positive Health* magazine, Dr Sandra Goodman.

Homeopathy

While, as I have said above, classical homeopaths would rarely prescribe a remedy without talking to the patient, Lynne Mcttagart, in her book *What Doctors Don't Tell You*, cites Dr Patrick Kingsley, who has had some success in treating menopause symptoms generally with the homeopathic preparation Lachesis at 30c potency, and silver nitrate, also at 30c. Dr Kingsley suggests that the Lachesis should be taken four times a day for a few days, reducing gradually to once a day just before bedtime.

Vitamins

Barbara Seaman includes a chapter in her book that is entirely on vitamins and minerals, which she suggests are useful for women generally. These include: vitamin B complex, vitamin E and vitamin C. In their 1987 book, *Nutritional Medicine*, Dr Stephen Davies and Dr Alan Stewart look at menopause only briefly, but suggest vitamin B and E supplementation and an adequate consumption of zinc and essential fatty acids. A study by Winlaw from 1994 suggests that 200mg of vitamin C, along with 200mg of bioflavonoids six times a day provides complete relief for 67 per cent of women, and partial relief of menopausal symptoms for an additional 21 per cent.[11]

Vitamin E and B complex are professionally regarded as being of value in treating menopausal problems. Seaman's section on vitamin E is heavily backed by studies and medical information, which show it to be effective.

Some studies suggest that ginseng, taken over a period of between 10 days and six weeks, with vitamin E, is good for the prevention of hot flushes.

---

11 DeMarco C. *Take Charge of Your Body*. Winlaw, British Columbia: Well Women Press; 1994.

Heather Biggs

When I rang Heather to arrange an interview, I mistook her lapses into silence for reluctance. By the distant sound of her voice, I was sure that she did not want to be interviewed. When I got to see her, however, I found out the real reason for the long pauses: Heather's memory and her concentration had been spirited away.

Halfway through the interview, I began to feel despondent about getting anything substantial from her; she seemed unable even to remember the adverse reactions from which she suffered.

'Can we try again?' I said. 'Besides the tiredness and the headaches, what else was there that made you feel seriously ill?'

Heather stared in front of herself looking down at her files, letters and documents which had been produced at an earlier time. She smiled slightly: 'What do you mean, "seriously ill"?', she said as if the words were foreign to her.

'Some women say that they have terrible pain, especially when they have been overdosed with implants.'

'Oh, yes, I did have to crawl up the stairs on my hands and knees at one point because of the pain.' She said this as if it were an aside, as if to say, 'Oh, that's what you mean by ill, is it?'

Then, slowly, she began to disentangle the memory and the present recollection of her illness and adverse reactions from the log-jam of half-focused thoughts.

'Some days I will have a runny nose, some days I produce too much saliva, other days I seem to produce none at all. Some days my eyes are very dry and sore. I have very dry skin, patches like eczema which are terribly dry, and I have lesions; they bleed and then the dry skin falls away leaving a dark mark.'

She rolled up her sleeve to show that her arms were patterned with purple patches and spots.

302

Heather is in her early fifties. She last had an implant in August 2000. At the time when she stopped accepting implants, her oestrogen levels were 3,500. Although, as she says, the figure could have been much higher previously, it was never measured. This test was the first and only one she had been given after beginning on HRT, following a hysterectomy in 1997. Now Heather is unsure as to whether or not she gave her permission for the implant. She imagines she must have done, otherwise the consultant would not have given it to her – 'Would he?'

The first three months after her operation were hell, but during the next couple of months she felt all right. Then, with the second implant, she started to feel unwell. She began to get very bad headaches, with feelings of pressure behind her eyes. She had extreme mood swings, one minute being on top of things and the next 'going under'. She lost all her energy. At the time, her work entailed using an industrial sewing-machine, producing material accessories for helicopters. It was a precision stitching work. She began falling asleep at her machine. Her company was good to her, firstly giving her work that she could do at home, and then taking her back into the factory.

However, the adverse reactions got worse as she received more oestrogen. She began to feel so ill with fatigue and headaches that workmates had to keep bringing her home. Then, when the company laid her off, she became seriously depressed, and just after her last implant her consultant put her on Prozac.

This was despite the fact that Heather was showing clear signs of adverse reactions to the high levels of oestrogen in her body, which would have been the cause of her depression. She had very high blood pressure. Her joints hurt – it was the joint pains that had her crawling up the stairs. She experienced a dull ache throughout her body, and constant fatigue.

Heather spent time, initially, writing letters and searching for information. She made enquiries about getting her medical notes, but found that the cost to her of obtaining them was too high.

As if to divert attention from HRT, her doctor has now diagnosed Heather with ME and fibromyalgia. While it might well be the case that Heather has developed these illnesses, none of the doctors she has seen have even hinted at the cause of them.

'When I did have a test and the level was 3,500,' she says, 'I was told that I would have to stop taking HRT. They didn't tell me that I would be ill for a long time afterwards. I have to rest now between everything I do, between getting up and washing, between washing and making my breakfast. My memory and my concentration have been badly affected.'

Osteoporosis

I think it is misleading to get into a discussion of the treatment of osteoporosis when looking at the menopause. In fact, it is falling into one of the holes dug for us by the pharmaceutical companies. The whole matter of osteoporosis arose in relation to the menopause, only because drug pushers wanted to bolster the advertised use of HRT for marketing purposes. The only link between osteoporosis and the menopause is that they can begin within two decades of each other.

The fact that osteoporosis usually starts to become evident some ten years or more after the menopause, with the greatest risk of fractures at age 75-plus, is a compelling reason not to use HRT to treat osteoporosis either at, or before, the menopause. By taking it for a decade or two, theoretically to prevent osteoporosis, you could be trading broken bones at 80 for heart attack, stroke, thrombosis or breast cancer in your 50s or 60s. Furthermore, if it is to be effective against osteoporosis (and a Danish study in 2000 on HRT and the incidence of forearm fracture in postmenopausal women, showed no significant reduction in breaks), it has to be taken for a long period of time, and as soon as you stop taking it, bone density starts to drop to pre-HRT levels.

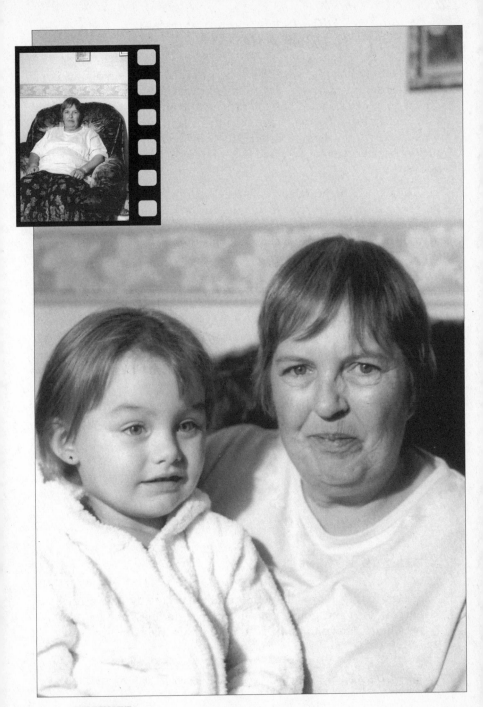

HEATHER

Growth in bone density cannot be precipitated by simply drinking milk or consuming dairy produce. Other factors help with the absorption and use of calcium once it has entered the human body. Calcium is used in the metabolism of protein, and for this reason and the fact that osteoporosis is very prevalent in societies that consume a lot of protein, many nutritionists believe that, to avoid osteoporosis, a low-protein diet is necessary.

The world's highest dairy consumers suffer most from osteoporosis. The best non-dairy sources of calcium include green, leafy vegetables, tahini (sesame paste), tofu, broccoli and sunflower seeds. Critics of vegetarian diets will tell you that these foods supply scant calcium, but consider the following.

In North America, female meat eaters at 65 have lost 35 per cent of their bone mass. Female vegetarians of the same age have an average bone mass loss of only 18 per cent.[12]

Seaman stresses that green vegetables, not milk and dairy products, are the best form of calcium. To ensure absorption of calcium into the bones, it must be combined with certain amounts of magnesium and phosphorous.

Women who avoid smoking and excessive alcohol, salt, caffeine, cola drinks and sugar have the strongest bones. Physical exercise appears to be the very best hedge against osteoporosis: women who do physical work or exercise heavily and regularly into their sixties are greatly protected against brittle bones.

Elizabeth Bowler

'On a bad day, I'm really poorly in the morning. It takes a couple of hours to get going, I'm slow, I have giddiness and nausea; sometimes I have to go back to bed. I have pains in my head,

12 Robbins J. *Diet for a New America*. Walpole, NH: Stillpoint Publishing; 1987.

very dry eyes and not enough saliva in my mouth. I get very tired; on some days I walk out to get my paper, and when I get back I go out like a light, sleeping very heavily. My nights are horrendous. I get bad pains in my head when I lie down, and I can't breathe. I am up and down to the bathroom; I cough because mucous builds up in my throat. I'm lucky if I get two or three hours' sleep. My sinuses are very painful; I usually reach a point in the night where I am absolutely exhausted.'

At 50, Liz had a hysterectomy and had her ovaries removed. She thinks now that there was no medical need for her to take HRT, and her first implant was put in without her permission. During the three years that she was given implants, Liz had no tests at all, not even of her blood pressure and certainly not of hormone levels. Liz had her last implant 15 years ago. She had previously been made ill by the Pill, which she took when she was younger. It gave her terrible headaches and the beginnings of a thyroid problem. Bitterly, she says now, that the consultant didn't ask her about the Pill; 'Actually,' she adds, 'he didn't ask me anything.'

Many of the women affected by HRT have an aura of loneliness, as if they have been battling in vain for years against confinement in an invisible prison. Like other women committed to their cases, Elizabeth has well-filed bundles of papers, replete with newspaper cuttings and letters to pharmaceutical companies. She campaigned hard on her case, she wrote many letters to Organon, who simply denied all responsibility.

Like the other women in this book, despite having a 'good' solicitor, Liz didn't even get started in her case to claim damages. She became a victim of the pharmaceutical-industry-supported 'expert witness' scam, which entails making bogus lists of experts for gullible lawyers – the 'experts' on the list, in this case, being entirely experts in prescribing HRT and ignoring its adverse effects. When Liz's lawyer found her an expert witness, this expert never saw her or examined her, but was happy to give an 'expert opinion'. This was, says Liz, quoting, 'that just because I had been made ill by HRT, that did not make the treatment bad or the consultant negli-

gent.' The solicitor and the barrister travelled personally to her flat
to tell me that they could not continue with the case. Like other
lawyers in similar circumstances, they refused to tell her who the
'expert witness' was or to take any responsibility for letting this fox
into the run in the first place.

Looking back, Liz thinks that as soon as she had been given the
first implant her life was over. By the end of the fifth day in hospital
after her surgery, she had a streaming cold and a sore throat. She got
home to other portents of a failing body. At home on the first day,
she fainted for only the second time in her life, and bashed her head
on the radiator. From that day onward, she didn't leave the house
for three years, except for hospital appointments; mainly because
she was dizzy all the time. After two years, she became very ill, and
after two-and-a-half years her health was wrecked. She was jaun-
diced, had lost two-and-a-half stone, couldn't eat, and had difficulty breathing. But even then, when she was too sick to get to the hospital to get her next implant, her GP told her not to let herself get low
on oestrogen: 'Go to the hospital,' he admonished her.

Liz was in and out of hospital, where consultants gave 'all the
usual suspects' diagnoses, none of which pointed the finger at HRT.
On one occasion she was thought to have meningitis. Her breasts
grew and were very painful, to the extent that, in the end, she had to
have a breast reduction operation. She had to have a thyroidectomy
and, following this, was unable to speak for three months. It has left
her with a legacy of continuous, serious throat infections.

'In my opinion, doctors are completely untrustworthy. At the
height of my illness, which I have suffered now for over 15
years, I was seeing a neurologist, a general surgeon, an eye specialist because my eyes were haemorrhaging, an ENT specialist,
a dermatologist. Not one of these consultants suggested that it
was the HRT making me ill, despite the fact that it was the only
medication that I was taking. Despite the huge lump on my neck
caused by the overgrowth of my thyroid, they sent me to see a
psychiatrist. When I saw the psychiatrist and talked to her for 45
minutes, she was adamant that I was not even depressed, and

LIZ

she ordered blood tests; these, of course, showed nothing because, as with all the others, they did not test for oestrogen.'

Despite her illnesses and her straitened circumstances, Liz tries, as far as she is able, to take some supplements and to pay attention to nutrition. 'I use garlic and ginger root and take milk thistle. On the whole, though, I find it too expensive to take these all the time. I eat lots of fruit and vegetables and drink lots of water. My digestion has been very badly damaged; there are foods that I can't tolerate.'

'It took ten years from the last implant to get the oestrogen out of my system. Unfortunately, the damage had been done over this period, and although I thought that I would get better once the levels had fallen, this has not been the case. I have now developed an auto-immune illness, which seems to be getting worse rather than better.'

A couple of days before I saw her, Liz had been to see a friend who was unwell, and had tried to help out around the house. The following day, alone in her flat, she had paid for it. She felt like a rag doll. 'I want to be part of my friends' and, for instance, my grand-children's lives and do things with them. I want to fight it, I tell myself that it isn't going to destroy me, but it is doing.'

Chapter Eleven

The Profit, the Whole Profit and Nothing but the Profit

The pain, dysfunction, disability and even anguish which result from technical medical intervention now rival the morbidity due to traffic, work and even war-related activities. Only modern malnutrition is clearly ahead.

Ivan Illich [1]

Other branches of commercial activity, such as passenger airlines, which also operate for the public interest, are subjected to strict liability in the case of an accident which can in no way be blamed on the company concerned.

Henning Sjostrom and Robert Nilsson [2]

Not long after I left college, having worked for 18 months in the West End with heroin addicts, I was offered a job carrying out research at the Institute of Community Studies. The research was into juvenile drug use in Bethnal Green in London's East End. I had to carry out some participant observation and interviewed some young people on a one-to-one basis. For the latter, I arranged interviews at the Institute close to Bethnal Green tube station.

---

1 Ivan Illich, *Medical Nemesis: The expropriation of health.* London: Calder & Boyers; 1975.

2 Henning Sjostrom and Robert Nilsson. *Thalidomide and the Power of the Drug Companies.* Harmondsworth, Middlesex: Penguin Books; 1972.

There were a wide range of questions and a discussion. One day I had to interview a slight, 14-year-old, who had persistently played truant and who, despite his tender years, had been involved in all kinds of criminal depredations. He was very confident and interested in the idea of being interviewed. I can recall him now, smiling and tipping back on his chair while he thought about the questions. We got on to the discursive questions and answers. My pen was poised over the paper as I asked him:

'How would you describe your ideal society?'

He thought for a moment, his brow furrowing.

'Don't understand, whatcha mean?'

'Ideal society? Well, you know, if you had a choice, what kind of world would you want to live in?'

He thought long and hard but evidently still didn't understand the question. I realised that I had misjudged his imaginative capacity. After all, he was stuck in the pragmatic reality of Bethnal Green.

'Ok,' I said, 'Put it like this.' I spoke slowly so that he would have no problem understanding.

'You have a choice between two societies.' I looked at him. 'Would you rather live in a society where everyone was at peace with each other, where everyone loved each other, where everyone was friends, where everyone had enough of everything? Where everyone was happy?'

I gave him a few seconds, while he stared at me blankly.

'Or would you rather live in a society where everyone was on their guard, competing? A place where you were never safe. Where some people were rich and others very poor, where everyone was fighting against each other?'

There was a beat, during which moment it seemed as if he had made up his mind minutes ago. The look on his face was one of disappointment – disappointment in me asking such a dumb question.

'The first one, of course. The one where everyone was happy. Not much of a choice, is there?' he said flatly.

My heart relaxed; he had vindicated my innate belief in human nature.

I thought I had better get some more information on this choice.

'OK. Great. I know it's a simple question, but could you tell me why you would rather live in that peaceful society?'

'Simple, innit?' He smiled wickedly at me. 'No one would be expecting you to thieve off of them. You could rob lots of people.'

I spent a couple of days recovering from that. Inasmuch as I still remember it and can see the kid's face some 35 years later, I suppose I still haven't really come to terms with it. Now, however, I have a different take on it. What more perfect metaphor could there be for the pharmaceutical industry? Suppose we were to put a similar question to a pharmaceutical executive, phrased perhaps in this way: 'What kind of society would you prefer to live in, one where everyone was always completely healthy or one where there were a proliferating number of illnesses and a high level of risk in relation to sickness?' Wouldn't the executive say, 'Simple, innit? No one would buy medicine in a society where everyone was healthy.'

This chapter of conclusions argues that, while HRT can be a damaging drug regime, it is still prescribed to those whom it damages, because the drug, its manufacturers and government agencies are embedded in a system of medicine that is hopelessly flawed. It is a system geared not to ridding the world of illness, but in many ways to creating and perpetuating conditions of illnesses, which provide markets for new drugs.

The problems with HRT are not just those about replacing hormones, of which there are many; they are also problems of the pharmaceutical industry, systems of medical welfare and consumer safety in advanced societies. The ten years to 2005 revealed an increasing number of serious problems in relation to the pharmaceutical industry. While pharmaceutical marketing techniques and billion-dollar budgets have driven drug sales up at the expense of safety, bad drugs have killed hundreds of thousands of patients.

The drug regulation agencies in both North America and the UK are controlled by the drug companies, and many of their licensing boards have been packed with 'experts' with a variety of company allegiances. In both Britain and North America, it has been shown that government leans heavily towards the pharmaceutical, chemical and bio-tech companies.

The pharmaceutical industry is today completely out of control. Rather than be accountable to government, it is now more often a *part of* government, helping to shape policy, not only in relation to health care, but also in relation to psychiatry, mental illness and social control. At the same time, it shapes important parts of the legal and medical landscape, such as consumer choice in health care and legal aspects of product lia-bility. This *pharmgov* has reached its nadir in North America, where school children have up to 15 mandatory vaccination shots, and where President Bush has recently ordered a psychiatric audit of the whole adult population with the seeming intention of creating a massive mandatory market for psychiatric drugs.

One aspect of the increasing power of the pharmaceutical compa-nies is their ability to deflect criticism, however radical. News of the mounting number of deaths caused by pharmaceuticals is passed over in a blur of rhetorical accusations and excuses, following which the indus-try returns to normal. Many pharmaceutical companies are now drag-ging around massive trust funds, which, well into the future, will be pay-ing off the casualties of their toxic products. And, unlike the asbestos and cigarette companies, the pharmaceutical companies have become so rich that there is little chance that they will have to declare themselves bank-rupt.

Amid all this medical degeneration, hormone replacement therapy stands out as a classic paradigm of corruption and quackery. Besides the drug companies we find selected physicians and political leaders with no real interest in health. Perhaps those most to blame for the continuing confusion about HRT are journalists.

In Britain, at least, medical journalism has become almost complete-ly debased. What you read, on the whole, in your newspaper, is often simply an arid regurgitation of PR items from Big Pharma. Matters of life and death, which should be argued in the most stringent regulatory terms, are discussed with the 'Do you prefer the red or the blue packet?' approach. Journalists seem to live in perpetual fear of writing 'unbal-anced' reports that might offend the pharmaceutical companies.

The more serious journalists, whose writing appears more profound, are also caught in the mill of information production, which grinds out a stream of constantly conflicting information without recording history or attempting to project future consequences. On the whole, contemporary newspapers, their proprietors and journalists have given up on moral or ethical crusades, preferring instead to sit on a rickety fence and to keep moving to ensure their own comfort.

It is not the purpose of this concluding chapter to make a singular case or argument against HRT. HRT is only one example of how the drugs industry, governments and the medical profession conspire to do limitless damage to the general population. To change society's response to the manufacture of drugs such as HRT means to change the whole way in which we understand health and health care. The summary strands of argument that follow are intended to make readers consider the questions that arise regarding the manufacture and prescription of HRT within a system of socialised health care such as the one that exists in the UK.

Generally speaking, the introduction of synthetic human hormones to women via the commercial market has been a disaster. Few other medical therapies so obviously manifest the inadequacies of the theory and practice of pharmaceutical treatments as hormone replacement.

If DNA represents the building blocks of life, hormones represent the mortar that holds life together, they are the alchemical fluids that make us individuals. Hormones, however, carry out none of their brilliant functions in isolation. The human organism is a complex whole, from which bits cannot be subtracted, or to which bits cannot be added, without inevitable serial effects. Some effects might appear inconsequential and, in the short term, hardly noticeable, but others can be fatal.

In the investigation, synthesis and commercial production of human female sex hormones, we see a major aspect of 20th century science in the clearest of lights. We also see the repercussions of irresponsible, profit-driven scientific production. We can glimpse the increasingly difficult problems of science and its Pandora's box, which, once opened, scientists cannot hope to shut.

Even when prescribed to help women with a variety of discomforts experienced during the menopause, hormone replacement therapy represents the medicalisation of a life condition, rather than the treatment of an illness. While, to the patient, there might be no quantifiable difference between adverse reactions suffered in medical pursuit of real illnesses, and those suffered as a result of interference with the natural processes of ageing, the doctor's role in these two situations raises quite different questions.

The medicalisation of life and its various stages is an important strategy for the medicines industry, equivalent to the car manufacturers' support for an intensification of the network of new motorways. The medicalisation of life ultimately swamps the body with pharmaceuticals, just as the building of new motorway networks leads to more and more cars.

In the medicalisation of human life, everything previously taken for granted as an aspect of nature is turned, as if by necessity, into a cause for intervention. In a world designed by men, women present an endless circumstance of changing states, which can be medicalised, mediated and managed.

Childbirth, perhaps more consistently than any of these life functions, has been medicalised by male doctors, who have convinced many women that pregnancies have to be monitored and scanned, induced by drugs and surgery, and must take place in hospitals.[3] And now, doctors and scientists are working on assisting elderly women to give birth on the grounds of their freedom to choose. Moving on past this contemporary period, when doctors are able to grow life outside the womb, who then will exercise the freedom to choose?

To help doctors in their mass act of cognitive behavioural therapy, which convinces women that childbirth and the menopause are medical conditions, our society produces a limitless supply of environmental toxins, bad food and poor health practices. Many of these, from cigarettes to pesticides, created by a malign partnership between drug, food and

---

3 Doubleday J. *101 Reasons Not to Have Your Baby in a Hospital* (Vol. 1). Spontaneous Creations Publishing. Also, *New Woman New Man Newsletter*. http://www.spontaneouscreation.org

leisure manufacturers, have been, and are still, uncriticised in health terms by the medical profession.

As with many other human conditions, the body's ability to get through 'the change' in a relaxed and smooth manner is heavily dependent upon good environmental care and preventive health prior to the event. In previous ages and other societies, the menopause has rarely been considered a period of illness, but, as with childbirth, scientists and doctors have now made its process dependent upon medical advice and a whole range of drug therapies.

It has been known for more than half a century, almost from the time that they were first developed, that the introduction into the human body, of exogenous hormones, especially oestrogen, or those chemicals that mimic hormones, causes breast and other cancers. The massive rise in breast cancer over the past 50 years can be put down, in large part, to the random and unmonitored introduction of very powerful 'medicinal' hormones into women's bodies. The male medical establishment, governments and regulatory bodies of developed countries, especially the UK and North America, have done nothing to halt this seemingly obvious environmental damage to women.

Well beyond the science of hormones and their role in 'health', their creation of adverse reactions and illness, there is another, even more appalling, problem relating to the artificial production of hormone chemicals and those that mimic them. To rid the earth of chemicals that 'mimic' human hormones is set to become one of the great environmental and health battles of the 21st century.

❦   ❦   ❦

Let us imagine that HRT is proven to be a perfect menopausal treatment for the model woman. However, because of its design and the inevitable complex internal biological interaction, it needs the most exact prescription and constant monitoring, without which it will be dangerous to the majority of patients. Who should be held responsible if a great number of women are damaged by this treatment?

Considering this question leads us quickly to the understanding that, although drug manufacturers and doctors try hard to dissociate themselves from each other, they have to be seen as colleagues and associates in the single venture of modern scientific medicine.

The manufacturing company is clearly responsible, because the principle of manufacturing a drug that suits only the model patient makes many patients vulnerable to adverse reactions. The physicians are responsible because they collude with the company in treating their patients as if they were modelled for the drug, rather than the other way round. In fact, in the case of HRT, 'scientific medicine' is an oxymoron; what gets in the way of the scientific working of hormone replacement therapy is the patient. Increasingly, pharmaceutical companies are suggesting that a drug is still a good drug, even if it kills a limited number of patients.[4]

Most contemporary manufacturers create products on the understanding that we live in an imperfect world. Automobile manufacturers would find it difficult to justify selling a car that ran only on flat roads and that, in a minor bump, assuredly killed the driver and all passengers. The confectionery industry would soon grind to a halt if it produced cakes that were not damaging, only if eaten on an empty stomach, at average room temperature, by people with blue eyes. And in none of these circumstances would the manufacturers gain much headway by blaming the consumer in the event of a legal wrangle.

It is even more unlikely that, if a major outbreak of food poisoning were traced to a specific source, or a faulty car design linked to a life-threatening mechanical failure, the manufacturers would get away with arguing that there was no link between their defective product and the 'ill health' it was accused of creating. Retailers of patently toxic food products that lead to ill health or death of consumers, inevitably feel the full weight of criminal and trade law. Officers with power of investigation,

---

4 In 2004, the Merck arthritis drug, Vioxx, was withdrawn from the market after it was admitted that it had created heart attacks and strokes in at least 60,000 patients. The withdrawal of Vioxx cast a cloud of suspicion over all COX-2 inhibitors, including Celebrex and another Pfizer drug, Bextra. Bextra was shown to increase the incidence of heart attacks and strokes by 219% in a study carried out by the American Heart Association. The cardiologist who presented the study, Dr Garret Fitzgerald, called Bextra 'a time bomb waiting to go off.' Pfizer, however, did not move immediately to withdraw Bextra or Celebrex, which are still prescribed with black box warnings imposed by the FDA. Pfizer plans to carry out major new trials of both drugs.

arrest and seizure are employed by the local authorities to detect and trace such cases, and there are mandatory, heavy fines and worse for miscreants.

In fact, it could be said of modern car design and even confectionery in developed societies that the best is done to ensure the health of the consumer in the most individual personal circumstances. And the history of litigation between the car industry and consumers, between the confectionery industry and consumers, has shaped the products involved and their availability on the market. Today, cars are designed to withstand all kinds of aberrant conditions, and many retailers now warn customers about the possible, idiosyncratically damaging ingredients in confectionery. The producer is considered, without question, to be responsible.

Relations between the pharmaceutical companies and consumers come nowhere near this end point of tort. The attitude of the pharmaceutical companies to citizens and consumers is exactly the same as that of the tobacco industry: 'F*** you – our immense power gives us the legal and moral right to kill and maim you.'

If a toy manufacturer retailed a toy with a fault that resulted in one child being blinded, it would not appear to be a reasonable defence for the manufacturer to plead, 'But only one child was blinded; the great majority of our customers are happy.' If a person died or was badly injured in police custody, it would not appear to be a reasonable explanation for the police to claim that they deal with thousands of people, generally speaking providing a good service, and that very few people die in custody. One can imagine the response of the jury to the man charged with the murder of a woman, who defended himself with the story that he had generally lived a blameless life, doing a lot of good for many people, and had known a great number of women, but killed only one.

How is it possible, in Britain, for pharmaceutical companies to get away with the frequent and often terrible damage that their products do to individuals? How is it possible for the perceived philanthropic qualities of the medical practitioner to have rubbed off on the money-grubbing, disease-mongering executives of pharmaceutical companies? [5]

---

5 In November 2005, British Vioxx claimants (mentioned above in North America), (*cont.*)

How has the situation arisen whereby physicians are able to disclaim liability for the damage that drugs do, when they have acted as agents distributing these drugs? In many other fields of liability, the distributive agent, the retailer or the seller is held to be as responsible as the producer or manufacturer.

On the whole, people need their illnesses explained, described clearly labelled and defined. Because most doctors are unwilling to admit to iatrogenic illness, to chart its course or its history, as well as making the patient ill, they can also rob them of the validation of their illness and send them into a kind of medical and personal limbo.

In a complex modern society, an understanding of the responsibility for damage to the individual, of cause and effect, of blame and justice, are crucial; they are also becoming more difficult to divine. This is not only because complexity brings difficulties of comprehension, but also because modern society is full of many groups who pursue, often secretly, vested interests that are inimical to the interests of individual personal happiness, community and public safety.

When you impose upon this governments who lack the will to challenge powers with which they are themselves in league – governments without moral values – you find a society in which the individual is made vulnerable, not only to the odd psychopathic personality within the community, but also and more consistently, to the greed and callousness of corporations. And the lack of linkage between personal damage and corporate responsibility is nowhere more evident than in medicine.

Iatrogenic illness goes to the very heart of the social contract between the State and the people. Its levels are also indicative of general levels of democracy in society. It sits awkwardly at the nexus between the public, its governance and private corporations. The State provides, regulates and is supposed to monitor the effects of pharmaceutical pro-

---

5 (*cont.*) were denied legal aid to pursue claims. While in the USA the Bush Administration is trying to pass new legislation to protect Big Pharma from compensation claims, in Britain the New Labour government has managed complete liability protection by simply denying legal aid in a number of important cases.

duction and distribution. Almost silently, these public functions have, in Britain and North America, been handed back to the pharmaceutical companies themselves. In the case of this production resulting in adverse effects, serious illness or death, the State stands aside from the debacle, pretending that it is not involved. This is often because, in the field of health, the interests of the pharmaceutical companies and their executives are now almost identical with those of government and its functionaries.

The social contract that exists between the State, its agencies, the citizen and corporations, and between retailers and consumers, has been, classically, a contract between agencies and individuals. In the case of pharmaceuticals and government agency dealings with them, science has been used to obscure the individual nature of the social contract. With pharmaceuticals, the social and legal contract is assumed to be between the government, corporations, the agents of both of these, and the mass of consuming citizens – not individuals.

Only 30 or 40 years ago, it seemed possible that the individual could influence government and social policy. The campaign that Maggie Tuttle mounted to help prisoners' wives and families was effective. It engaged with the prison service, with government and with local authorities, to influence thinking and the debate around such things as visiting conditions.

The citizens' right to voice criticism and to be involved in the discourse around subjects that directly affect them is not an arbitrary aspect of democracy, it is an absolute. This absolute exists, however large, complex or technical society becomes.

Over the past half century, in some 'developed' countries, most particularly Britain, an airlock has formed between the citizens and their government. While this process has affected all areas of relations between government, corporations and the citizen,[6] where professionalisation has

---

6 Along with this process, the history and idea of common law – one of the most democratising social elements – has been purged from any handbook of activism and from the minds of the people.

deflected the involvement of the common people in the processes of social organisation, it is perhaps nowhere more evident than in medicine.

Although definitions of 'post-modern' society are clearly open to argument, because they are constructs that sometimes bear little relationship to real communities, in the case of medical practice, 'post-modernism' represents an ideal analysis. There is an utter fracture between any textural continuity of ideas in pharmaceutical production, the objectives of medically-trained professionals, and the receipt by citizens of health care. This hopeless dislocation can be witnessed in the fate of the Menopausal Helpline.

When Maggie Tuttle first began her campaign, she actually wrote to some pharmaceutical companies, asking if they would co-operate. Left over from her campaigning 30 years ago was her view of a communal world. Her consciousness still resided in a world where, despite struggle and conflict, it might just be possible to move together as a community.

There is little doubt that the Menopausal Helpline stirred the debate about HRT in the late 1990s. Looking at this debate as it jumped back and forth across the pages of the press in 1998, any observer can, however, very quickly diagnose the real difficulty. While some users, separated from any mechanisms of power and the media, tried to find a public voice or to engage with the authorities, doctors controlled by the drug companies, who had access to power and the media, simply kept repeating the message that HRT was clearly beneficial to those suffering problems of menopause and possible osteoporosis.

Behind this conflict between professional doctors and the laity is another, more complex conflict between science and personal experience. And behind this, again, is another conflict, which centres upon the continuing disintegration of our communities and the hopeless divide that has opened between the individual and the producers and reproducers of professional and commercial health care.

While the clearest of links has been established on a number of occasions between the prescription of drugs, their adverse reactions and ill health in the community, physicians have seemingly so far escaped censure for the incredible, rising levels of iatrogenic illness and death by medicine. The strongest and most committed measures have to be brought to bear on this problem of physician-induced illness. The only physicians who should escape the most intense scrutiny are those who do not prescribe pharmaceuticals of any kind.

It is to link illnesses with their causal agents that we have epidemiologists. For some obscure reason, however, while epidemiologists help in moving heaven and earth against the butcher, fishmonger or sandwich bar owner who gives even a couple of individuals a salmonella stomach upset, they seem not to operate in the area of drug damage.[7] While the greatest of them will work assiduously for years on behalf of corporations, proving that their products could not possible damage anyone, few, if any of them, will work on behalf of local communities, and next to none of them, apparently, in community epidemiology.

In its list of 'demands' to help women suffering from adverse reactions to HRT, the Menopausal Helpline suggested double-blind trials, which would look at adverse reactions.

There has been no attempt in Britain to institute agencies like the North American Environmental Protection Agency. Agencies such as the Medical Research Council, which initially attempted research in defence of consumers or citizens, are today deeply involved in the secret agendas of governments and corporations.

Over the past 20 years, all the British organisations that might at some previous time have claimed 'independence' with respect to research in defence of citizens or consumers, have been *turned* by industry.

There are now, in any case, few organisations in Britain that could carry out such 'independent' research. Our first demand should be for an agency that carries out research into toxicity on behalf of the citizen and consumer, an agency that defends the health of the laity against all comers. Such an independent agency would be able to serve the citizen and consumer in all the various areas that have become matters of contention during the past 20 years: pesticides, vaccines, a large number of pharmaceuticals, dioxins, etc.

---

7 Perhaps even more worrying than their absence from the field of adverse drug impact in the community, many of Britain's most highly regarded epidemiologists, such the late Sir Richard Doll, have consistently worked on trialling pharmaceuticals, lending their good name for science to that notoriously unstable aspect of the scientific and regulatory process which gets pharmaceuticals licensed. Such epidemiologists, however, steer well clear of post-licensing surveillance or the reporting of adverse reactions.

In the present political climate, however, with a government that, even more than its predecessor, sides with the big industrial corporations, has no core moral values and no view on individual rights, such an agency is a distant dream. Its establishment would mean the positive reversal of all the trends that have come to support Britain's toxic industries.

During the period of industrial capitalism, trade unions acted in defence of workers while they were at work, and the common law, together with a concept of civil rights, defended the citizen outside of work. With the passing of the classic 19th century relations between capital and labour, and, consequently, of the power of the manufacturing 'working class', a new, unprotected class of 'consumers' – citizens who buy goods, consume services or, in some cases, have services forced upon them – has arisen.

In North America, the absence of institutions to protect the public from toxic products and processes led consumers, aided by lawyers, understandably to use the courts and civil law to claim damages. The use of toxic tort and its development to a fine art in North America has infuriated pharmaceutical, chemical, asbestos and other toxin producers and, more recently, the President himself.[8] Between the lines, these companies appear to articulate the idea that they should not be held responsible because they did not initially intend to injure anyone.

In an attempt to evade responsibility for the damage that various corporations have done to thousands of people and the environment, these corporations have developed strategic arguments about society and litigation. According to the corporate mind, we have developed a culture of litigation, in which professionals and corporate executives are likely to have their lives ruined by greedy lawyers and irresponsible litigants, and in which it becomes impossible for companies to make realistic profits, because anti-capitalist complainants are continually sniping at them. We now live in a society, they whinge, in which a doctor cannot treat a

---

8 Bush has recently made pronouncements about curtailing the rights of citizens and lawyers to make claims against corporations.

patient for fear of being sued; a society in which consumers and patients are denied products of great personal advantage and social good, by campaigns of biased, irrational and unjust criticisms.[9]

However, despite their corporate whining, toxic tort has done a favour to irresponsible companies: in the event of their killing thousands of people, they can salve their consciences by financial pay-outs. Such damages, usually minimal in terms of overall profit, leave them free to kill or harm more people in the future. Toxic crime against individuals and communities is, in fact, one circumstance where the death penalty – for a corporation – is the only proper solution.

Apart from direct action and demonstration against individuals and corporations, the law is the only recourse for those suffering iatrogenic illness. Claimants can, using civil litigation, sue a number of people, depending on who their lawyers consider most demonstrably culpable. In England, this kind of law, up until the advent of New Labour, had a noble and distinctive history, whether for workers wanting better conditions, individuals wrongly arrested or imprisoned, servants wanting to protest against wrongful dismissal, or individuals sold faulty goods.

There is nothing greedy or morally reprehensible about using the law to claim, in some form, compensation for damaged goods or a damaged life. In fact, the constant bombardment of legal cases, together with boycotts and popular demonstrations, are the *only ways* in a modern society riven by conflicting interests that corporations or professionals can be censured or made accountable.

It might even be worth arguing further than this. Post-industrial society needs instruments of democracy to return to it a sense of community. Independent individuals with equal power have to be locked into social groups by a sense of responsibility; such social organisations might be created by the consistent use of common law.

---

9 North American manufacturers became so utterly convinced that no criticism could be fair criticism that they backed a law in the mid-1990s which introduced the prosecution of anyone who endangered production with unjustified criticisms. The first person to be prosecuted under the Act was Oprah Winfrey, for comments made on one of her programmes about BSE and beef production. Winfrey was found not guilty and the beef producers incurred enormous costs, as well as dire embarrassment.

In the UK, where there is not the same open legal market as there is in North America, there has been no legal backlash against the health-damaging effects of toxic corporations. The British Government and lawyers themselves conspire to keep the laity at bay; the law is principally for the advantage of professional players, and not an instrument for establishing the rights or freedoms of the individual in battles with corporations. While, in North America, corporate apparatchiks complain that the only people to gain from toxic tort are the lawyers, in the UK, the only people to continue profiting from toxicity are the corporations who produce it.

❦   ❦   ❦

One way in which British legal professionals have radically failed the laity and kept iatrogenic illness out of the courts has been by refusing to train, to look for or to cultivate good expert witnesses. This, in turn, has been affected by the decline of radical or politically-thinking professionals. By refusing to do battle at this very first stage of the legal process, lawyers acquiesce to the fallacy that there is no alternative point of view in relation to pharmaceuticals and therapies such as HRT. Although inexperienced lawyers in Britain will always pass the buck to claimants when they have been turned down by expert advice, the fault lies with lawyers.

A claims lawyer, like any other lawyer, is acting on behalf of the client, and in this position is responsible for assembling a representation that will win the case for the client in court. It is obviously of the utmost importance that any expert is researched in great detail before being approached[10] and that the lawyer has the confidence in the client to bring into court an expert who, though perhaps shunned by the establishment, is professionally on the side of his client. It is the height of folly to approach an 'independent expert' who is thought to be 'acceptable to the court', without the strong understanding, from their record, that their opinion is likely to support the client.

---

10 Any opinion given by a witness approached by either the defence or the claimant has to be presented to the court and can, therefore, if it does not support the case, be used by the other side.

At the end of the day, however, lawyers don't act powerfully for claimants because, with the increasing professionalisation and commercialisation of society, fewer and fewer lawyers or doctors feel the need, or have the desire, to commit to their clients or patients. Over the past 25 years, the British professional classes have suffered from an irreversible leakage of moral fibre.

❦   ❦   ❦

Despite a reputation that often precedes it, the criminal law in Britain is relatively cautious. And despite class prejudice, nationalism, corruption and simple mistakes, the record of the criminal law and the pursuit of justice over the past rapidly-changing half century, can be said to show our society at its inquiring and, to some extent, liberal best.

The same cannot be said of medicine and the pursuit by professionals of health. While the axiom seems to have been taken to heart by the judiciary that 'it is better for any number of guilty men to go free than one innocent man be hanged', there is no equivalent rubric, which safeguards the individual patient against damage and death, in medicine. What was, centuries ago, the first Hippocratic principle, to 'do no harm', has long been forgotten by the majority of medical professionals in an age of pharmaceuticals. Its modern equivalent, to 'do as little harm as possible to the majority', leaves thousands vulnerable.

There are many reasons why judicial procedure has retained some kind of integrity and still entertains notions of justice, but medical professionals have drifted far from concepts of healing. The first and perhaps the simplest explanation is that, after the judicial confusion of the 18th century, in the 19th century legal thinkers resolved a detailed penal code, which, over the coming years, they tried to act out. Central to the new judicial thinking was, at least, an attempt at independence from both the executive and the surrounding industrial system.

The new juridical codes in England did not stop the prisons from filling up with working-class people, it did not stop judges from settling labour disputes invariably in favour of bosses, or stop the police and the judiciary from acting in favour of the prevailing power. However, the very existence of codes of professional behaviour in the public domain meant that, within the boundaries of the law, the individual had some protection from arbitrary decisions and prejudicial processes. These codes have been continuously updated since their introduction.

Doctors, although mainly professionally 'incorporated' in the second half of the 20th century, have never officially been seen as part of the State. And, because, from the beginning, the notion that physicians might do unethical or dishonest damage to their patients was not entertained, the profession has never felt the need to define a set of rules described for the benefit of the public, to protect patients from its power. Nor has it been felt right to make them answerable to anyone in the form of the State or the people – only to their own professional body.

Physicians emerged from the anarchy of power, prejudice and corruption in the 18th century, and continued as normal throughout the 19th. They wandered into the 20th century, and on into the 21st, as a powerful but chaotic, secretive and highly-protected body, lately, inappropriately, melded with private, industrial and State interests.

One of the most public differences between the medical profession and the judiciary lies in the fact that wrongful arrests and wrongful acts by the judicial authorities have always been protested. As a result, they have often, historically, been resolved by inquiries and investigations, while it is only recently that doctors have been subject to popular protests and campaigns. In turn, this is perhaps because judicial proceedings are inevitably more public than the 'private' administrations of physicians.

So it occurs now in the 21st century, that a relatively 'small number' of judicial mistakes – albeit with tragic consequences – have led to constant reappraisals of society's policing and juridical functions, while, on the medical front, today, pharmaceuticals provided by doctors and hospitals as institutions, kill hundreds of thousands of potentially healthy people every year. There exist no clear mechanisms for addressing these wrongdoings, except common law or hearings completely organised by the professional body of doctors, the General Medical Council (GMC).

Just how great this risk of modern medicine is, and whether or not it is justified or proportionate to the profession's ability to heal, is a question that rarely comes under scrutiny. Only on those odd and improbable occasions when electricity supply failures or general strikes shut down the hospitals does it become evident that, just as the crime rate rises, the death toll declines.

Perhaps worse and more confusing, when considering a comparative critique of medicine, is the fact that, while jurists tend ultimately to acknowledge their mistakes as a consequence of their humanity, many medical professionals blindly cite science as incontrovertible proof that they cannot possibly be in error. Even more maddeningly, they use statistical arguments when discussing adverse reactions and deaths. In fact, as jurists recognise with their 'one innocent man' argument, statistics are of no consequence to that individual who goes innocently to the gallows, or to the one whose life is ended by the intervention of a physician or a pharmaceutical.

From 1965 until the mid-1980s, there were a series of internal inquiries into the Metropolitan Police, into the squads that dealt with pornography, vice, drugs and armed robbery. As a consequence of these inquiries, over 20 years, the ranks were thinned, some officers went to prison, a number stood trial, a larger number were disciplined, and some were dismissed or retired from the force.

Those who observed this rendering of the Met saw that it did two things: it reasserted the control of masters over its servants, at the same time separating them from the criminal undergrowth in which they had become entangled. As well, the investigations acted as a lesson to a new force that was being built; it was an act of discipline and punishment.

Given the growth in iatrogenic illness and death by medicine, why does the State not embark upon a similar exercise in relation to doctors and pharmaceutical medicines? Why should doctors who injure and kill people, even accidentally, continue in their profession? Why should doctors who have broken the first rule of healing, to 'do no harm', and who are enmeshed in a twisted relationship with pharmaceutical cartels, keep the confidence of the people? Why should we not expect our doctors to be honest, and to believe their patients rather than their pharmaceutical masters, when, for instance, the patients say that they might be suffering adverse reactions? Why should the State not try to rebuild the medical services on the principle that doctors act in support of their patients and not the drug companies?

Interestingly, authorities have moved against technicians and scientists in similar circumstances. They have recalled patients and disciplined whole laboratories for shoddy work and mistakes. Why does it appear so indelicate to suggest that the government set in motion a recall of all women prescribed with HRT over the past ten years, in order to ask them simple, specific questions – for example: 'Have you reported ill health after taking HRT to your doctor?' 'Did your doctor ever say that none of your bad health could be due to HRT?' 'Has your doctor monitored your health after prescribing HRT?' 'Did your doctor make sure that you were not part of a risk group before he prescribed HRT?' Such an exercise, if well organised and co-ordinated, could be accomplished in weeks, given the resources of the Department of Health.

It is time that we considered the relationship between science and medicine. In the late 19th century and the beginning of the 20th, science advanced the development of medicine. The model was simple: communities were faced with illness, physicians reported it, then scientists worked with them to bring about a solution.

There was always, however, and there has continued to be, an increasing aspect of 'medical' science that worked independently of pragmatic issues. Now that this form of science is in the ascendancy, ideas about health rarely originate from empirical evidence in the community, but problems and their solutions are passed down by science to be implemented or 'sold' to the general population.

Many of the ideas that originate in this way have not been given any or sufficient ethical, social or political consideration. The idea of a vanguard of physician scientists researching treatments is not necessarily a bad model, so long as their inquiries are motivated by everyday concerns of independent-thinking communities. But, just as industrial scientists are the wrong people to be involved in food production and distribution, so they are entirely the wrong people to be involved in health and the production and distribution of health care.

While individuals and communities have to reassert their control over their own health, it should be done in co-operation with physicians and alternative therapists, who are the only people able to keep track of the community's health problems and to correlate and develop treatments.

The beginning of scientific medicine meant the end of healing as an art and the end of a holistic view of the human identity. Science drove out of medicine any sense of wholeness or individual, subjective understanding or intimacy between the healer and the treated. The introduction of scientific medicine, which began late in the 18th century in Britain, put the patient in the background and the supposedly healthy doctor centre stage. From this point onwards, doctors became the only people allowed to hold knowledge of illness.

The advent of scientific medicine robbed individuals of any right to understand their own bodies and any power to treat and heal themselves. The advent of scientific medicine meant, not exactly Huxley's Brave New World, but a slightly different form of slavery, in which the laity became victims of an inhuman science, forced upon them by physicians who had become apprentices to a master of whom they had a diminishing understanding.

Often, when science is pressed upon human groups, its form is authoritarian, its very nature undemocratic.[11] The facts of science become the acts of medicine, and they brook no individual dispute. The idea of personal choice disappears with scientific medicine, for in order for it to sustain itself, there can be no discussion of alternatives, and there can be no dissent from the plans of the corporations who produce uniform medications for the masses.

Science turns us all, except for those who control it, into laity, and, therefore, renders us unable to make an informed contribution either to any policy discourse or to our own health.

When I came to read the letters written by women to the Menopausal Helpline, two things stuck in my mind. The first was just how damaging were the 'minor' adverse reactions that women suffered – how, in many cases, women's lives were destroyed by these adverse reactions, jobs lost, families broken up. The second matter that began to loom large in

---

11 In the late 18th century, when they built the first railway station in East London, hundreds of houses were knocked down and their inhabitants made homeless.

my thoughts was the thread of continuous references to doctors who denied that HRT was responsible for the side effects that were repeatedly reported.

At first I suppose I thought, 'Well, despite being in the business of healing, these are professional men first and foremost and unlikely to take women patients at their lay word.' Then I began to notice the accounts of women doctors who had acted in the same manner. The denial by doctors of women's concerns about adverse reactions is such a majority experience that we are forced to consider a theory that might explain it.

Are some doctors unwilling to enter into a discourse or partnership with their patients, and frightened of joining the laity in a search for the truth, simply because they don't want their professional status challenged? Or is it more sinister than this? Do some doctors have their reasoning faculties cauterised at medical school? Is it actually impossible for them to consider that pharmaceuticals can cause damage? As I considered these alternatives, I was suddenly forced up against a third possibility, which did not bear thinking about. Is it possible that doctors are involved in a conspiracy with pharmaceutical companies to push HRT and override all objections? Could it be the case that women are actually, and not just metaphorically, being experimented upon?

As I went over these matters and re-read the letters that women had written to the Menopausal Helpline, I was forced to realise just how sleazy professional Britain had become. The letters are heart-rending, they strip the life of the writer down to sheer pain. How was it possible for doctors to sit and listen to these patients again and again, without even going back to the data sheets? How was it possible to ignore the cries of women whom these doctors themselves had injured? And still, even now, with the reports of increased breast cancer and heart attack, stroke and thrombosis, how could they continue fighting the corner for the drug companies?

Class, status and the State have a lot to do with just about everything that happens in England. A man whose car gets ensnared on a railway line is prosecuted and imprisoned for the deaths of the passengers when the train crashes into it. Despite a public outcry, rail company executives are not prosecuted after their company has let stock fall into disrepair resulting in deaths. Parents who let their children play by a railway line are prosecuted when the children are killed by a train. A woman who takes her child to hospital after he has fallen off a chair and banged his head, is visited by social services accompanied by police officers and the child is taken into care.

It is against this background that a doctor can be continuously involved in the declining health and even death of a patient, without attracting the attention of any social authority. I am not talking about Harold Shipman here. 'Professional' criminals are devious and will always find ways of committing their crimes, while presenting alibis and excuses; this is, after all, an aspect of their professional capability.

In my opinion, any doctor should go before a disciplinary hearing, if he or she has told a patient that she need not worry about breast cancer with HRT (even worse, of course, if the patient then actually contracts breast cancer). Or if he or she has repeatedly refused to entertain the possibility that specific illnesses suffered by a patient taking HRT could be adverse reactions related to the treatment.

Personally, I could never be convinced by the argument put forward by some doctors that they simply facilitate a patient's choice of a treatment that best suits them, after an exchange of perfect information, which approaches all the minutiae of risk and responsibility. That's a bit like an airline saying after a plane crash, 'Well, the passenger chose to fly with us in the full knowledge that our planes have a history of crashing.' Most allopathic doctors are not facilitators, anyway; they are drug dispensers.

The whole process of dispensing pharmaceutical medicines is, at best, authoritarian. Bad medicines are prescribed to people who know nothing, by people who will later claim to know even less. Allopathic health consultations and the prescription of pharmaceutical medicines are organised in such a way that doctors can simply avoid responsibility for any damage they incur.

Doctors, general practitioners and consultant specialists clearly have to be held to be as responsible as garage mechanics who make mistakes in mending cars, which then leads to death or injury. Doctors have to learn that they must pay for the damage that has been done to patients through the prescription of bad products.

There are ways of preserving a government-sponsored and financed structure of socialised medicine that gives consumers choice, but which entail breaking the monopoly of the allopathic doctors and drug companies.

The most obvious and permanent way of transforming the system of primary health care in Britain would be to give equal power and resources to other forms of medicine besides allopathic, drug-based medicine. Money, capital and teaching resources could be diverted into different medical paradigms, setting discriminatory employment practices in favour of different medical models, and supporting diverse community practices, so that individuals could have a wide range of choice of both preventive health and specific treatments.

A simpler policy would be to pay out all health care funding derived from taxation in the form of vouchers to citizens. Individuals could then trade in the vouchers against any therapies they chose.

Such policies would, however, necessitate any government taking a firm stand against the pharmaceutical companies and letting go of the allopathic monopoly. It would be idealistic to imagine that this could happen within the present economic model of British society.

It is clear, now, that the medical profession is *unable* to regulate itself, while the pharmaceutical industry has no intention of introducing honest regulation. Agencies such as the MHRA, and schemes such as the yellow card system, whereby health professionals and – at last – patients can now report adverse drug reactions, are purposefully designed for failure.

The pharmaceutical companies have to be brought to heel, with powerful legislation, which describes the production and distribution of medicines and drugs that do damage to patients as serious criminal offences. Senior pharmaceutical executives should be held personally responsible and liable to long prison sentences, with the confiscation of their money and assets in cases where numbers of people die as a consequence of taking prescribed drugs.

It should be a criminal offence for pharmaceutical companies or their agents to have any contact of any kind with practising doctors. The retailing of pharmaceuticals to individual doctors or their joint practices should be carried out by independent organisations also able to provide all contextual and quality information to buyers. Doctors or their practices should approach these organisations with the brief for the illnesses for which they need treatments, not for specific drugs. An integrated system should be designed to retail herbs, homeopathic remedies and other treatments to practitioners without them having to come into contact with producing companies.

The most effective way of picking up toxic threats in the community would be through independent public health departments that had epidemiologists ready to investigate and correlate reports of pharmaceutical adverse reactions.

Because it is clear that physicians are now in thrall to pharmaceutical companies and are unable, because of time and other pressures, to consider all the literature on a wide range of drugs, it must be assumed that knowledge of side effects and toxicity is, at present, beyond their competence. All physicians should be made to attend monthly day courses on pharmaceuticals, their manufacturing companies and the marketing techniques they use. All GPs should have to reach a level of competence in their knowledge of adverse reactions.

It should be a reportable disciplinary offence for any physician to deny knowledge of known adverse reactions, or even possible adverse reactions, to pharmaceuticals that he or she has prescribed. Any physician who is found to have knowingly denied highly probable adverse reactions and blamed the patient, accusing him or her of, for example, exaggerating physical symptoms or having psychiatric problems, should be stopped from practising for a limited period while attending education courses on adverse reactions. Any physician insisting that a patient is suffering from a new and distinctly separate illness, when the patient is actually suffering adverse reactions, should have to undergo similar courses.

Courses should be run by authorities entirely independent of the medical profession or the pharmaceutical companies.

Physicians should have to give clearly-printed and independently-written and published literature to all patients to whom they prescribe drugs. This literature should explain the purpose of the drug, its potential toxicity and possible side effects. Such data sheets should also give references to newspaper articles and books available in local libraries, and the names and addresses of campaigning organisations that have criticised the drugs, for whatever reason.

These sheets should contain reference to the condition for which the drug is being prescribed, with information about natural remedies for such conditions. No physician should be able, for instance, to prescribe HRT to encourage bone density growth, without, at the same time, providing the patient with information about nutritional sources of supplementation and the role of exercise in bone density growth. No physician should be able to suggest the surgical removal of gallstones without explaining to patients self-administered natural processes for the removal of stones.

Those doctors who respond to such suggestions by saying that most patients only come to the surgery to demand pills, should have to attend community-based courses on preventive health care and environmental medicine. Doctors have to realise that often patients' education about their health begins with their GP. They, therefore, have to take this role seriously.

No drugs, apart from a very limited range of simple compounds with few known side effects, should be prescribed without a 'cooling off' period between the patient and the doctor. During this time, the patient should be able to ascertain information about the prescription drug, through local agencies, the Internet, and local libraries, which should have reference sections solely for this purpose.

In the event of a patient being dissatisfied with more than one consultation with their doctor – for instance, in the case of an adverse reaction being ignored in any way – the patient should be able to ask for a tape-recorded or video consultation with the doctor, and receive a copy of this recording. Similarly, where a doctor feels that he or she is being pressurised into the wrong course of action, or where they might feel that the patient is being unreasonable, this doctor should have the right, with permission of the patient, to tape-record any consultation.

Any qualified medical doctor should be barred from making any public statement in favour of or against any pharmaceutical treatment, and all journalists or interviewed pundits and politicians who make public statements about any pharmaceuticals should have to declare any vested interests, however slight.

All physicians, in whatever kind of practice, health centres and trusts, should be made to comply with a statement of vested interests and funding, which is transparent, visible to patients in bold, clear type, and preferably placed at head height, behind the physician's consulting-room chair.

❦   ❦   ❦

The double-think of a medical profession that, on the one hand, claims to cure the sick, and, on the other, makes large numbers of almost healthy people more sick, can be seen in the fact that it refuses even to use the word that describes the damage it causes – 'iatrogenic'.

When a person suffers iatrogenically-induced illness, their experience is reported as anecdotal, their story is reduced to the rudiments of explanation. On the other hand, when a drug or medical procedure apparently contributes to the maintenance of health, however superficially, this story and that of the patient becomes imbued with all the authority of science, and the subject is presented as an example of a great and beneficial movement, a product of man's infinite ability to understand the human body and its biological environment. Science reduces those whom it damages to illiterates who have, somehow, been unable to understand or accept science. In an extension of Darwin's theory of survival of the fittest, these victims become physical failures, people unable to keep up with science.

If you suffer iatrogenic illness, you are made to appear stupid and unable to appreciate the great gains of science. You are blamed for your own fate, because you are apparently different from the majority; your condition does not fit with contemporary thinking; you become a complainer or a neurotic. On the other hand, if a drug or a procedure works for you, it is suggested that you are near perfect because you resemble science's collective perception of the modern identity.

Physicians, more than most professionals, have to learn to listen. While the physician might be in control of any treatments, the patient has to be in control of his or her own body, and it is part of the physician's task to help the patient, to explain the details and the context of their condition, and then to equip the patient with enough information to make good decisions. If physicians complain that they do not have the time to help patients constructively to review their health, they should either change the system within which they practise, or stop being physicians. Most of all, however, some physicians have to regain a sense of their vocation and position in the community.

There are few circumstances, in advanced society, apart from military service, in which a person can be asked in all seriousness to lay down his or her life, apparently for the common good. Medicine is one of the only exceptions. One common defence used by the pharmaceutical industry and physicians when faced with the question of serious side effects linked to drugs is to say that the drug in question has played a crucial role in ridding society of such and such a condition.

This statement is often made by scientists and doctors. It is made in the same way that it might be made in defence of a rogue cop who had just wiped out a family with indiscriminate gunfire, and whose senior officer argues, not only that the man's job is difficult, but that in his years in the service he has done a great deal to rid society of miscreants.

Those who suffer and die *from* medicine are not suffering and dying *for* medicine, but for the profits of the medical industry.

Appendices

QUESTIONNAIRE ON THE SIDE EFFECTS OF HRT

Please tick the relevant boxes	Yes	No	Unsure (or any comments)
Allergies to food or environment			
Breast Cancer (only if confirmed by GP)			
Burning in the Body/Vagina and/or Mouth			
Clitoris Extension/Enlargement			
Depression			
Diagnosed ME symptoms or similar			
Digestive Problems			
Discharge from the Vagina			
Dizziness			
Dry Eyes			
Dry Hair			
Ear problems, loss of hearing, balance			
Erratic Behaviour			
Eyesight Problems			
Feelings of Insecurity			
Fluid Retention			
Hair Growth on Face and Body			
Hair Loss			
High Blood Pressure			
Hot Flushes/Night Sweats			
Joint Pains, Hips etc			
Leg and Foot Cramps			
Liver and Kidney problems			
Loss of Sex Drive			
Memory Loss			
Migraine or Head Pains			
Muscle Spasm in neck and shoulders			
Nervous Disorders, Twitching etc			
Pain In Gums (as if teeth are loose)			
Psoriasis/Skin Disorders			
Sleeplessness			
Sticky Discharge from Mouth			
Stomach Cramps			
Suicide			
Swollen breasts/lumps			
Thinning Bones			
Thyroid Problems			
Vaginal Dryness			
Voice Deepening			
Weeping Eyes			
Weight Gain, bloated feelings			

CERTIFIED COPY   OF AN ENTRY
Pursuant to the Births and   Deaths Registration Act 1953

DEATH	Entry Number 207

| Registration District   Greenwich | Administrative area |
| Sub-district   Greenwich | London Borough of Greenwich |

1. Date and place of death

TWENTY SECOND JANUARY 1995
The Brook Hospital. Greenwich

2. Name and surname	3. Sex Female
Irene BRANKIN	4. Maiden surname of woman who has married McKELLAR

5. Date and place of birth

TWENTY THIRD AUGUST 1950   GLASGOW. SCOTLAND

6. Occupation and usual address

Publican
Wife of Bernard BRANKIN Publican
The Glenmore Arms. 41. Edison Grove. Plumstead

7. (a) Name and surname of informant   (b) Qualification

Certificate received from Selena Shippey Assistant Deputy Coroner
for Inner South London. Inquest held 7th April 1995

(c) Usual address

8. Cause of death

1a   Pulmonary Embolism (Operation)
b   Hormone Replacement Therepy.

    Accidental death

9. I certify that the particulars given by me above are true to the best of my knowledge and belief.

Signature of informant

10. Date of registration	11. Signature of registrar
Tenth April 1995	J.A. Jefferies Registrar

Certified to be a true copy of an entry in a register in my custody.

.... KAJamncu .... Superintendent Registrar   4ᵗ August, 1995. Date

GA 6008

SAMPLE MEDIA ALERT FOR LOCAL MEDIA BRIEFING

WORLD MENOPAUSE DAY

MEDIA ALERT!   MEDIA ALERT!   MEDIA ALERT!

[Insert the Name of Your Organization's Menopause Society]
Briefing
Menopause in an Aging Society

How does estrogen loss affect the body as women age?
How will an increasing population of postmenopausal women impact national heart disease, Alzheimer's and osteoporosis rates?
What are the unanswered questions about menopause management?
Is our nation prepared to care for **[INSERT ESTIMATED NUMBER OF MENOPAUSAL WOMEN IN YOUR COUNTRY]** *menopausal women?*

These are important public health issues that we are just now beginning to address. To help highlight these important public and personal health issues, **October 18** has been deemed World Menopause Day, a time to spotlight attention on menopausal health issues facing women and society.

Some Basic Facts:

- **[Insert approximate number of women entering menopause by 2010 in your country or nationality]** women will enter menopause within the next decade and many will live up to ONE-THIRD of their lives post-menopausal.
- Many women don't know that menopause increases the risk of heart disease. Yet, cardiovascular disease - largely heart attacks and strokes - is the leading cause of death in the world today.
- **[Insert approximate number of women in your country with osteoporosis and the name of your country]** women are at risk for osteoporosis. There is a significant cost for treating fractures from this debilitating brittle bone disease, running into the **[Insert the approximate cost of treating osteoporosis in your country using your local currency]**, yet the incidence of this disease can be reduced.
- Maintaining a healthy lifestyle can have an enormous impact on overall well-being. Women entering menopause are encouraged to stop smoking, get adequate exercise, and to eat a healthy diet that includes vitamins and minerals including vitamin D and calcium.

When: **[Insert the Date and Time of the Event]**
Where: **[Insert the Location of the Event]**
Who: **[Insert the Names, and Titles of the Event Speakers]**

- ✓ What is menopause and how does it change the body?
- ✓ The latest research on menopause and the effects of estrogen loss

---

To attend the briefing, contact: **[Insert the name of the person to be contacted and their contact information]**

343

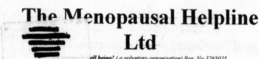

The Menopausal Helpline Ltd

...ell being! (a voluntary organisation) Reg. No 3265025

DIRECTORS: M TUTTLE (Chairman); J WILLIAMS LLB
SECRETARY: I F HARRIS
228 Muswell Hill Broadway, LONDON N10 3SH Tel:0181 444 5202, Fax: 0181 444 6442
PATRONS: Dr. Adel Badr Dr. Erik Enby

AGENDA RECOMMENDED BY THE MENOPAUSAL HELPLINE TO TRY TO IMPROVE HEALTH CARE FOR WOMEN:

1. Local Health Authorities should ensure that all doctors are aware of the very real risks of Thrombosis, Breast Cancer and Gall Bladder Disease after taking synthetic hormone drugs.
2. They should also ensure that all patients are informed of any other possible side effects of these drugs and warn those who have a family history of cancer or thrombosis of the increased risks involved.
3. The government should pass a measure to make it obligatory for doctors to fill in the forms provided to them under the yellow card system. Doctors are presently under no legal obligation to fill in details of side effects of drugs and send these back to the Committee for Safety of Medicines. As a result there is a real lack of awareness of the full extent of the problems they can create.
4. The information leaflets now made obligatory under EU regulations of 1995 are still not always supplied and do not always give all the information.
5. Government should make nutrition an obligatory part of medical training. It is extraordinary that the recent controversy over Vitamin B6 ever occurred.
6. The government should not sign the EU document MLX 249. It is not helpful to give GP's control over health supplements when they have no knowledge of nutrition. It is also not helpful to deprive consumers of these over the counter health supplements (MLX 249) when many depend on them for good health.
7. A comprehensive randomised control trial should take place to monitor the full side effects of these drugs.
8. Doctors should be trained how to solve the side effects of these drugs before prescribing them. At present there is no UK specialist who has this knowledge.

Huntercombe Lane South
Taplow, Maidenhead
Berkshire, SL6 0PH
Tel: 01628 604377
Fax: 01628 666368

23rd September 1998

Dear Practice Manager

You may have become aware recently of media coverage condemning the use of Hormone Replacement Therapy. This publicity will have alarmed women because it includes a wide range of unsupported claims. We write to advise you that the organisation behind the recent media coverage is scheduling a meeting in your area at the Brighton Conference Centre on 26 September under the title of 'The Other Side of HRT'.

We are particularly disturbed by the alarmist tone of the campaign and believe that publicity from this meeting may cause concern to your patients. The advertising campaign promotes the event with statements such as "never again should a woman die from Hormone Replacement Therapy" and "revealed the scandal of unnecessary hysterectomies and the removal of healthy ovaries". The meeting will apparently also be the launch vehicle for a new book entitled 'Killed by HRT'.

Symptoms of the menopause can be extremely distressing for a woman. As a GP, you will understand that it is important that the situation is not exacerbated with misleading and alarmist information. We have, for this reason, taken the decision to write to you to forewarn you of the meeting so that you are in a position to respond to any concerns expressed by your patients following publicity from it.

To help you address concerns, if they arise, please find enclosed 10 copies of 'Living with the Menopause', a magazine that has proved popular with both women and GPs and is designed to provide women with all the latest information about the menopause.

As the UK's leading manufacturer of HRT, Wyeth also have available a range of informational materials entitled 'Menopause and Women's Health' which have been designed to help you provide the kind of information patients need when undergoing the menopause and contemplating HRT.

We thank you for your attention and if you would like more information on our informational materials, please contact Charlotte Messer on 01892 516020.

Yours sincerely

Dr P G Brock
Medical Director, Wyeth

John Wyeth & Brother Limited
Registered in England No. 139937
Registered Office: Huntercombe Lane South
Taplow, Maidenhead, Berkshire, SL6 0PH

INVESTOR IN PEOPLE

Incorporating: Wyeth Laboratories
SMA Nutrition
Genus Pharmaceuticals

Colditz GA, Hankinson SE, Hunter DJ et al (1995). The use of estrogens and progestins and the risk of breast cancer in postmenopausal women. *NEJM*, 332, 1589-1593.

Dale E, Vessey MP, Hawkins MM et al (1996). Risk of venous thromboembolism in users of hormone replacement therapy. *The Lancet*, 348 977-980.

Grodstein F, Stamfer MJ & Manson JE (1996). Post-menopausal estrogen and progestin use and the risk of cardiovascular disease. *NEJM*, 335, 453-461.

Grodstein F, Stampfer MJ, Goldhaber SZ et al (1996). Prospective study of exogenous hormones and risk of pulmonary embolism in women. *The Lancet*, 348, 983-987.

Hemminki E & McPherson K (1997). Impact of postmenopausal hormone therapy on cardiovascular events and cancer: pooled data from clinical trials. *BMJ*, 315, 149-155.

Pike MV, Peters RK, Cozen W et al (1997). Estrogen-progestin replacement therapy and endometrial cancer. *Journal of the National Cancer Institute*, 89, 1110-1116.

Case number	Surname, Forename			Date of birth	Sex	Lab sort code	
not given.	GALE, ROSALIND			05/11/1949	F	804	GP122
For the on of		At		Originated by			
Dr ▓▓▓▓▓▓▓		▓▓▓▓ Road Surgery		Dr ▓▓▓▓▓▓▓			

Copy sent as requested

Serum   collected 27/10/2003   at 09:00 ID: BB629459Q

SAS SENT FOR GROWTH HORMONE. IGF-1 AND IGF-3 NOT AVAILABLE.

    Cortisol (9am) - -   -   -   301   nmol/L   (150 - 680)
    17-Beta Oestradiol - -   -   1514   pmol/L
    Growth Hormone - -   -   -   Result to follow

Bibliography

Advisory Committee on Human Radiation Experiments. *Final Report.* Washington, DC: U S Government Printing Office; 1995.

Archer, John. *Bad Medicine.* Australia: Simon & Schuster; 1995.

Batt S. *Patient No More: The politics of breast cancer.* London: Scarlet Press; 1994.

Bealle MA. *House of Rockefeller: how a shoestring was run into 200 million dollars in two generations.* Washington, DC: All America House; 1959.

Behan M, Haslam B. *The Benzodiazepines. Submission to the Home Office Advisory Council on the misuse of drugs.* 26 July 2003.

Bell SE. *The Synthetic Compound Diethylstilbestrol (DES) 1938-1941: The social construction of a medical treatment* [dissertation]. Waltham (MA): Brandeis Univ; 1980.

Campion K. *A Woman's Herbal.* London: Century; 1988.

Clorfene-Casten L. *Breast Cancer: Poisons, profits and prevention.* Monroe, ME: Common Courage Press; 1996.

Coney S. *The Menopause Industry: A guide to medicine's 'discovery' of the mid-life woman.* (British edition) London: Women's Press; 1996.

Coney S. *The Menopause Industry: How the medical establishment exploits women.* (US edition) Alameda, CA: Hunter House; 1994.

DeMarco C. *Take Charge of Your Body.* Winlaw, British Columbia: Well Women Press; 1994.

Doubleday J. *101 Reasons Not to Have Your Baby in a Hospital* (Vol. 1). Spontaneous Creations Publishing; 2005.

Dumontet S, Grimme H, eds. *Biology, Biologists and Bioethics: Concerns for scientists, politicians and consumers.* Naples: Foxwell & Davies Italia; 2004.

Dutton D. *Worse Than the Disease: Pitfalls of medical progress.* Cambridge: Cambridge University Press; 1988.

Effectiveness and costs of osteoporosis screening and hormone replacement therapy. Vol. II: *Evidence on Benefits, Risks, and Costs.* Washington, DC: OTA; 1995.

Farmer A. *Prophets and Priests: The hidden face of the birth control movement.* London: Saint Austin Press; 2002.

Glenville M. *The New Natural Alternatives to HRT.* Kyle Cathie Ltd; 1997.

Gorney S, Cox C. *After Forty.* New York: Dial Press; 1973.

Grant ECG. *The Bitter Pill.* London: Corgi; 1986.

Grant ECG. *Sexual Chemistry: Understanding your hormones, the Pill and HRT.* London: Cedar; 1994.

Greer G. *The Change: Women, aging and the menopause.* London: Hamish Hamilton; 1991.

Griffin J. *Mother Nature's Herbal.* Llewellyn Publications; 1997.

Grisham J. *The King of Torts.* New York: Doubleday; 2003.

Grisham J. *The Runaway Jury.* London: Arrow; 1996.

Harr J. *A Civil Action.* New York: Vintage Books; 1996.

Holmes D. Tears Behind Closed Doors: Failure to diagnose an underactive thyroid. NPL Publication; 2002.

Hubbard B. *Secrets of the Drugs Industry.* London: What Doctors Don't Tell You; 2002.

Illich I. *Medical Nemesis: The expropriation of health.* London: Calder & Boyers; 1975.

Jenner H. *Silicone – Gate: Or the scandal behind breast implants;* 1995.

Kenton, Leslie. *Passage to Power*. UK: Random House; 1995.

Kloss J. *Back to Eden*. Loma Linda, CA: Back to Eden Books Publishing Company; 1988.

Kushner R. *Breast Cancer: A personal history and investigative report*. New York: Harcourt, Brace Jovanovich; 1975.

Liebenau J. *Medical Science and Medical Industry: The formation of the American pharmaceutical industry*. London: Macmillan; 1987.

Mamone Capria M. *Is science worth pursuing?* In: Dumontet S, Grimme H, eds. *Biology, Biologists and Bioethics: Concerns for scientists, politicians and consumers*. Naples: Foxwell & Davies Italia; 2004.

McTaggart L. *What Doctors Don't Tell You: The truth about the dangers of modern medicine*. London: Thorsons; 1996.

The Merck Index of Chemicals and Drugs. 6th ed. Rahway, NJ: Merck; 1952.

Mintz M. *The Pill: An alarming report*. Greenwich, CT: Fawcett; 1969.

Mokhiber R. *Corporate Crime and Violence: Big business power and the abuse of the public trust*. San Francisco, CA: Sierra Club Books; 1988.

National Women's Health Network. *The Truth About Hormone Replacement Therapy: How to break free from the medical myths of the menopause*. Prima Publishing, 2002.

Pearse IH, Crocker LH. *The Peckham Experiment: A study in the living structure of society*. London: G Allen and Unwin; 1943.

Rampton S, Stauber J. *Trust Us We're Experts: How industry manipulates science and gambles with your future*. New York: Tarcher/Putnam; 2001.

Read C. *Preventing Breast Cancer: The politics of an epidemic*. New York: HarperCollins; 1995.

Rees M, Purdie D. *Management of the Menopause*. Marlow, Bucks: British Menopause Society; 2002.

Rinzler CA. *Estrogen and Breast Cancer: A warning to women*. New York: Macmillan; 1993.

Robbins J. *Diet for a New America*. Walpole, NH: Stillpoint Publishing; 1987.

Robbins J. *Reclaiming Our Health: Exploding the medical myth and embracing the source of true healing*. Tiburon, CA: H J Kramer; 1996.

Royal College of Physicians. *Allergy, the Unmet Need: A blueprint for better patient care*. London: RCP; 2003.

Schell O. *Modern Meat: Antibiotics, hormones and the pharmaceutical farm*. USA: Random House; 1984.

Seaman B. *The Doctors' Case Against the Pill*. New York: P H Wyden; 1969.

Seaman B. *Free and Female: The sex life of the contemporary woman*. New York: Coward, McCann & Geoghegan; 1972.

Seaman B. *The Greatest Experiment Ever Performed on Women: Exploding the estrogen myth*. New York: Hyperion; 2003.

Seaman B, Seaman G. *Women and the Crisis in Sex Hormones*. New York: Rawson Associates; 1977.

Sjostrom H, Nilsson R. *Thalidomide and the Power of the Drug Companies*. Harmondsworth, Middlesex: Penguin Books; 1972.

Sobel LA, ed. *Cancer and the Environment*. New York: Facts on File; 1979.

Stewart M. *Beat the Menopause Naturally*. Natural Health Publishing; 2003.

Trombley T. *The Right to Reproduce: A history of coercive sterilization*. London: Weidenfeld and Nicolson; 1988.

Walker, Martin J. *Brave New World of Zero Risk: Covert strategies in British science policy*. London: Slingshot Publications; 2005. <www.zero-risk.org>.

Walker, Martin J. *Dirty Medicine: Science, big business and the assault on natural health care*. London: Slingshot Publications; 1993.

Walker, Martin J. *Skewed: Psychiatric hegemony and the manufacture of mental illness in Multiple Chemical Sensitivity, Gulf War Syndrome, Myalgic Encephalomyelitis and Chronic Fatigue Syndrome*. London: Slingshot Publications; 2003.

Indexes

Three separate indexes follow.

Index One: Chapter guide.

Index one is a chapter guide which lists the main subjects of each chapter.

Index Two: Major subject index.

Index two lists the most important contents of the book under six main headings: HRT; HRT and adverse reactions; HRT, general practitioners, doctors and patients; HRT and pharmaceutical companies; HRT, lobbying and marketing; HRT, legal cases; together with a few salient entries, unconnected with the major subjects.

Index Three: The names index.

Index three lists the names in the book by page.

A Chapter Guide

Major Subject Index

A

All Party Group on Men's Health
(APGMH), 201.
Associate Parliamentary Group on Health
(APGH), 196-8, 201, 203.
Association of the British Pharmaceutical
Industry (ABPI), 166, 182, 197-8,
200, 203-4.
British government and, 166,
182, 197-8, 200, 203-4.

C

Calcium,
non-dairy sources of, 306.
brocoli
green, leafy vegetables
sunflower seeds
tahini (sesame paste)
tofu
Cancer, xi, 6, 128-9, 137, 172, 254.
DES and, 16, 140-2, 144.
endometrial, 14, 16-8, 141, 148-50, 153,
168, 232.
oestrogens and,
oral contraceptives and, 146-7.
ovarian, 87, 271.
See also Breast cancer *under* HRT.
Charity Commission, 40-1, 53, 229.
Commissioners, 40-1.
Corporations, industrial and commercial
concerns,
ABN AMRO, 170, 170n.
BASF, 139, 159.
Chase Manhattan Bank, 162.
Exxon Mobil, 165, 169.
Halliburton Company, 169.
JP Morgan Chase, 165.
& Co, 164, 169.
bank, 171.
International Advisory Council of,
170-1.

Royal Dutch Petroleum, 170-1.
Unilever, 170, 248.
board, 170-1.

D

Department of Health (DoH), 21-2, 38, 46,
152, 183-4, 189, 199, 201, 228, 246,
249, 330.
Department of Trade and Industry (Dti),
194-6, 199.

F

Fibromyalgia, 291, 304.

G

General practitioners, 44, 78-80, 109, 122,
184, 264-6, 268, 335-6.
adverse reactions to HRT and, 21, 24,
50, 63-6, 72, 84-5, 90, 92, 97, 99,
101-3, 110, 112-4, 116-7, 119, 247,
270, 275, 295, 308, 335.

H

HealthWatch, 252-3.
Heart and Estrogen/Progesterone
Replacement Study (HERS), 18,
209.
HRT
adverse reactions to, 8, 13, 14n, 22, 24-
7, 32, 35, 39-41, 43, 47, 49, 50-1, 55-
9, 60-122, 150, 179, 205, 216, 239,
252, 256, 265, 277, 280-1, 323, 331,
333.
all in the mind, 37, 77, 99, 101.
ankles, damaged, 295-6.
anxiety, 271, 274.
severe, 272.
balance, affected, 272-3.
blackouts, 91, 112.
bleeding, 90, 96, 98, 140, 263, 271,
285, 295, 302.
profuse, 36, 295.
bloated feeling, 92, 101.

influence in
  journals, newspapers and
    publications, 165, 174, 207, 225-
    6, 232, 237, 242, 245, 247, 249-51,
    254-5, 314, 337.
  See also *Feminine Forever* and
    *The Amarant Book on Hormone
    Replacement Therapy* under
    HRT, lobbying and marketing.
  legal system, 46-7, 47n, 50-1, 69,
    167, 314, 319, 326.
  legal claims against, 48-50, 142, 173-4,
    181-2, 216, 325-6.
  lobby groups/organisations, 155, 193-
    221, 223-56.
  marketing, xi-ii, 15-6, 32, 57, 148, 157-
    8, 162, 167-8, 171, 173, 177, 182,
    184, 200, 231, 233, 240, 243, 304,
    313, 335.
    distribution, 193-221.
    Huntsworth plc, 202.
  medicalisation of menopause and, 224,
    289, 316.
  NHS and, 81, 166, 175, 177, 179, 183,
    195, 198-200, 202, 204-5, 229.
  Parliament and, 177, 193-221.
  patient information and, xii, xvi, 14,
    14n, 26, 50, 60, 95, 110, 117-8, 122,
    168n, 178, 184-5, 119, 212, 215-6,
    336.
    See also influence in journals,
    newspapers and publications.
  PR companies and, 152, 168, 173, 202,
    207, 209, 212, 217, 223-56.
  press propaganda and, 223-56.
  quality control and, 190.
  responsibility of, 21, 161, 163, 177-8,
    262, 307, 315, 317-20, 324-5, 334.
  separating doctors and, 329.
  US Government and, 145, 166-7, 180-1,
    185, 187-9, 313-5, 320-1, 323.
  voluntary sector and, 41n, 48n, 166,
    177, 224, 227-230.
Pharmaceutical Fordism, 125-128.
Pharmaceutical industry,
  British Government and, 314-5, 334.
  See also British Government *under*
    Pharmaceutical/drug companies.
Population Council, 147.

Q
Quackbusters, 68, 172, 253-4.

R
Radiation experiments, human, 133.
Richard and Judy, 51.

S
Science,
  industrial, xii, 21, 132, 254, 330.
  medicine and, 3, 12, 23, 26, 58, 82, 129-
    30, 132-3, 151, 159-60, 224, 329-31.
Scientific Medicine, History of, 128-32.

T
Tamoxifen, 12, 210.
Thalidomide, 21, 21n, 129.
Trilateral Commission, 169-70.

V
Vaccines, 32, 159, 166-7, 175, 179-85, 187-
  90, 193, 200, 203, 323.
  DPT (diphtheria-pertussis-tetanus),
    180-1, 185.
  FluMist, 181-2.
  meningitis C, 183.
  polio, 181.
  Prevnar, 184-7.
  RotaShield, 186-8.

W
What Doctors Don't Tell You, 70, 182.
  See also McTaggart, Lynne in the
    Names Index.
Women's Health Initiative (WHI)
    study/trials, 21-3, 151-2, 153-4,
    213, 218-9, 234, 244-5, 252-4.

Names Index

A

Alexander, Clifford L., 164.
Allen, Edgar, 135.
Amess, David, MP, 200-1, 201n.

B

Bailar, John, 56, 56n.
Baker, Dr Maureen, 153, 153n.
Barlow, David H., 245.
Barrett, Don, 194, 194n, 246, 246-7n.
Bart Classen, Dr J., 185.
Batt, Sharon, xi, xin, 56n, 131, 131n, 145n, 146.
Baum, Prof. Michael, 153.
Beecham, Stephanie, 212.
Behan, Michael, 177-8, 178n.
Bellerby, C.W., 136.
Bennack, Frank A., Jr, 163-4.
Beral, Prof. Valerie, 20, 20n, 152n.
Beresford, S. A., 17, 17n.
Bernard, Claude, 14, 134.
Black, Dr Steven, 185.
Blair, Isla, 212.
Blair, Tony, 46, 203, 170, 216.
Bottomley, Virginia, 170.
Brankin, Bernard, 47-8, 50.
Bremer, Paul, III, 170.
Bright, Martin, 183.
Brittan, Lord, 170.
Brown-Séquard, Charles Edouard, 14, 134-5, 134n.
Bush, George H. W., 162-3n, 167, 314, 324, 324n.
    from 1991 to 1993, 169.
Butenandt, Adolf, 135, 136n.

C

Calman, Prof. Kenneth, 199, 199n, 202n, 203.
Capesius, Dr Victor, 139.
Cartwright, Prof. Keith, 183n, 184.

Chang, Dr Min-Cheuh, 145.
Clorfene-Casten, Liane, xi, 136n, 141n, 150, 150n.
Cohen, Abraham E., 170.
Colin-Thome, David, 199.
Collins, Joan, 212.
Coney, Sandra, x-xii, xn, 232n, 236n.
Cook, J.W., 136.
Cooper, Wendy, 43, 43n, 232.
Cox, Claire, 231, 231n.
Cumberlege, Baroness, 200-2.
Cushman, M., 23n.

D

Dent, Julie, 199.
Dobson, Frank, 41.
Dodds, Charles, 136-7, 140.
    in 1938, 136.
Doisy, Edward, 135.
Donaldson, Liam, 183-4.
Drew, David, MP, 200.
Dunkley, Bernard, 199.

E

Eaton, Duncan, 199, 199n.
Eckhart, Wolfgang, 138.
Edwards, Kathryn, 185, 188.
Endby, Dr Eric, 43.
Epstein, Samuel, MD, viiin.
Estes, Dr Mary, 188.

F

Finkle, W. D., 16n.
Finnigan, Judy, 212, 238.
Ford, Gerald, 165.

G

Gascoine, Jill, 212.
Gidley, Sandra, MP, 200-1.
Glenville, Dr Marilyn, xi, xin, 43.
Godfree, Dr Val, 229, 230.
Goldblatt, Prof. David, 183n, 184.
González, Claudio X., 171.